Cosmic Rays, Supernovae
and the Interstellar Medium

NATO ASI Series

Advanced Science Institutes Series

A Series presenting the results of activities sponsored by the NATO Science Committee, which aims at the dissemination of advanced scientific and technological knowledge, with a view to strengthening links between scientific communities.

The Series is published by an international board of publishers in conjunction with the NATO Scientific Affairs Division

A Life Sciences	Plenum Publishing Corporation
B Physics	London and New York
C Mathematical	Kluwer Academic Publishers
and Physical Sciences	Dordrecht, Boston and London
D Behavioural and Social Sciences	
E Applied Sciences	
F Computer and Systems Sciences	Springer-Verlag
G Ecological Sciences	Berlin, Heidelberg, New York, London,
H Cell Biology	Paris and Tokyo
I Global Environmental Change	

NATO-PCO-DATA BASE

The electronic index to the NATO ASI Series provides full bibliographical references (with keywords and/or abstracts) to more than 30000 contributions from international scientists published in all sections of the NATO ASI Series.
Access to the NATO-PCO-DATA BASE is possible in two ways:

– via online FILE 128 (NATO-PCO-DATA BASE) hosted by ESRIN,
Via Galileo Galilei, I-00044 Frascati, Italy.

– via CD-ROM "NATO-PCO-DATA BASE" with user-friendly retrieval software in English, French and German (© WTV GmbH and DATAWARE Technologies Inc. 1989).

The CD-ROM can be ordered through any member of the Board of Publishers or through NATO-PCO, Overijse, Belgium.

Series C: Mathematical and Physical Sciences - Vol. 337

Cosmic Rays, Supernovae and the Interstellar Medium

edited by

Maurice M. Shapiro
Department of Physics and Astronomy,
University of Maryland, College Park, MD, U.S.A.

Rein Silberberg
Code 4150, Gamma and Cosmic Ray Astrophysics,
Naval Research Laboratory, Washington, DC, U.S.A.

and

John P. Wefel
Department of Physics and Astronomy,
Louisiana State University, Baton Rouge, LA, U.S.A.

Kluwer Academic Publishers

Dordrecht / Boston / London

Published in cooperation with NATO Scientific Affairs Division

.4280428

ASTRONOMY

Proceedings of the NATO Advanced Study Institute on
Cosmic Rays, Supernovae and the Interstellar Medium
Erice, Italy
July 26–August 5, 1990

```
Cosmic rays, supernovae, and the interstellar medium / edited by
  Maurice M. Shapiro and Rein Silberberg and John P. Wefel.
        p.   cm. -- (NATO ASI series. Series C, Mathematical and
  physical sciences ; vol. 337)
     Selected lectures presented at the 7th course of the International
  School of Cosmic-Ray Astrophysics in Erice, Italy, July-Aug. 1990.
     Includes indexes.
     ISBN 0-7923-1278-3 (alk. paper)
     1. Cosmic rays--Congresses.  2. Galactic cosmic rays--Congresses.
  3. Supernovae--Congresses.  4. Interstellar matter--Congresses.
  5. Astrophysics--Congresses.   I. Shapiro, Maurice M. (Maurice
  Mandel), 1915-    .  II. Silberberg, Rein, 1932-    .  III. Wefel, J.
  P.  IV. International School of Cosmic-Ray Astrophysics.  V. Series:
  NATO ASI series.  Series C, Mathematical and physical sciences ; no.
  337.
  QC484.8.C68   1991
  523.01'97223--dc20                                      91-16898
```

ISBN 0–7923–1278–3

Published by Kluwer Academic Publishers,
P.O. Box 17, 3300 AA Dordrecht, The Netherlands.

Kluwer Academic Publishers incorporates the publishing programmes of
D. Reidel, Martinus Nijhoff, Dr W. Junk and MTP Press.

Sold and distributed in the U.S.A. and Canada
by Kluwer Academic Publishers,
101 Philip Drive, Norwell, MA 02061, U.S.A.

In all other countries, sold and distributed
by Kluwer Academic Publishers Group,
P.O. Box 322, 3300 AH Dordrecht, The Netherlands.

Printed on acid-free paper

TABLE OF CONTENTS

PREFACE ix
    M. M. Shapiro

I. COSMIC RAYS AND THE INTERSTELLAR MEDIUM

A BRIEF INTRODUCTION TO THE COSMIC RADIATION 1
    M. M. Shapiro

THE COMPOSITION OF THE COSMIC RAYS: AN UPDATE 29
    J. P. Wefel

INTERSTELLAR DUST-GAS RELATIONSHIPS 57
    J. M. Greenberg

DUST, GAS AND COSMIC RAYS IN THE INTERSTELLAR
       MEDIUM 69
    A. W. Wolfendale

COMPARISON BETWEEN GREENBERG AND MATHIS
    MODELS OF GRAINS FOR THE H_2 FORMATION INDUCED
    BY COSMIC RAYS 81
    D. Averna, V. Pirronello, W.L. Brown, and L.J. Lanzerotti

II. SUPERNOVAE, ACCELERATION, PROPAGATION AND SOURCE COMPOSITION

SHOCK ACCELERATION OF COSMIC RAYS 87
    L. O'C. Drury

SOURCE COMPOSITION, SITES OF ORIGIN AND
    ACCELERATION OF COSMIC RAYS 97
    R. Silberberg, C. H. Tsao, M. M. Shapiro and P. L. Biermann

COSMIC-RAY AGE AND THE INTERSTELLAR MEDIUM.................... 119
  V. S. Ptuskin

THE PRODUCTION OF ANTIPROTONS IN THE INTERSTELLAR
  GAS BY PROPAGATING COSMIC RAYS.................................... 137
  M. Simon and U. Heinbach

THE SOURCE COMPOSITION OF GALACTIC COSMIC RAYS
  AND THE CONDENSATION PROCESS OF THE ELEMENTS
  IN CIRCUMSTELLAR AND INTERSTELLAR GASES...................... 153
  K. Sakurai

THE DISTRIBUTION OF SUPERNOVA REMNANTS IN THE
  GALAXY 163
  D. A. Green

GAMMA RAYS FROM SUPERNOVA 1987A 167
  R. S. White

ACCELERATION OF COSMIC RAYS AT YOUNG SUPERNOVA
  REMNANTS 177
  T. Stanev

THE EFFECT OF RELATIVISTIC PARTICLE BEAMS ON THE
  EVOLUTION OF SUPERNOVA ENVELOPES:
  SELF-CONSISTENT SOLUTIONS.. 187
  J. H. Beall

RADIO SPECTRAL VARIATIONS IN THE CYGNUS LOOP 207
  D. A. Green

III. GAMMA RAYS AND THEIR ROLE AS COSMIC RAY TRACERS

GAMMA RAY ASTROPHYSICS AT ENERGIES UP TO 10 GEV 213
  R. S. White and R. Silberberg

VHE AND UHE GAMMA RAY SOURCES 249
  R. S. White

GAMMA-RAYS FROM ELECTRON, PROTON BEAM
  INTERACTIONS WITH MATTER AND/OR RADIATION:
  APPLICATION TO CYG X-1, GEMINGA, AND 3C273..................... 271
  F. Giovannelli, L. S. Graziati, W. Bednarek, S. Karakula,
  and W. Tkaczyk

GAMMA RAYS AND NEUTRINOS FROM ACCRETION
PROCESSES ONTO COLLAPSED OBJECTS:
APPLICATION TO 3C273 289
    F. Giovannelli, L. S. Graziati, S. Karakula, and W. Tkaczyk

NEARBY GALAXIES IN HIGH ENERGY GAMMA RAYS 307
    M. E. Özel

IV. ULTRA-ENERGETIC COSMIC NUCLEI

COSMIC RAYS AT THE HIGHEST ENERGIES 313
    A. W. Wolfendale and J. Wdowczyk

PARTICIPANTS 325

AUTHOR INDEX 335

SUBJECT INDEX 345

PREFACE

The Galactic cosmic rays have far-reaching effects on the interstellar medium, and they are, in turn, profoundly affected by the particles and fields in space. Supernova remnants and their expanding shock fronts pervade the Galaxy, heating the interstellar medium, and accelerating the cosmic rays. The interplay among the cosmic rays, the interstellar medium in which they propagate, and supernovae has been investigated for decades; yet these studies have generated as many enigmas as they have resolved. These puzzles continue to challenge observers and theorists alike.

This volume is devoted to selected lectures presented in the 7th Course of the International School of Cosmic-Ray Astrophysics in Erice, Italy in July-August, 1990. Alltogether, some 400 participants have attended the biennial sessions of this School since its inception in 1978. As its name implies, the School deals with cosmic-ray phenomena viewed in the broader context of astrophysics. Students and Lecturers are attracted from many astrophysical disciplines. Like earlier courses in this series, the present one was organized under the aegis of the Ettore Majorana Centre as a NATO Advanced Study Institute. Given the diverse scientific backgrounds of the students, it was deemed useful to include lectures at the introductory level. Other lectures and contributed talks were at a more advanced level, featuring new developments. If this collection is useful pedagogically, and if it provides some stimulus and information for the mature research worker, then the editors will feel well rewarded.

We acknowledge the lively contributions of Lecturers and other senior participants to the sessions. For their substantial support and encouragement, we are grateful to the following: the NATO Scientific Affairs Division and Dr. L. V. da Cunha, Director of its ASI programme; Professor Antonino Zichichi, Director of the Majorana Centre; Dr. Alberto Gabriele, Administrator of the Centre; the Italian Ministry of Education; the Italian Ministry of University and Scientific Research; the European Physical Society; the Sicilian Regional Government; the U.S. National Science Foundation and the Scientific Advisory Committee of the School, especially Professors Pierre Auger, G.P.S. Occhialini, Bruno Rossi, John Simpson, and James van Allen. We appreciate the cooperation of Kluwer Academic Publishers and of Mrs. N. M. Pols v.d. Heijden. The Director of the School warmly thanks J. P. Wefel and R. Silberberg for their fruitful collaboration. Professor Wefel efficiently co-directed the Course, and he and Dr. Silberberg served as co-editors.

A final word: the Table of Contents contains a "singularity" — Sec. IV has only one paper, and it may seem somewhat extraneous to the main theme of the Course. After all, the very highest-energy cosmic rays are suspected to be of extragalactic origin. Yet this supposition has not been firmly nailed down. Moreover, a fuller understanding of these extraordinary particles (up to some 10^{20} eV, or even greater energy), may eventually help us clarify the provenance and nature of the less spectacular, but far more numerous, cosmic rays. Stranger things have happened in the history of science!

-- Maurice M. Shapiro

A BRIEF INTRODUCTION TO THE COSMIC RADIATION

MAURICE M. SHAPIRO*
Department of Physics and Astronomy
University of Maryland
College Park, MD, USA

ABSTRACT. Some prominent features of the Galactic Cosmic Rays (GCR) are summarized for the non-specialist. These include the composition of the "primaries" reaching the earth and the "primordial" or source composition; the energy spectra and their modulation in the heliosphere; the effects of magnetic fields, notably on the directional distribution; the propagation of the GCR in the interstellar medium (ISM), and what is inferred about abundances, especially the isotopic ones; lifetime of the GCR; acceleration of the particles and their injection into the ISM. Finally the significance of cosmic neutrinos, cosmic gamma rays, and antiprotons is briefly treated.

1. INTRODUCTION

The Galactic cosmic rays are mostly relativistic atomic nuclei that pervade the interstellar medium, with an energy density comparable to that of starlight. This much has been known for some years, but for several decades after their discovery in 1912, their essential nature was in dispute. And even today, their origin is not firmly established. Yet we have learned a great deal about this ubiquitous phenomenon--enough to fill many volumes of conference proceedings. Hence, a treatment of some salient features of the cosmic radiation in a couple of lectures--even qualitatively--must be sketchy at best. Some topics will scarcely be mentioned; the Bibliography may help to fill the voids.

In Sec. 2 the cosmic-ray discipline is related to the other contemporary astronomies. This is followed by an historical perspective on the first half-century of cosmic-ray research. The rest of the paper describes some important characteristics of the cosmic rays: Sec. 3, their composition as observed locally, i.e., the "arriving composition;" Sec. 4, energy spectra and solar modulation;

*Address for Correspondence: 205 Yoakum Parkway, #1720
                                 Alexandria, VA 22304 USA

1

M. M. Shapiro et al. (eds.), Cosmic Rays, Supernovae and the Interstellar Medium, 1–27.
Reprinted from J. M. Greenberg and V. Pirronello (eds.), Chemistry in Space, 43–69.

Sec. 5, magnetic fields and isotropy; Sec. 6 propagation, pathlength,
source composition; Sec. 7, injection and acceleration; Sec. 8,
isotopic composition; Sec. 9, high-energy neutrinos and gamma rays;
Sec. 10, other aspects of cosmic radiation.

2. HISTORICAL PERSPECTIVE

The discovery of cosmic rays by Hess in 1912 marked the advent of the
first new astronomical discipline of the 20th century--although an
appreciation of its astrophysical nature and impact was not to be
realized for many years. Two decades later Jansky opened up the
channel of radio astronomy, which was to acquire a special symbiotic
relationship to the cosmic radiation. In the sixties the X-ray sky
was revealed by Friedman, Giacconi, Rossi and their colleagues. Soon
thereafter came gamma-ray astronomy, and today we are at the
threshold of two more channels of cosmic information--neutrino
astrophysics and gravitational wave astronomy. All of these
contemporary astronomies are complementary to each other and to the
classical discipline of optical astronomy

   The mutability--and, indeed, the fallibility--of cherished
physical theories is exemplified by the early history of the cosmic-
ray discipline (yet, paradoxically, certain concepts, such as Fermi's
mechanisms of acceleration, persist like the proverbial cat with nine
lives.) Widely held views as to the identity of the penetrating
"primaries" changed radically from decade to decade. First they were
gamma rays; then, successively, electrons (and positrons), protons,
heavier nuclei up to iron and beyond, culminating in the periodic
table of the elements. The progression came full circle with the
advent of high-energy gamma ray astronomy--albeit the relevant fluxes
are a thousand times lower that those of the relativistic nuclei.
Electrons are present among the primaries, but they only comprise
about 10^{-2} of the nuclear component. To the radioastronomer, they are
the most "visible" of the relativistic particles. High-energy cosmic
neutrinos--tracers of cosmic-ray sources--are yet to be observed, but
their detection seems imminent.

2.1 <u>The Development of Particle Astrophysics</u>. From observations in
his manned balloon flights, Victor Hess concluded that a penetrating
radiation of extra atmospheric origin was responsible for the response
of his electroscope. He could hardly have imagined that his discovery
portended the birth of two new sciences--elementary-particle physics
and high-energy astrophysics. We are here concerned mainly with
astrophysics; the field of elementary particles--in its experimental
embodiment--has become the province of huge, ground-based
accelerators.
   In the decades of the twenties and thirties, particle physics at
high energies (far beyond those then available in the laboratory) was

the main concern of cosmic-ray scientists, both experimental and theoretical. Among the noteworthy discoveries were the positron, the process of pair production of electrons, electromagnetic cascades, muons, "stars", i.e. nuclear disintegrations, and extensive air showers. These phenomena were successfully incorporated into a coherent theory of secondary cosmic-ray production and propagation through the atmosphere, thanks to the work of Bethe, Heitler, Oppenheimer, Bhabha and their collaborators. Some remaining enigmas about the atmospheric secondaries, e.g., the origins of the soft and hard components (i.e., the electron-photon showers and the muons) were resolved in the late forties and early fifties through the discoveries of neutral and charged pions, repectively.

Meanwhile, the latitude effect, discovered by Clay and established by Compton, showed that the "primaries" striking the top of the atmosphere must be charged particles. These are predominantly positive as determined by the East-West affect, and at first they were thought to be positrons. In 1941 Schein, Jesse and Wollan disproved this assumption. Their findings were consistent with the primary particles being penetrating protons.

In 1948 Freier et al. a team of Minnesota and Rochester physicists, discovered that the arriving protons were accompanied by nuclei of elements from helium to iron. (In due course, Fowler was to find evidence for cosmic-ray nuclei much heavier than iron, in fact up to the actinides). Soon thereafter, V.L. Ginzburg and others (notably Pikelner, Shklovsky, and Hayakawa) interpreted the synchrotron radiation emanating from the Crab Nebula as due to a copious flux of relativistic electrons. The mechanism responsible for energizing electrons could be expected to accelerate protons and other heavy ions as well.

For the first time one could point to an object in the sky that generated cosmic rays, albeit the clear evidence was only for relativistic electrons. The idea of supernovae as cosmic-ray sources was attractive. Astronomical evidence showed that the fast electrons were moving in large-scale magnetic fields. Moreover, the theory of nucleosynthesis in stars, developed in the fifties by Burbidge et al. and by Cameron, predicted the production of heavy elements in supernova explosions, and the cosmic rays were known to be rich in those elements. The source strength seemed to meet the requirements of cosmic-ray replenishment in the Galaxy. Fermi's stochastic mechanisms of acceleration, which encountered difficulties in interstellar space, might work more efficiently within the confines of supernova remnants. (Concern over adiabatic losses in the expanding shells came later.)

We have reviewed rather briefly certain landmarks in cosmic-ray history during its first half-century. We shall now elaborate on some salient features of the cosmic radiation, as they are understood today.

4

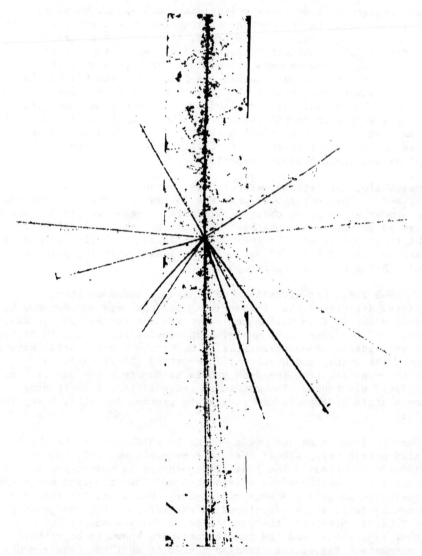

Figure 1. Breakup of a heavy primary cosmic-ray nucleus in collision
with a nucleus in a photographic emulsion detector. The narrow-angle
shower of particles proceeding beyond the star-like collision point are
fragments of the incident cosmic-ray nucleus. The other, lateral tracks
radiating from the collision point are fragments of the "complex-target"
nucleus; these would be absent in a collision with a hydrogen nucleus
in the ISM.

3. COMPOSITION OF THE COSMIC RAYS NEAR THE EARTH

The Galactic cosmic rays (GCR) arriving in our vicinity include a
substantial admixture of secondaries generated en route by progenitor
nuclei in collision with interstellar matter. These transformations
of source particles into secondaries--e.g., nuclei, electrons,
antiprotons, gamma rays--provide a veritable Rosetta Stone that helps
us unravel the complexities of cosmic-ray propagation and origin.
Figure 1 is a photomicrograph of an "event" observed in a photographic
emulsion exposed near the top of the atmosphere. It portrays the
breakup of a heavy cosmic-ray nucleus into lighter fragments. In this
case the target was an atomic nucleus within the emulsion. The
corresponding events in outer space would usually involve collisions
with hydrogen or helium targets. By investigating the details of such
interactions we have learned much of what is known about the many
effects to which cosmic rays are subject in their tortuous paths from
sources to earth.

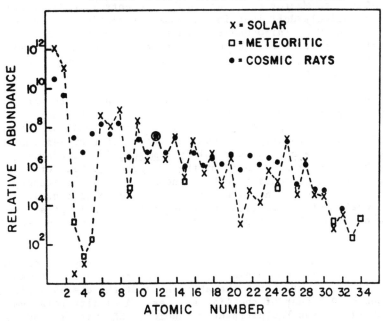

Figure 2. The relative abundances of elements in the cosmic rays
and in the solar system. The abundance of solar hydrogen is normalized
to 10^{12}, and the cosmic-ray abundances are normalized to the solar values at magnesium.

Figure 2 compares the composition of the arriving GCR with the (thermal) composition of solar system material. In the diagram solar abundances are plotted relative to 10^{12} hydrogen atoms, and the cosmic-ray composition has been normalized to the solar one at Mg. Looking first at the cosmic-ray values, represented by circles in the figure, we see that hydrogen and helium are more abundant than the principal heavier elements by some two orders of magnitude. In the solar system the disparity is greater, three orders of magnitude. Carbon and oxygen are distinctly more plentiful that the other principal nuclides--those of Li, Be, B, N, Ne, Mg, Si and Fe. Still lower in flux than Ne, Mg, Si are the odd-Z nuclei of F, Na, Al. The elements S, Ar, Ca, Ti, and Cr--all some 10 times lower in abundance than Mg or Fe--show enhanced abundances relative to their odd-numbered neighbors, phosphorus to vanadium. However, for all Z > 8, and especially for the sub-iron group, the odd-even ratios are less pronounced than they are in the solar abundances. This is consistent with the production of secondary nuclides by collision in the interstellar medium (ISM).

Comparing the cosmic-ray and solar compositions, it is noteworthy that, normalized to Mg (or to other "peak" elements like Si or Fe) H and He are relatively deficient in the cosmic radiation. To a lesser degree, O, N, and C are also underabundant relative to the solar values, although this seems like a small effect in the logarithmic scale of Figure 2. The fluxes span ten orders of magnitude, so many of the abundances look deceptively close.

The deepest "valley" in the solar distribution, due to the extreme scarcity of Li, Be, and B, contrasts sharply with their abundance in the arriving cosmic rays. The observational uncertainty -- and prolonged controversy--surrounding these light nuclei [do they truly come from space or are they solely atmospheric secondaries?] was disspelled by the definitive work of the NRL group (O'Dell et al. 1962). These three elements have been the most revealing breakup products, i.e., secondary nuclides, of cosmic-ray collisions in space, yielding a wealth of information on propagation, path lengths, and source composition. These topics will be treated further in Sec. 6 below.

Until the decade of the sixties the cosmic-ray composition had been investigated only for elements up to the iron group. It was known that in the solar system the abundances of the elements with Z ≳ 30 comprises < 10^{-6} that of the lighter ones. A similar relative scarcity characterizes the ultra-heavy nuclei (UHN) with Z ≳ 30 in the cosmic rays. The latter were first detected in meteoritic crystals through ancient particle tracks developed by chemical etching (Fleischer et al. 1967). The formidable task of accumulating enough data for useful studies of contemporary UHN was tackled by P. Fowler et al. (1967). They deployed very-large-area stacks of photographic emulsions at balloon altitudes. Soon hybrid stacks, consisting of layers of plastics and emulsion, were used for detection and identification of UHN. Since the density of tracks in emulsions increases with Z^2, the tracks of UHN are very dense indeed, as shown in Figure 3.

On NASA's HEAO-3 (High-Energy Astronomy Observatory), a consortium of physicists from Washington University, Caltech, and the University of Minnesota improved the precision of charge resolution for the UHN (see Binns 1986 and references therein). Their apparatus incorporated ionization chambers for measuring dE/dx and a Cerenkov counter. Figure 4 is a histogram showing the "charge spectrum" of elements with $Z \geq 50$. These abundances contain information about the special reactions of nucleosynthesis (Burbidge et al. 1957) that are considered to be responsible for most of the UHN, i.e., the s-process ("slow" addition of neutrons) and the r-process ("rapid" capture). The terms "slow" and "rapid" are relative to the rates of beta decay. Owing to the rarity of the heaviest (actinide) elements, the data on these have thus far been scanty.

4. ENERGY SPECTRA, SOLAR MODULATION

The differential intensities of arriving protons and helium nuclei at solar-quiet (Q) times and in active (A) periods are displayed in Figure 5. Over a wide interval of energies, starting at a few GeV/amu, the intensities of H, He, and heavier nuclides conform to a power law $E^{-\gamma}$, where $\gamma = 2.7 \pm 0.1$. At energies ≤ 1 GeV/amu during solar-active times the intensities are suppressed by solar modulation. Thus the cosmic-ray flux observed inside the "solar cavity" has an inverse correlation with solar activity in the 11-year cycle (see Figure 5). [Contrary behavior would be expected if the particles were mainly of solar origin.] As cosmic rays enter the heliosphere, their intensity is reduced by the action of the solar wind, especially at low energies and at times of solar maximum.

Various aspects of solar modulation are shown schematically in Figure 6. The solar wind moves out from the sun into the solar cavity and, owing to the sun's rotation, solar magnetic fields are drawn out into a spiral structure. The solar wind also transports irregular components of the magnetic field. The paths of cosmic rays entering the heliosphere are altered: while diffusing, the particles are also being convected outward. As they interact with the expanding magnetic fields, the charged particles are adiabatically decelerated. Hence, those observed at a given energy had posessed considerably higher energies before reaching the solar system.

5. MAGNETIC FIELDS AND ISOTROPY

The Galaxy is pervaded by plasma clouds and by large-scale magnetic fields aligned approximately along the spiral arms. The magnetic fields deflect and store the cosmic-ray ions so that, to a first approximation, the incidence of cosmic rays striking the earth's magnetosphere at energies $> 10^{10}$ eV is nearly uniform in direction and

8

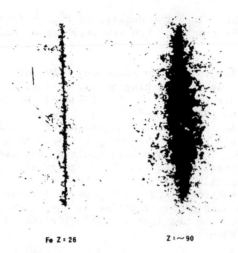

Fe Z = 26   Z ≈ 90

Figure 3. Comparison of tracks of an Fe nucleus and that of a very heavy primary. (Courtesy of P. H. Fowler).

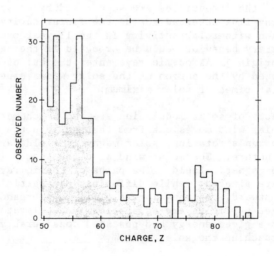

Figure 4. Histogram of nuclides in the region of atomic numbers between 50 and 90 (after Binns et al.)

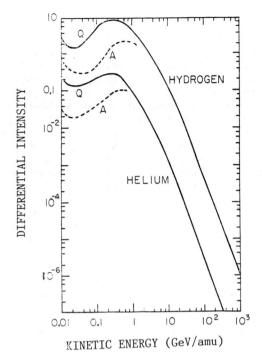

Figure 5. Energy spectra of cosmic-ray protons and helium nuclei at solar-quiet (Q) and solar-active (A) periods.

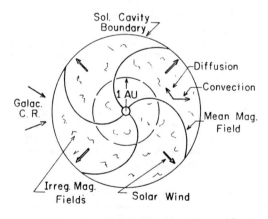

Figure 6. Aspects of solar modulation. The effects are described in Section 4.

time of arrival.

Actually, both anisotropies and time variations have been observed in the GCR. At energies near 10^{12} eV the magnitude of the anisotropy is $\simeq 10^{-4}$. At still higher energies the reported anisotropies are less well known, but they seem to increase with energy; the effects are of the order of a few per cent or less. At the highest energies, $> 10^{19}$ eV, larger anisotropies have been reported (e.g., a higher flux from the direction of the Virgo cluster), but the statistical weight of these observations is low. The study of time variations, on the other hand, has provided a rich harvest of information, e.g., on solar modulation (results based heavily on the work of Forbush and on the Simpson neutron monitors), and on cosmic-ray chronology over geologic time spans.

The substantial isotropy of the cosmic-rays--the fact that the particles have "forgotten" their initial directions--distinguishes charged-particle astronomy from the electromagnetic channels. Indeed, it was a long time before many classical optical astronomers recognized the cosmic radiation as a branch of astrophysics. It is worth noting parenthetically that another branch of particle astronomy--that of high-energy cosmic neutrinos, closely related to cosmic rays--does not suffer from loss of directionality. Since neutrinos, like photons, travel in straight lines, it follows that neutrino astronomy can "point back" to the locations of sources, as do the established channels in astronomy.

6. PROPAGATION, PATH LENGTH, AND SOURCE COMPOSITION

The propagation of the GCR in the Galaxy from the time of birth to their egress from the CR reservoir (by escape or energy loss) encompasses the history of the particles in space and time, once the constituent nuclei have been formed by element synthesis. Among the processes comprising "propagation" are diffusion, acceleration (see Sec. 7), fragmentation that generates secondary nuclei, including radioactive ones (see Sec. 8), and other secondaries (to be discussed in Sec. 9).

A prime task of propagation theory, however, is to deduce the composition of the cosmic rays at the "sources(s)," for the light that it can shed on CR origin. The theory is subject to the constraint that it must yield, finally, the observed, arriving composition. The latter is bound to be very different from the source composition, especially in its isotopic constitution.

The first comprehensive program of calculations on the transformation and propagation of CR nulcei in the interstellar medium (ISM) was carried out by the NRL group (Shapiro, et al, 1970a, b, and c). They applied the latest cross sections and took account of their dependence on energy, as well as the effects of ionization loss and geomagnetic and solar modulation. Clearly, a knowledge of nucleon-nucleus interactions is essential for these computations. Only a fraction of the needed cross sections, however, have been measured; most have been calculated by semi-empirical methods that depend on nuclear systematics. Silberberg and Tsao (1973) have used experimental cross sections for products from proton interactions with various nuclides to formulate semi-empirical formulae for cross sections. These relations have been widely utilized by CR observers: they are applicable to all products having a mass number A $\gtrsim$ 6, and for targets ranging from lithium to uranium. For targets with atomic number Z $\gtrsim$ 30, the relations are applicable from 100 MeV up to many GeV.

An important parameter for CR propagation is the mean path length of the particles. It tells us how much material the CR have penetrated during their space travels. The magnitude of this path length is connected with the regions and mechanisms of cosmic-ray diffusion and trapping; it was used, together with interstellar densities, to get a preliminary estimate of the mean confinement time of the nuclei. Also, a knowledge of the path length is needed for deducing the cosmic-ray source composition. The best source of information on path lengths is the abundance ratio of the so-called "light" nuclei to heavier ones arriving at the top of the atmosphere. Since the light nuclei are the breakup products of heavier ones that have collided with interstellar gas and dust, the relative flux of light nuclei reflects the amount of material traversed. An NRL investigation (O'Dell et al. 1961) on the relative flux of Li, Be, and B nuclei showed that the ratio for CR in the GeV range "light"/"medium" = 0.25 ± 0.02. (The "medium nuclides are C,N,O,F.) This result has been confirmed by subsequent work.

The simplest approach to deducing a mean path length from the foregoing data involves the so-called slab approximation, in which all the cosmic-ray nuclei are assumed to have the same path. By applying the appropriate diffusion equations, a mean path length λ_e = 5g/cm^2 was inferred. This value has also been confirmed through studies of the isotopic composition of cosmic-ray helium; in "stripping" reactions ^{4}He is converted to ^{3}He. In fact, the distribution of path lengths does not conform to a delta-function (slab model). No unique value of λ_e could satisfy both (a) the observed production and survival of the group of light nuclides, and also (b) the production, from Fe, of the "sub-iron" set of nuclides having 17 $\leq$ Z $\leq$ 25. Investigation of various distribution functions revealed that an exponential type of distribution can satisfy the abundance ratios in both regions (a) and (b).

The transformation of CR nuclei by collisions in the ISM can be described by a diffusion equation (sometimes called a transport equation) of the type published by Ginzburg and Syrovatskii (1964); see also Shapiro et al. 1972, and Silberberg et al. 1989. In simplified form, the solution to this equation can be written:

$$J_i(E) = (J_{i,1} + J_{i,2} + J_{i,3} + J_{i,4}) f_m, \qquad (1)$$

where J_i is the total flux of primary i-type nuclei; $J_{i,1}$ is the intensity of <u>primordial</u> i-type nuclei surviving a path x, and arriving at the top of the atmosphere with energy E; $J_{i,2}$ is the flux of i-type secondaries generated over a path x; $J_{i,3}$ and $J_{i,4}$ are the tertiary and quaternary products; f_m is the modulation coefficient that incorporates both solar and geomagnetic effects.

For a path-length distribution of the form e^{-x/λ_e}, where λ_e is the mean path, the first and second terms of Equation (1) are, respectively:

$$J_{i,1}(E) = \frac{1}{\lambda_e} \int_0^\infty f_{ion}(E,x)\, J_{i,o}\, e^{-x/\lambda_i}\, e^{-x/\lambda_e}\, dx \qquad (2)$$

$$J_{i,2}(E) = \frac{1}{\lambda_e} \int_0^\infty e^{-x/\lambda_i}\, e^{-x/\lambda_e} \left\{ \sum_j \frac{P_{ji}}{\lambda_j}\, J_{j,o} \cdot \right.$$

$$\left. \int_0^x f_{ion}(E,x_i)\, f_{col}(E')\, f_{ion}(E',x_j)\, e^{-x_j(\frac{1}{\lambda_j} - \frac{1}{\lambda_i})}\, dx_j \right\}\, dx \qquad (3)$$

$J_{i,o}$ and $J_{j,o}$ are the intensities of i- and j-nuclei in the absence of interstellar matter and of modulation effects. f_{ion} is an ionization loss factor, and f_{col}, the collision energy loss factor. E' is the energy of a j-type nucleus just before it collides. In Equation (3) x_i is the path of the daughter nucleus and x_j that of the parent; $x_i + x_j = x$. The tertiary and quaternary intensities, $J_{i,3}$ and $J_{i,4}$ involve more complex expressions which have been used in the calculations. Actually, cross sections rather than mean free paths are usually measured. So it is convenient for purposes of calculation to replace the latter in Equns. (2) and (3) by suitable transformations (see Shapiro et al. 1972)

In order to deduce a source composition, one can solve the diffusion equations numerically: the fragmentation of the primordial nuclei, and the production and attenuation of the secondaries are calculated in successive increments of path length. First, however, one adopts a trial source composition resembling, say, the solar one, and also a path-length distribution. One then derives an <u>arriving</u> composition, and compares it to the observed one. Both the trial source composition and the distribution function of path lengths are modified to improve the fit with observations.

Results of this iterative procedure are displayed in Figure 7 showing the relative abundances of cosmic rays at the sources and near the earth. The arriving particles are subdivided into the surviving "original" nuclei and the secondaries generated en route. All abundances have been normalized to a value of 100 for the total flux of arriving carbon. For each element in the figure (with few exceptions), there are two adjacent ordinates. The diagonally hatched column gives the source abundance; the black-and-white column represents the overall abundance of the <u>arriving</u> nuclide. In the latter, the white portion gives the surviving flux of nuclei from the <u>source</u>, and the dark portion specifies the surviving <u>secondary</u> nuclei produced en route. In order that the abundances of the rarest elements be visible, the right side of the histogram was expanded in scale compared to the left side. We see that, of the principal arriving cosmic-ray elements, substantial fractions of C, O, Ne, Mg, and Si have survived. On the other hand, each of these is accompanied by an appreciable admixture of secondaries. Li, Be, and B are entirely secondary, as is flourine, and the total arriving nitrogen exceeds the primordial contribution. Owing to its large geometric cross section, cosmic-ray iron is sharply depleted, much of it being transformed into nuclides of the sub-iron group.

7. INJECTION AND ACCELERATION

How and where do the cosmic rays acquire their prodigious particle energies? In recent years some promising advances have been made in answering these questions. The favored mechanisms of acceleration can be traced to the concepts of magnetohydrodynamics (MHD) due to Hannes Alfven. Enrico Fermi built upon these ideas in his seminal theories of acceleration. Alfven emphasized that the acceleration of ions in space arises from variations in the magnetic fields, and is produced by "magnetic pumping". He argued that ions can be energized in the earth's magnetosphere, in the interplanetary medium, in the ISM, and even in extragalactic space as well. In the light of subsequent observations, his predictions seem well founded.

Fermi devised a scheme of stochastic acceleration in which charged particles gain energy by encounters with irregularities in moving magnetic fields. These could be clouds of plasma in the ISM; if a moving ion and a cloud are approaching each other, then the ion gains energy in the "collision" at the expense of the cloud. To be sure, if the ion is overtaking the cloud, it loses energy. However, on the average, head-on-collisions occur more often than overtaking ones, so the particle gains energy in the long run. A success of

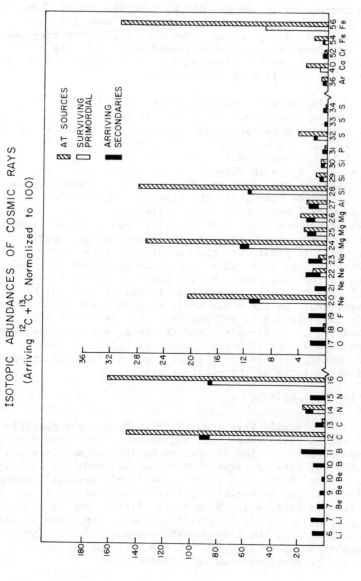

Figure 7. The relative abundances of nuclides at cosmic-ray sources and near the earth. In the arriving columns, the secondaries and the surviving source component are shown separately.

Fermi's so-called "second-order" theory was that it yielded a power-law energy spectrum, as is observed. Some difficulties with this early theory were that it generated a relatively slow, inefficient acceleration, and required what seemed to be a high threshold for injection--especially for the heavier particles having a high rate of ionization loss. In his later ("first order") theory, Fermi proposed that the spiral arms of the Galaxy might operate as magnetic bottles with a configuration like that of a plasma "mirror machine". Suppose that the magnetic field lines in a segment of a spiral arm converge toward the ends. If the magnetized plasma near the two ends of the "trap" approach each other, then the confined ion will gain energy. A special, analogous case of such efficient acceleration would be the relative approach of two contiguous clouds, with an ion between them gaining energy in successive collisions. This could happen efficiently within the confines of a supernova remnant, as realized by Ginzburg (1953).

Implicit in early theories of acceleration was the supposition that particles of modest energy (say, 1-10 MeV) are somehow injected into the regions where a further boost in energy occurs. The nature of the injection process has been elusive, but evidence has been accumulating that initially the thermal particles destined to become cosmic rays are pre-selected according to the first ionization potential (FIP) of the parent atoms. Generally, elements with low FIP are more abundant than those with higher FIP, as can be seen in Figure 8 (Silberberg et al. 1989). The data in this figure are based mainly on the satellite HEAO-3 experiment of the French-Danish collaboration (Lund, 1984).

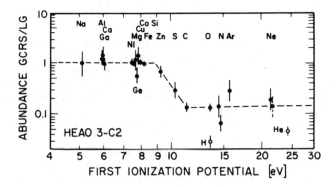

Figure 8. Comparison of the relative abundances of the galactic cosmic-ray source and the local galactic abundances, normalized at Mg. [Courtesy Silberberg et al. (1989)]

For many years, supernova explosions were regarded as the "machines" that could produce the GCR (see Shapiro 1962 and references therein). About 10^{53} ergs are released from the outburst within seconds after collapse of the stellar core, most of the energy going into neutrinos. Some 10^{51} ergs appear as kinetic energy of the ejected debris. In the precursor star, successive generations of nucleosynthesis have reached the stage of silicon-burning, with the formation of an iron core. As its exothermic energy sources are exhausted, the stellar core collapses to a neutron star, while the outer envelope explodes, giving rise to a supernova remnant, of which the Crab Nebula is the most famous example. If only one percent of the kinetic energy goes into high-energy particles, the source strength of supernovae suffices energetically to produce the observed CR intensity. (The frequency of these stellar explosions is estimated to be about twice per century). Current theories attribute the main acceleration of CR to their encounters with shockwaves in the ISM. The direct evidence that shocks occurring in outer space can boost particle energies comes from observations with space probes in the interplanetary medium. The shocks in the ISM are believed to be mainly those at the leading edge of expanding shells of supernovae. An important difference of this view from the older supernova theories of origin is that formerly the CR were thought to be boosted directly from freshly ejected material within the supernova remnant. Likewise, the acceleration itself was supposed to occur within the remnant. While modern theories still regard the supernova explosions as the main energy source, the ions that are ultimately promoted to CR energies reside in the ISM, and are accelerated by the shock fronts that they encounter (see, for example, Axford 1981). It will be noted that shock acceleration is still basically a Fermi mechanism, in that it is due to the ion's interaction with the magnetic inhomogeneities in the shock front.

We may now ask, is injection into the ISM really needed in order to start the accelerating process? There are experts (e.g., Eichler 1979) who believe that the "seed" particles can be boosted to CR energies directly from the thermal pool in the ISM. Others, however, such as Casse (1983) and Meyer (1985) have argued that the CR source composition precludes such direct acceleration. One reason is that the temperature in the ISM--notably in the hot phase that fills most of the Galactic volume--are not conducive to FIP selection. Accordingly, injection of, say, 1-10 MeV ions into the ISM from suitable sources is most probably required. Though many eruptive stars are likely to contribute some seed ions into the ISM, two particularly favorable classes of stars seem to be the dMe and dKe stars (Shapiro 1987). The possibility that these flare stars might provide seed particles has cropped up several times in recent years, but a detailed argument establishing energetic and compositional plausibility has only recently been advanced (Shapiro 1989). It appears that the powerful and frequent flares of the numerous dMe and dKe red dwarfs can populate the ISM with the seed particles required for the shock acceleration of the bulk of the cosmic rays.

8. ISOTOPES IN THE COSMIC-RAY COMPOSITION

The GCR nuclei arriving in the solar system are a mixture of stable and radioactive species. It has been demonstrated that the interactions occurring en route must have a profound effect on the relative abundances detected near the earth. As a result, the composition of the cosmic rays arriving at the top of the atmosphere is quite different from that just after production at the sources, not only in their elemental makeup, but particularly in their isotopic distribution. For example, such nuclides as ^{3}He, ^{7}Be, and ^{15}N are relatively abundant in the arriving cosmic rays, though absent or scarce in the general composition of matter.

In theories of origin and propagation of cosmic rays a central problem is this: what are the relative cosmic-ray abundances when the particles are just leaving the sources? This composition provides a starting point for calculating the production and attenuation of secondary nuclides. To do so requires, as we have seen, the solution of diffusion equations in which the path length distribution, the partial cross sections for fragmentation, and the particle energies are among the parameters.

The composition at the cosmic-ray sources has been calculated by adjusting the values of the source-abundances in the diffusion equation until the _calculated_ arriving composition near the earth agreed with the _observed_ composition of cosmic-ray nuclei at the top of the earth's atmosphere. The calculations require detailed knowledge of the many modes of cosmic-ray spallation and their respective cross sections as a function of energy.

8.1 _Cross Sections for Fragmentation_. In recent years, progress has been made both in Laboratory measurements and in calculations of break-up cross sections. Originally, the group at the Bernas Laboratory in Orsay applied mass spectrometry to this problem, and the NRL group devised semiempirical relationships based upon nuclear systematics and the available measured values. Meanwhile, relativistic beams of heavy ions were developed at Berkeley, Dubna and other accelerator laboratories, with energies exceeding those hitherto available by two orders of magnitude. In this way, it became possible to measure the production rates of many more secondaries. The predictive value of the semiempirical formulations could be tested and confirmed, and the formulae themselves could be further refined.

8.2 _Calculation of Isotopic Composition_. These developments enhanced our confidence in deducing the relative abundance of the cosmic ray elements at the sources. Once a source composition has been derived (by a best fit to the arriving _elemental_ composition), the procedure can be turned around to estimate the arriving _isotopic_ composition. Starting with their calculated elemental source composition, the NRL group computed the expected _isotopic_ distribution of cosmic rays at the top of the earth's atmosphere (Tsao et al. 1973). The isotopic abundances of the various elements at the sources were taken to be the same as those in the solar system, according to Cameron. Some typical results are depicted in Figure 9 which compares some of the predicted cosmic-ray abundances with the corresponding nuclidic abundances in the general (thermal) composition found in the solar system.

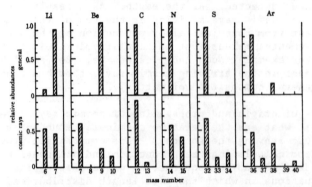

Figure 9. Comparison of the calculated isotopic abundances for several elements in the arriving cosmic rays with observed abundances in solar system material (Tsao et al, 1973). The columns are adjusted so that the total for each element is normalized to unity.

It can be seen that for most of the elements the two distributions are strikingly different. For example, in the general composition, 93 per cent of lithium consists of ^{7}Li; in the cosmic rays, about half of it is expected to be ^{6}Li. "Normal" beryllium is almost entirely ^{9}Be, while in the arriving cosmic rays, only about 30 per cent of this element should be ^{9}Be, about 60 per cent ^{7}Be, and $\leq$ 10 per cent ^{10}Be. (As discussed below, nuclei like ^{7}Be, that decay only by electron capture, are expected to survive in cosmic rays.) ^{15}N comprises only 4 x 10^{-3} of ordinary nitrogen, but it should constitute very nearly one half of the element in cosmic rays. For sulfur, argon, potassium, and calcium, the lightest isotopes predominate in the general abundances, while in the arriving cosmic rays, the heavier isotopes contribute about half of the total.

Measurements of relative isotopic abundances for many of the cosmic-ray elements are still in their infancy. Certain striking qualitative features, however, have already been confirmed: the predominance of ^{7}Be among the beryllium isotopes, and the comparable fluxes of ^{15}N and ^{14}N in the arriving cosmic rays.

Thus far, the measured and calculated isotopic compositions of the elements from lithium to oxygen agree rather well. This suggests that the NRL model is a reasonable representation of the isotopic composition at the sources. Any significant isotopic <u>differences</u> that may be discovered between predicted values for the local cosmic rays and observations, would show that the isotopic composition at the sources must differ from that elsewhere in nature. Such discrepancies would provide guidelines for modifying an initially adopted source model; they would tell us about special conditions at the sources, (or at least at some sources), and the processes of nucleosynthesis operating there. (See Sec. 8.6 below).

8.3 The Helium Isotopes. Among the well-established results on galactic cosmic-ray isotopes are those for helium at low energies. About ten per cent of helium nuclei at energies of $\sim$ 100 to 500 MeV are ^{3}He. The flux of ^{3}He is virtually all secondary, for its relative abundance in the general composition is hundreds of times lower. If we inquire what mean path length of interstellar material is required to produce by spallation the observed fraction of ^{3}He, the answer (4 to 6 g/cm^2) agrees rather well with the mean path deduced from the production of Li, Be, and B.

Stripping of ^{4}He in collisions with interstellar gas is the main source of the ^{3}He, both indirectly (by stripping off a neutron) and directly, through proton stripping and the subsequent decay of tritium. It may be remarked that the sizeable cross sections for nucleon stripping of energetic ions make this process one of the more important agents of cosmic-ray transformations. Thus, the two nuclides next in abundance to ^{4}He, i.e., ^{16}O and ^{12}C, undergo stripping, and give rise to rather copious fluxes of ^{15}N and ^{11}B, respectively. These two nuclides, somewhat like ^{3}He, are generated directly--by proton stripping--and also indirectly, through the intermediate production of radioactive ^{15}O and ^{11}C by neutron stripping.

8.4 Electron-Capture Isotopes and Cosmic-Ray Chronology. Among the radioactive cosmic-ray nuclides are some neutron-deficient species that decay by capturing one of their K-electrons, rather than by emitting a positron. However, at high velocities in a tenuous medium, a K-capture nucleus is effectively stable since in cannot then capture an electron. A striking example is ^{7}Be which has a half-life T of 53 days at rest. At energies $\gtrsim$ 10 MeV it can survive for millions of years in interstellar space, and it is in fact the most abundant of the three Be isotopes arriving in the cosmic rays. If it is to avoid decay the ^{7}Be ion must, of course, be completely stripped of its orbital electrons--a condition satisfied by cosmic-ray nuclei that have been accelerated to relativistic energies: of these, K-capture nuclei can survive as long as they have not been unduly slowed down (to $\sim$ 10 MeV/nucleon for light nuclei like ^{7}Be, and to $\sim$ 300 MeV/nucleon for the Fe group).

Cosmic-ray ^{7}Be is a secondary fragment of heavier nuclei. Certain other K-capture nuclides are formed mainly during nucleosynthesis rather than by subsequent spallation. Among these are three--^{57}Co, ^{44}Ti, and ^{59}Ni-- which have been proposed as tracer-clocks for estimating the magnitude of the time t_a from nucleosynthesis until acceleration up to, say, $\sim$ 300 MeV/nucleon. A fast K-capture atom which has not decayed in the time t_a will have been stripped of its electrons during the period of acceleration, and thereby avoid decay indefinitely while propagating through interstellar space. Thus ^{57}Co (T = 1 year) will be present in the arriving cosmic rays if these were accelerated within a year after nucleosynthesis, and will be essentially absent if acceleration requires more than a few years, for it will have decayed into ^{57}Fe. Since the present state of our knowledge by no means precludes time t_a >> 1 year, we may require chronometers of longer half life; two such nuclides are ^{44}Ti (with T = 47 years) and ^{59}Ni (T = 8 x 10^4 years). The approximate bounds that can be placed upon t_a by detecting the survival or decay of these tracers--and of ^{57}Co are shown in the following table:

K-Capture Nuclide	Time for Acceleration t_a (years) if nuclide is	
	Present	Absent
^{57}Co	≤ 1	> 1
^{44}Ti	≤ 50	> 50
^{59}Ni	≤ 10^5	> 10^5

Available data on the relative abundances of cobalt and nickel in the cosmic rays imply that ^{57}Co has decayed, hence that t_a > 1 year. Isotopic measurements of nickel may tell us which of two models is more tenable--acceleration of fresh supernova material or acceleration of old interstellar gas. In the former case, ^{59}Ni should be present in the arriving cosmic rays, in the latter case it should be absent. Similarly, various models of acceleration in supernova remnants predict different values of t_a which can be tested from the presence or absence of ^{44}Ti.

8.5 The Residence Time of Cosmic Rays. Among the long-lived radioactive tracers for measuring cosmic-ray lifetime in the Galaxy, ^{10}Be has been especially useful (Hayakawa et al. 1958; Peters 1963; Shapiro and Silberberg 1967, 1968, 1970). The ^{10}Be has a mean life of 2.5 x 10^6 years; it decays into ^{10}B.

In 1969, the NRL group reported (11th Conf. Budapest) based on a measured rate of Be/B at relativistic energies, an estimate of T < 10^7 y for the age of the CR nuclei. Later, measurements of the Be isotopes at low energies became feasible through satellite experiments.

The observed abundance of ^{10}Be must be compared with the calculated rate of beryllium production in space, from the heavier cosmic rays. If very little of the isotope is found in the arriving cosmic rays, this means that they have been traveling for a long time --long enough to allow the radioisotope to die out. If, on the other hand, most of the beryllium has survived, this would signify that the cosmic rays have lived for a time short compared to the "mean life" of the beryllium nuclei. The principle of the "nuclear tracer-clock" in determining the CR dwell time is illustrated in Figure 10. Limiting values of calculated relative abundances of the tracer are displayed for the extreme cases of total survival and complete decay of a long-lived radionuclide. The dashed curve refers to a hypothetical case in which the half-life is somewhat shorter than the escape time.

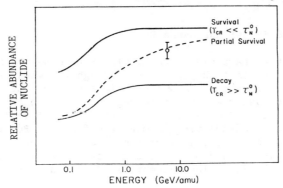

Figure 10. Tracer method for determining the galactic confinement time of cosmic rays. Limiting values of calculated relative abundances of the tracer are shown for the extreme possibilities of total survival and complete decay of a long-lived radionuclide. The dashed curve (and experimental point) illustrate an hypothetical case in which the half-life is somewhat shorter than the dwell time.

The Chicago group, in a satellite experiment, obtained sufficient, well-resolved isotopic data to estimate the cosmic-ray age (Simpson 1983). Taken together with subsequent work by Wiedenbeck (1983), a reasonable value of the residence time is ~ 10^7 years.

8.6 Isotopic "Anomalies" at the Source

Of the major isotopic differences thus far deduced between cosmic-ray source material and local (e.g., solar) matter, the abundance of ^{22}Ne in the sources is very striking: it has about 3.5 times the solar value. In addition, ^{25}Mg, ^{26}Mg, ^{29}Si and ^{30}Si appear to be "excessive" in the sources. These anomalies suggest that at least some of the CR sources may have had different conditions for nucleosynthesis (e.g., neutron-rich environments) than the sources responsible for the solar system composition.

As we acquire more reliable information about isotopic abundances in the cosmic rays, it should become possible to solve fundamental problems of their propagation, chronology, acceleration, and sites of origin. Consider, for example, the primordial nuclidic material prior to acceleration: is it young, newly born in nucleosynthesis, is it old (swept up from the interstellar medium), or does it consist of a mixture of these two? Assuming that it is fresh material, must it be produced in special processes of nucleosynthesis or can its composition be generated in the same processes that give rise to ordinary thermal matter? How much time is then required for acceleration? This time--and also the duration of magnetic trapping in the galaxy--can be estimated from measurements of radioactive tracers in the cosmic rays. The total time since nucleosynthesis can also be inferred from radioactive species, i.e. those of thorium and uranium.

9. HIGH-ENERGY NEUTRINOS AND GAMMA RAYS

Neutrinos are neutral particles with little or no mass which interact so weakly with matter that they can pass through the whole earth--and even through a star like the sun--without interaction. Relativistic electrons have been detected in remote regions of space through the radiations they emit, and especially the "synchrotron" radiation produced by electrons circulating in magnetic fields. But the more numerous cosmic-ray nuclei, mainly protons, have not been observed in sources at great distances from our solar system, owing to their tortuous paths in the ISM. The nascent field of neutrino astronomy can help solve this problem.

Neutrinos pervade all of space, along with photons and cosmic rays. However, according to the standard big-bang cosmology, the density of neutrinos is about a billion times higher than the average space density of atoms in the universe. That we have only begun to see extraterrestrial neutrinos poses a tantalizing challenge.

9.1 Neutrinos as Tracers of Cosmic-Ray Sources. Most of the neutrinos are exceedingly low in energy and extremely difficult to detect. Actually all neutrinos tend to elude observation. For the high-energy neutrinos that arise from cosmic-ray collisions with matter, however, the prospects of detection are brighter. It is these very energetic neutrinos that may reveal observationally the origin of cosmic-ray nuclei in exotic objects like pulsars and quasars and the cores of other active galaxies.

One may ask: could not radio astronomy, or x-ray or gamma-ray astronomy provide such information? Radio emission is produced by high-energy electrons in magnetic fields, and x-rays when such electrons collide with photons. They thus point back to the locations of sources of the cosmic-ray electrons. But the energy distribution of electrons becomes distorted by energy losses in magnetic fields, which actually prevent the acceleration of electrons to the higher energies. This is a severe shortcoming; to learn about the acceleration process, it is essential to know the energy spectrum. Furthermore, a study a cosmic-ray protons is required, since they vastly outnumber the electrons arriving at the earth.

Gamma-rays are produced as tertiary offspring of cosmic-ray nuclei colliding with matter; the ephemeral "neutral pions", (directly produced) disintegrate into gamma-rays. These could, in principle, tell us about the sites of acceleration of cosmic-ray protons and of heavier nuclei. However, gamma-rays are _also_ generated by the Compton effect--electrons colliding with photons. Other gamma rays are produced by the "braking" of electrons giving so-called "Bremsstrahlung." These latter processes seem to dominate over those due to proton interactions in their production of gamma rays. Thus, in important respects, neutrinos provide a unique test for models of cosmic-ray sites and acceleration processes.

9.2 _Detection of Cosmic Neutrinos_. Neutrino astronomy is beset by the great difficulty in observing the elusive particles. Due to their very low cross sections for interaction, a large detector volume is required. This problem could be solved by the proposed DUMAND (Deep Underwater Muon and Neutrino Detection) experiment: an appreciable fraction of a cubic kilometer of ocean would be the basic detector, and the target mass as well. Neutrino-initiated showers and muons will be "seen" in this detector by photo-electric particle sensors, spaced in an array some tens of meters apart.

For over a decade intensive studies have been carried out to identify candidate celestial sources of neutrinos. These studies have focused principally on the high-energy domain (above 10^{11} eV). Much of the pioneering work was done by participants in Project DUMAND whose efforts have stimulated research on lower-energy cosmic neutrinos as well. With the detection of neutrinos from Supernova 1987a, neutrino astronomy has finally emerged as an observational science. This, in turn, has prompted the design of new instrumental arrays for cosmic _high-energy_ neutrino and gamma-ray detection. The main neutrino background is due to cosmic-ray collisions in the earth's atmosphere. Some promising sources of cosmic neutrinos have been investigated. Among these are the expanding shells around young pulsars or neutron stars formed in a supernova collapse.

Outside of our galaxy, if a central massive black hole is the power source of a Seyfert galaxy like NGC 1068 or NGC 4151, these are also plausible candidate sources. NGC 1068 is the Seyfert closest to us (some 15 megaparsecs away). Its compact core pours out as much power as 200 billion suns. Neutrino astronomy gives promise of teaching us about acceleration mechanisms and other processes occurring, e.g., in pulsars, in compact binary systems and in active galactic nuclei.

9.3 _Very-High-Energy and Ultra-High-Energy Gamma Rays_. Cosmic gamma rays have come into their own as an astronomical discipline, and also as tracers of cosmic-ray interactions. At energies up to the GeV domain much has been learned from the SAS-2 and COS-B satellites (see, for example, Ramana Murthy and Wolfendale 1986 and Chupp 1976). Here we shall call attention to recent discoveries at ground-based observatories in the VHE (10^{11} - 10^{14} eV) and the UHE (> 10^{14} eV) regions. The former has depended on mirrors for collection of

Cerenkov light; the latter has employed extensive-air-shower (EAS) arrays.

There is a growing body of data on celestial sources that generate these UHE and VHE photons. Among these are the binary systems Cyg X-3, Her X-1, Vela X-1, and the Crab Nebula. The EAS apparently generated by UHE photons, have aroused controversy and even skepticism. Confusion has arisen partly because of the sporadic character of the signals and partly because of the anomalously high muon content in their cascades. Extragalactic sources have also been reported, e.g., Cen A, 3C 273, and M 31; the reports will require confirmation. The discovery by Samorski and Stamm (1983) of pulsed UHE gamma rays from Cyg X-3 excited great attention mainly because the nuclear primaries of the putative photons (up to $\simeq 10^{15}$ eV) would have to be about 20 times as energetic. Thus a "point source" of cosmic rays capable of boosting protons up to $\sim 10^{16}$ eV would be established. Hillas (1984) and Wdowczyk and Wolfendale (1983) emphasized the importance of such gamma-ray sources as possible sites of copious cosmic-ray production. Several large ground based arrays are now being enlarged or constructed with a view to clearing up the enigmas engendered by these UHE observations.

9.4 <u>Antiprotons</u>. A small but finite flux of antiprotons must be expected in the primaries detected above the atmosphere. These are secondaries of cosmic-ray collisions in the ISM. Some measurements of this intensity have yielded values higher than those predicted by propagation theory. One result, especially puzzling, was the considerable number of <u>low</u>-energy $\bar{p}$ reported by Buffington (1981). Within the past year, however, upper limits obtained for the antiproton flux at energies of a few hundred MeV have shown that the earlier results must have been in error. The new measurements (Salamon et al. 1988, Moats et al. 1988) agree with "standard" propagation theory.

10. OTHER ASPECTS OF THE COSMIC RADIATION

Constraints of time and space have led to omission of important topics in CR astrophysics. A few that come to mind are the Anomalous Component, the highest-energy CR, extragalactic CR, nucleosynthesis, components and properties of the ISM, the role of CR in the dynamics of the Galaxy, low-energy cosmic rays as catalytic agents in space chemistry, gamma-ray spectroscopy, instrumental advances in CR detection, etc. The interested reader is referred to the literature, some of it in the General Bibliography.

REFERENCES

Axford, W. I. (1981), in G. Setti, G. Spada, and A.W. Wolfendale
    (eds.), Origin of Cosmic Rays, D. Reidel Co., Dordrecht, p. 339 ff.
Binns, W. R. (1986), in M.M. Shapiro and J.P.Wefel (eds.), Genesis and
    Propagation of Cosmic Rays, Reidel Publ. Co., Dordrecht, p. 71 ff.
Buffington, A., Schindler, S.M. and Pennypacker, C.R. (1981), Ap. J.
    248, 1179
Burbidge, E.M., Burbidge, G.R., Fowler, W.A., and Hoyle, F. (1957),
    Rev. Mod. Phys. 29., 547
Casse',M. (1983), in M.M. Shapiro (ed), Composition and Origin of Cos-
    mic Rays, Reidel Publ. Co., Dordrecht, p. 193 ff.
Chupp, E. L. (1976), Gamma Ray Astronomy, Reidel Publ. Co., Dordrecht
Eichler, D. (1979), Ap. J. 229, 419
Fleischer, R.L., Price, P.B., and Walker, R.M. and Hubbard, E.L. (1967)
    Phys. Rev., 156, 353
Fowler, P.H., Adams, R.A., Cowen, V.G., and Kidd, J.M. (1967), Proc.
    Roy. Soc. A 301,39
Freier, P.S., Lofgren, E.J., Ney, E.P., Oppenheimer, F., Bradt, H. L.,
    and Peters, B. (1948), Phys. Rev. 74, 213
Ginzburg, V.L. (1953) Uspekhi Fiz. Nauk 51, 343
Ginzburg, V.L. and Syrovatskii, S.I. (1964), Origin of Cosmic Rays,
    Pergammon Press, New York
Hayakawa, S., Ito, K., Terashima, Y. (1958), Prog. Theo. Phys., Kyoto,
    Suppl. 6, 1
Hillas, A.M.,(1984), Ann. Rev. Astron. and Astrophys. 22, 425
Lund, N. (1984), in M.M. Shapiro (ed.), Cosmic Radiation in Contempo-
    rary Astrophysics, Reidel Publ. Co., Dordrecht, p. 1, ff.
Meyer, J.P. (1985), Ap. J. Suppl., 57, 173
Moats, A., Bowen, T., Golden, R., Strittmatter, R. Stochaj, S., Ormes,
    J. and Lloyd-Evans, J. (1988), in M.M. Shapiro and J.P. Wefel (eds.),
    Kluwer Academic Publ., Dordrecht, p. 475 ff.
O'Dell, F., Shapiro, M.M., and Stiller, B.(1962), J. Phys. Soc. Japan,
    Supplem. A-III, 17, 23
Peters, B. (1963), Pontif. Acad. Sci. Scripta Varia 25, 1
Ramana Murthy, P.V. and Wolfendale, A.W. (1986), Gamma Ray Astronomy,
    Cambridge University Press
Salamon, M.H. et al., (1989), in M.M. Shapiro and J.P. Wefel (eds.),
    Cosmic Gamma Rays, Neutrinos, and Related Astrophysics, Kluwer Aca-
    demic Publ., Dordrecht, p. 465 ff.
Samorski, M. and Stamm, W. (1983), Ap. J. 268, L17
Schein, M., Jesse, W.P., and Wollan, E.O. (1941), Phys. Rev. 59, 615
Shapiro, M.M., (1962) Science 135, 175
Shapiro, M.M., (1987), Proc. 20th Internat. Conf. on Cosmic Radiation
    (ICRC), Moscow, 2, 260
Shapiro, M.M. (1990), Proc. 21st ICRC, Adelaide, Australia, Paper
    OG 9. 1-7
Shapiro, M.M. and Silberberg, R. (1967), in B.P.S. Shen (ed.), High
    Energy Nuclear Reactions, W. A. Benjamin, Inc., Addison-Wesley
    Publ., Reading, Pa., p. 33 ff.
Shapiro, M.M. and Silberberg, R. (1970), Acta Phys. Hungarica 29,
    Suppl. 1, 485

Shapiro, M.M., Silberberg, R., and Tsao, C.H. (1970a), Acta Phys. Hungarica, 29, Suppl. 1, p. 463 ff.
_____ (1970b), ibid., p. 471 ff.
_____ (1970c), ibid., p. 479 ff.
_____ (1972), in F. Reines (ed.), Cosmology, Fusion and Other Matters, Univ. of Colorado Press, Boulder, Co., p. 124 ff.
Silberberg, R. and Tsao, C.H. (1973), Ap. J. Suppl. 25, 315 and 335
Silberberg, R., Tsao, C.H. and Letaw, J.R. (1989), in M.M. Shapiro and J.P. Wefel, Cosmic Gamma Rays, Neutrinos, and Related Astrophysics, Kluwer Acad. Publ., Dordrecht, p. 491 ff.
Simpson, J.A. (1983), in M.M. Shapiro (ed.), Composition and Origin of Cosmci Rays, Reidel Publ. Co., Dordrecht, p. 1, ff.
Tsao, C.H., Silberberg, R., and Shapiro, M.M. (1973), Conference Papers, 13th ICRC, Denver, University of Denver, 1, 107
Wdowczyk, J. and Wolfendale, A. W. (1983), Nature 305, 609
Wiedenbeck, M.E., (1983), in M. M. Shapiro (ed.), Origin and Composition of Cosmic Rays, Reidel Publ. Co., Dordrecht, p. 65 ff.

GENERAL BIBLIOGRAPHY

Proceedings of the International Conferences on Cosmic Radiation (ICRC), sponsored by the International Union of Pure and Applied Physics:
17th ICRC (1981), Paris, France
18th ICRC (1983), Bangalore, India
19th ICRC (1985), La Jolla, CA, USA
20th ICRC (1987), Moscow, USSR
21st ICRC (1990), Adelaide, Australia

Books

Creutz, E. (ed.) (1958, Nuclear Instrumentation, in Hdb. Physik (Encyclop. of Physics), 45/1 and 45/2 Springer-Verlag, Berlin
Fleischer, R.L., Price, P.B., and Walker, R.M. (1975), Nuclear Tracks in Solids, Univ. of California Press, Berkeley
Ginzburg, V.L. and Syrovatskii, S.I. (1964), Origin of Cosmic Rays, Pergammon Press, New York
Hayakawa, S. (1969) Cosmic Ray Physics, Wiley-Interscience, New York
Longair, M.S. (1981), High Energy Astrophysics, Cambridge University Press
Morrison, P. (1959)Hdbk. d. Physik, 46/1, Springer-Verlag, Berlin
Powell, C.F., Fowler, P.H., and Perkins, D.H. (1959), The Study of Elementary Particles by the Photographic Method, Pergammon Press, New York
Shapiro, M.M. (ed.) (1982), Composition and Origin of Cosmic Rays, Reidel Publ. Co., Dordrecht
Shapiro, M.M. (ed.) (1984), Cosmic Radiation in Contemporary Astrophysics, Reidel Publ. Co., Dordrecht
Shapiro, M.M. and Wefel, J.P. (eds.) (1986), Genesis and Propagation of Cosmic Rays, Reidel Publ. Co., Dordrecht

Shapiro, M.M. and Wefel, J.P. (1989) (eds.), Cosmic Gamma Rays, Neu-
   trinos, and Related Astrophysics, Kluwer Academic Publishers,
   Dordrecht
Sitte, K. (ed.) (1963), Hdbk. d. Physik 46/2, Springer-Verlag, Berlin
Stecker, F.W. (1971), Cosmic Gamma Rays, NASA Publication SP-249
Wilson, J.G. and Wouthuysen, S.A. (eds.) (1958-67), Prog. Elementary
   Particle and Cosmic-Ray Physics, Vols. IV to IX, North-Holland
   Publishing Co., Amsterdam, and John Wiley & Sons, Inc., New York
Wolfendale, A. W. (1963), Cosmic Rays, Philosophical Library Inc.,
   New York

Review Articles

Cesarsky, C.J. (1980), Confinement of Cosmic Rays in the
   Galaxy, Ann. Rev. Astron. Astroph., 18, 289
Fleischer, R.L., Price, P.B. and Walker, R.M., Ann. Rev.
   Nucl. Sci., 15,1.
Meyer, P. (1969), Cosmic Rays in the Galaxy, Ann. Rev.
   Astron. Astroph., 7, 1
Shapiro, M.M. (1958), in Creutz, E. (ed.), Nuclear Instru-
   mentation, in Hdbk. d. Physik, Vol. 45, Springer-Verlag,
   Berlin
Shapiro, M.M. (1962), Supernovae as Cosmic-Ray Sources,
   Science, 135, 175
Shapiro, M.M. and Silberberg, R.,(1970), Heavy Cosmic-Ray
   Nuclei, in Ann. Rev. Nucl. Sci., 20, 323
Shapiro, M.M. and Silberberg, R. (1974), Phil. Trans. Roy.
   Soc. London, A 277, 319
Simpson, J.A. (1983), Ann. Rev. Nucl. Part. Sci. 33, 323

THE COMPOSITION OF THE COSMIC RAYS: AN UPDATE

John P. Wefel
Department of Physics and Astronomy
Louisiana State University
Baton Rouge, LA 70803-4001 USA

ABSTRACT. The relative abundances of elements and/or isotopes in the cosmic radiation are the source of information on both the sites of cosmic ray origin and acceleration and the conditions in the interstellar medium through which the particles travel. Recent (1988-90) measurements and interpretations have provided new information on cosmic ray composition and source abundances. These new results are described and compared to previous work.

1.   Introduction

The composition of the cosmic rays, both elemental and isotopic, provides information on the regions of acceleration of these high energy particles as well as on the interstellar medium (ISM) through which the particles propagate during their journey from the sources to the Earth. It is the nuclear interactions of the cosmic ray primaries (nuclei leaving the source regions) with the ambient matter in the ISM that produces secondary nuclei which can be used as tracers of the particle propagation process, providing estimates of the mean density, the total amount of material traversed and the distribution of matter in the confinement/propagation region. The importance of the secondary nuclei has been realized for over forty years since the discovery that Li, Be and B (the light L elements) were orders of magnitude more abundant in the cosmic rays than they were in solar system material. The main progenitors of the L-elements are Carbon, Nitrogen and Oxygen (the medium M nuclei), and the L/M secondary to primary ratio has been employed, most often, as a tracer of the particle propagation process.

There are other secondary components. The interaction of cosmic ray electrons with the galactic magnetic field produces radio-synchrotron emission. Moreover, interactions of cosmic rays with both matter and photon fields produce gamma rays, as well as anti-protons and positrons. All of these other secondary radiations are important, complementary sources of information on both the cosmic rays and the ISM, but will not be discussed here. Gamma ray measurements are presented in detail in other papers in this volume, and anti-proton measurements have been reviewed recently by Stephens and Golden (1987; 1988).

29

M. M. Shapiro et al. (eds.), Cosmic Rays, Supernovae and the Interstellar Medium, 29–55.

The cosmic rays are composed primarily of nuclei of the elements Hydrogen and Helium with the remaining few percent of the particles encompassing all of the other elements in the periodic table, at least up to Uranium. However, the presence of secondary nuclei in the cosmic radiation complicates the interpretation of composition measurements. The secondary component must be unfolded to obtain information on the primary particles. In addition, particle energy losses (gains) and escape from the galaxy must be considered to determine the nature of the matter at the cosmic ray source(s).

Several different "compositions" can be identified. The Measured Composition is the relative abundance of nuclei actually observed by the detectors. This must be corrected for interactions or energy loss in the apparatus or in any atmosphere (for balloon experiments) above the instrument to obtain the Arriving Composition at the top of the Earth's atmosphere. This composition must be further corrected for any effects of the Earth's magnetic field to obtain the Interplanetary Composition. Satellite experiments outside the Earth's magnetosphere measure the Interplanetary Composition directly. The Local Interstellar Composition is obtained by correcting the Interplanetary Composition for the effects of Solar Modulation due to the outflowing solar wind. Finally, the Source Composition is determined by correcting for propagation of the cosmic rays in the ISM. (Most often, a Source Composition is assumed, propagated through the ISM to determine the Local Interstellar Composition which is then modulated into the orbit of Earth to provide a calculated Interplanetary Composition at 1 A.U. to which the experimental data can be compared.) The important astrophysical information from cosmic rays is contained in the Source Composition and in the Local Interstellar Composition.

The cosmic radiation encompasses a broad range in energy, from tens of MeV/nucleon to the highest known energies, $\sim 10^{20}$ eV. The measured kinetic energy spectrum, a power law with a spectral index of ~ 2.7 above a few GeV/nucleon, rolls off at low energies due to the spectral form and to the effects of solar modulation, which must be considered in interpreting the data. The bulk of the cosmic rays fall in the range 0.1-10 GeV/nucleon in which the composition is known most reliably. However, direct measurements are now becoming available at energies up to almost 100 TeV, and these very high energy results provide much of the recent data.

The Arriving Composition is slightly dependent on energy due, mainly, to the energy dependence of the confinement and propagation process, particularly escape from the confinement region and energy dependent nuclear reaction cross sections. This implies that the composition must be measured as a function of energy, and, indeed, the energy dependences, particularly for secondary to primary ratios, provide a major constraint on models for the origin, acceleration and propagation of the particles.

The experimental techniques used to measure cosmic ray composition also vary with energy. Below several hundred MeV/nucleon, the particles can be brought to rest in detector stacks and both elemental and isotopic abundances have been measured, mainly by satellite experiments. From several hundred MeV/nucleon to about a GeV/nucleon, the experiments are performed, predominately, by balloon borne instruments (see White and Silberberg, 1991, this volume) using a variety of different techniques. At higher energies, there have been both balloon and satellite measurements using Cherenkov, transition-radiation and calorimetry techniques. Above ~ 100 TeV (10^{14} eV) the flux is so low that air shower techniques must be employed. Here it is not possible to determine the identity of individual particles. Instead, an average composition must be deduced from the data sample.

A complete review of cosmic ray composition is beyond the scope of this paper. Instead, this report focuses on some of the recent measurements and their interpretation. For additional background information, the reader is referred to reviews by Wefel (1988), Silberberg and Tsao (1990) and Garcia-Munoz et al., (1987). Specific recent reviews of elemental and isotopic composition have been presented by Simpson (1983), Mewaldt (1983; 1989), Waddington (1988), Lund (1989), and Binns et al. (1989a). A fuller treatment of the important problems in cosmic ray astrophysics can be found in previous volumes of this series (Shapiro and Wefel, 1988; 1989; Shapiro, 1983; 1986) and in the proceedings of the biennial International Cosmic Ray Conferences.

The present "update" covers new measurements of the composition up to ~100 TeV (air shower data is not included) and new or revised interpretations of the measured data. Cosmic ray propagation will not be discussed in detail nor will the work on "reacceleration" during cosmic ray confinement. These topics are covered elsewhere in this volume. The elemental composition of cosmic rays, for the $Z \leq 30$ elements, is presented in Section 2, beginning with the lowest energies and proceeding upward in energy. Section 3 discusses the Source Composition, followed by a review of the current state of UH (Z>30) cosmic ray measurements and interpretation. Finally, in Section 5, the isotopic composition of cosmic rays is discussed briefly. This "update" covers data and interpretations of the last 1-2 years, particularly results presented at the 21st International Cosmic Ray Conference in Adelaide, Australia.

2.   Elemental Composition ($Z \leq 30$)

The elemental composition of the cosmic rays up through the iron peak has been, and remains, the major source of information on the origin, acceleration and transport of this high energy sample of "galactic" matter. Studies of secondary to primary ratios have determined the exponential character of the cosmic ray pathlength distribution (PLD), the mean of the PLD and its variation with energy. Solar modulation has been studied in detail so that corrections to the cosmic ray spectra can be made accurately to determine Local Interstellar Spectra (LIS) from the measurements or to modulate calculated LIS into the heliosphere to compare to data. Finally, the derived elemental source composition provides clues to the nature of the cosmic ray source regions.

2.1 LOW AND INTERMEDIATE ENERGY RESULTS

New work on the low energy cosmic ray elemental composition comes from the Voyager spacecraft (Ferrando et al., 1990) at 22 A.U. from the sun, from the ISEE-3 satellite (Leske and Wiedenbeck, 1990) near the Earth in interplanetary space, from the Salyut-6 orbital station (Gagarin et al., 1990) in 1978-79 and from the Anuradha experiment on board Spacelab-3 (Biswas et al., 1989; 1990; Durgaprasad et al., 1990) within the Earth's magnetosphere. At intermediate energies (700-800 MeV/nucleon), results from the ALICE balloon experiment have become available (Henkel et al.,

32

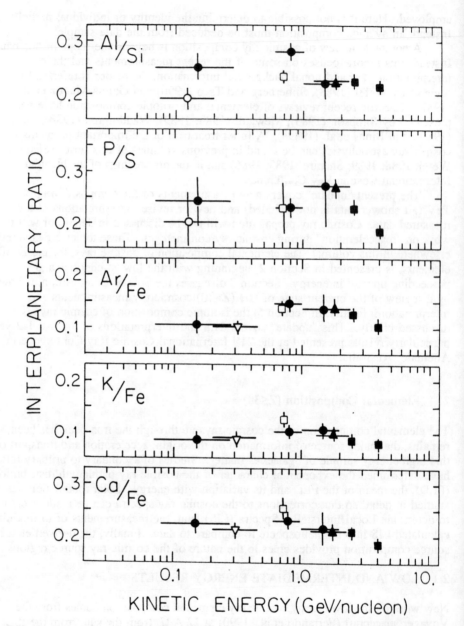

Figure 1. Measurements of the Al/Si, P/S, Ar/Fe, K/Fe and Ca/Fe ratios comparing new results (open symbols) to previous data (filled symbols). Data are from ● -- Simpson (1983), ○ -- Ferrando et al. (1990), □ -- Henkel et al. (1990), ▲ -- Dwyer and Meyer (1985), ■ -- Engelmann et al. (1983) and ▽ --Leske and Wiedenbeck (1990).

1990). Individual element ratios from these experiments (open symbols) are shown in Figures 1 and 2 compared to previous data (filled symbols) from the review by Simpson (1983), Dwyer and Meyer (1985) and the HEAO-C2 experiment (Engelmann et al., 1983). For the HEAO-C2 results only two points at 2.5 and 4 GeV/nucleon are plotted to indicate the behavior at high energy.

For almost a decade, the IMP-8 results have been the only comprehensive satellite dataset at low energies. This has now changed with the publication of the ISEE-3 and Voyager results. These three datasets show remarkable overall consistency, and together provide a firm measurement of the low energy Interplanetary Composition. The Voyager data was recorded at ~22 A.U. from the sun, with a level of solar modulation about half of that for the IMP and ISEE data. The expectation is that the measured ratios from Voyager should be lower than the 1 A.U. data (see e.g. Garcia-Munoz et al., 1987), and this is the trend observed in Figures 1 and 2. Somewhat surprising is the very low abundance of Aluminum and Vanadium reported by Voyager.

At intermediate energies, the ALICE balloon results are in good agreement with previous balloon data except for reduced abundances of Aluminum, Manganese and, possibly, Scandium. The first two of these appear to be significant differences that warrant further investigation.

Overall, however, the new data reported recently is in reasonably good agreement with previous results indicating that the composition in this charge and energy region is moderately well known. Note that these ratios show only a moderate energy dependence below a few GeV/nucleon and this dependence appears to be similar for all of the ratios shown. This implies that the relative abundances determined in different energy intervals are nearly the same. More precise measurements will be required to determine any difference in the energy dependences of these ratios.

Secondary to primary ratios of iron fragmentation products to iron (i.e. sub-Fe/Fe) have played an important role, historically, in determining the shape of the distribution of pathlengths (PLD) traversed by the cosmic rays (Shapiro and Silberberg, 1970; Garcia-Munoz et al., 1984; 1987; Osborne and Ptuskin, 1988; Soutoul, Ferrando and Webber, 1990). Briefly, the PLD which reproduces light secondary to primary ratios such as B/C predicts a sub-Fe/Fe ratio below the measured data, particularly at low energies. This need for additional iron fragmentation has led to the suggestion of a depletion of short pathlengths, i.e. a truncation of the exponential PLD. This, in turn, suggests that there may be more than one confinement volume for the cosmic rays (Guzik and Wefel, 1984). The Voyager, ISEE and ALICE data shown in Figures 1 and 2 are in essential agreement with the older results and do not qualitatively change this conclusion.

Measurements of the sub-Fe/Fe ratio (Sc-Cr/Fe) at still lower energies have produced an even more surprising result. Figure 3 shows data from the Anuradha experiment and the Salyut-6 investigation compared to previous results and to the experiments discussed above. In addition, an earlier result from Skylab (Durgaprasad and Biswas, 1988) is shown for comparison. The Anuradha, Salyut-6 and Skylab experiments all find Sc-Cr/Fe ratios significantly larger (up to factors of 2) than the low energy satellite results from IMP-8, ISEE-3 and Voyager. The dashed curve in

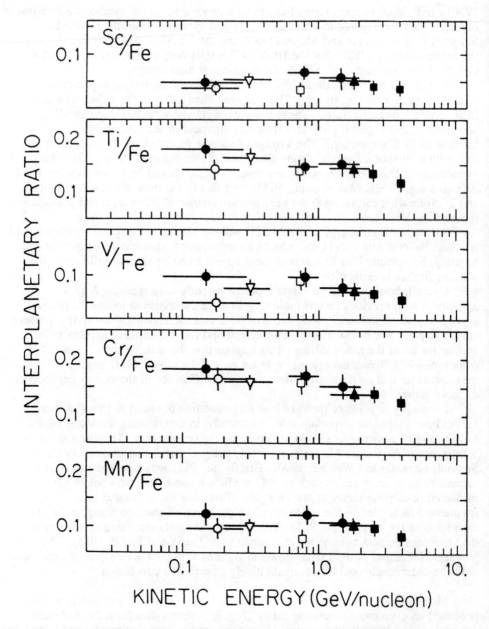

Figure 2. Measurements of the Sc/Fe, Ti/Fe, V/Fe, Cr/Fe and Mn/Fe ratios comparing new results (open symbols) to previous data (filled symbols). Data references are the same as Figure 1.

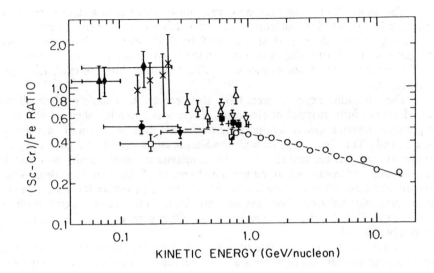

Figure 3. Compilation of (Sc-Cr)/Fe observations adapted from Durgaprasad et al., 1990. The lowest energy points (▲ and ◆) are from the Anuradha experiment (Durgaprasad et al., 1990) and the 50-250 MeV/nucleon point (◆) is from the Skylab experiment (Durgaprasad and Biswas, 1988). The Salyut-6 observations (✕) are from Gagarin et al. (1990), IMP-8 data (●) are from Simpson (1983), Voyager results (□) are from Ferrando et al. (1990) and ISEE data (▼) are from Leske and Wiedenbeck (1990). Other results shown include (△) Maehl et al. (1977), (▽) Young et al. (1981), (■) Webber (1982), (+) Lezniak and Webber (1978, 1979), (◪) Henkel et al. (1990) and HEAO-C2 (○) from Soutoul et al. (1985).

Figure 3 shows the result of a "representative" propagation calculation, which becomes flat and turns over at low energies due, largely, to ionization energy loss (see e.g. Garcia-Munoz et al., 1981; 1987). To obtain the amount of iron fragmentation required to explain the large Sc-Cr/Fe ratios measured by Anuradha, Skylab and Salyut-6 would require extreme truncation of the PLD or a major change in the propagation model.

The Anuradha, Salyut-6 and Skylab experiments all employed plastic track detectors, CR-39, Lexan or polyethyleneterephthalate. The charge resolution of such detectors in the charge region around iron is often not very good, but the charge distribution presented for the Skylab and Salyut-6 experiments do show reasonably resolved element peaks. With three separate experiments all showing the same result, the explanation is probably not "poor" charge resolution. It is interesting to note that while the Skylab point in Figure 3 covers the energy interval 50-250 MeV/nucleon, most of the excess Sc-Cr events were found at the lowest energies, 50-80 MeV/nucleon, which is about the energy interval (50-100 MeV/nucleon) reported by the Anuradha experiment. Thus, the Anuradha and Skylab results would not be completely inconsistent with the IMP, ISEE and Voyager data if the excess of sub-iron secondaries was predominantly at energies below ~80 MeV/nucleon.

The Salyut-6 investigation, however, shows a decreasing ratio with decreasing energy below ~250 MeV/nucleon. This is due to an increasing flux of iron nuclei with decreasing energy, the energy spectrum of the Sc-Cr events being almost constant (Gagarin et al., 1990). This is opposite to the trend reported for Anuradha and Skylab and brings the Salyut-6 observations into direct conflict with the IMP, ISEE and Voyager data.

The Anuradha experimenters have also reported that some of their observed nuclei are not fully stripped of electrons. There was a moving sheet of plastic in the experiment which allowed, by matching tracks, the time of arrival of each event to be determined. This time, coupled with the Shuttle flight ephemeris, gave the geographic location of the particle arrival. Then, the geomagnetic cutoff rigidity was calculated for this location and compared to the measured energy of the particle to determine the maximum charge state that the ion could possess to penetrate the geomagnetic field at the particular location. Four events were found to have low maximum charge states as: Ti (+5), Ti (+16), Cr (+6) and Fe (+10). Of course, each of these particles could be singly charged.

Combining the charge state observations with the enhanced Sc-Cr/Fe ratios, the authors suggest that this represents a "new" component of the cosmic rays which is trapped in a large molecular cloud, where fragmentation, energy loss and electron capture take place. These ions are subsequently accelerated to 30-100 MeV/nucleon, but do not pass through sufficient matter on their way to the Earth to restrip the electrons. The initial origin of this "new" component is different than the origin of the anomalous cosmic rays, but the acceleration and subsequent propagation of these particles in the heliosphere is suggested to be similar to that for the anomalous component.

Before accepting the existence of a "new" component in the cosmic rays, additional possibilities should be considered. There are two common features to the Skylab, the Salyut-6 and the two Anuradha observations; (1) all show a large proportion of iron secondaries, and (2) all of the experiments were performed within the Earth's magnetosphere in low altitude orbits. It is not possible for these heavy ions to be stably trapped particles, such as the Van Allen belt protons, but they might be quasi-trapped for up to one bounce period. A possible scenario is as follows. Incident (normal) iron nuclei just above cutoff arrive near the end of the magnetic field line connected to the spacecraft point of observation. These nuclei go through the upper layers of the Earth's atmosphere losing energy by ionization, fragmenting in the atmosphere and capturing orbital electrons. Some small fraction survive to become quasi-trapped. These gyrate along the field line and can be observed as arriving particles by experiments in low altitude orbits. Such "albedo" particles have been observed previously in a large UH cosmic ray balloon experiment employing plastic track detectors (Blanford et al., 1972). In that experiment, both iron and a large number of secondaries were found, consistent with the observations of the Anuradha, Skylab and Salyut-6 experiments.

The flux of "albedo" particles reported by Blanford et al. (1972) is too small to explain the low altitude satellite experiments, but the two experiments are not really comparable. The UH experiment had a specific scanning/event detection criterion which was different than the techniques employed by the recent experiments. Moreover, the balloon flight was from Texas under 4 g/cm^2 of residual atmosphere, which would reduce the observed number of "albedo" events. Finally, the balloon experiment was at a fixed location, connected magnetically to specific sites in the northern and southern hemisphere, while the satellite experiments in orbit sample a wide variety of magnetically connected regions.

Accepting that the "albedo" source provides a possible explanation for the Anuradha, Salyut-6 and Skylab observations, it is premature to postulate a "new" cosmic ray component. What is needed is a new experiment, sensitive to particles down to 30 MeV/nucleon, that can be flown in interplanetary space, outside the Earth's magnetosphere. Such an experiment could provide a definitive answer to the origin of these very low energy, heavy particles.

2.2 HIGH ENERGY INTERPRETATION

The most significant feature of the high energy (1-100 GeV/nucleon) composition is the decrease of secondary to primary ratios with increasing energy, as illustrated in Figure 4 for the B/C ratio (see also Figure 3). The decreasing number of secondaries implies that the amount of matter being traversed by the particles during propagation is decreasing with increasing energy. Thus, the composition measured at the highest energies is closer to the true source composition, since the correction for propagation effects is smaller.

This approach has been taken by Binns et al. (1988) and updated by Vylet et al. (1990). These authors combine data from the two experiments on the HEAO-3 spacecraft to obtain element ratios from ~1 to ~200 GeV/nucleon. Assuming that the elements K, Sc, Ti and V are purely secondary, the energy dependence of the ratios, e.g. Sc/Fe, are fit to a power-law. These fits then allow the energy dependence of the secondary component of mixed (secondary plus primary) elements such as Ar and Ca to be interpolated. Then, the secondary contribution can be subtracted to determine source abundance ratios. Binns et al. (1988) report Ar/Fe and Ca/Fe source ratios of $2.6 \pm 0.7\%$ and $8.8 \pm 0.7\%$, respectively. Vylet et al. (1990) have used improved data from the two experiments to refine the energy dependence of the measured ratios which, in turn, refines the source abundances.

The method of Binns et al. (1988) assumes that the matter traversal continues to decrease with increasing energy, i.e. the secondary component becomes smaller with increasing energy. This would imply that a mixed ratio such as Ca/Fe would show a flattening at high energy as the source component begins to dominate the secondary component. Such a flattening is observed in the data presented by Vylet et al. (1990). Alternatively, the matter traversal may not continue to decrease, but may stop at some value, i.e. all particles pass through some minimum amount of material. The secondary component, then, would become a constant value leading to a flattening of the ratio with increasing energy.

Mewaldt and Webber (1990) employed essentially the same data but have analyzed it in a series of full cosmic ray propagation calculations, altering the source abundances of the elements Ar, Ca, Cr, Mn and Ni to try to fit the measured ratios over the full energy range. They use the (Sc + Ti + V/Fe) ratio, assumed to be a pure secondary to primary ratio, to trace the propagation history of these heavy particles. An example of this method is shown in Figure 5 for the Cr/Fe ratio. (This figure is adapted from Mewaldt and Webber (1990) with the addition of the results from ISEE,

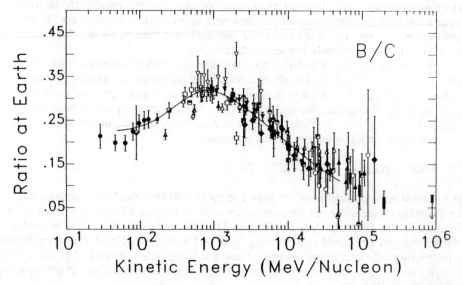

Figure 4. B/C ratio as a function of energy, adapted from Garcia-Munoz et al. (1987) who describe the data points. The CRN results have been added at high energy, (▮) -- Swordy et al., (1990). The curve shows the result of a propagation calculation (see Garcia-Munoz et al., 1987, for details).

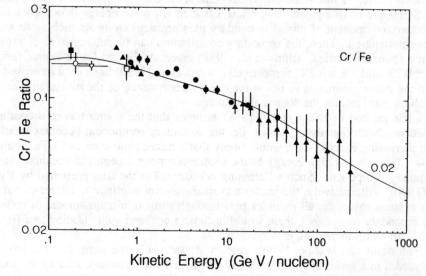

Figure 5. Cr/Fe ratios as a function of energy, adapted from Mewaldt and Webber, (1990) who describe the filled data points. Additions are the Voyager results (O), ISEE results (▽) and ALICE data (□). The curve shows the result of a full propagation calculation which assumed Cr/Fe = 2% at the cosmic ray source.

Voyager and ALICE discussed above.) The curve shows the calculated ratio for a source abundance of Cr/Fe = 2%, which is very close to their best fit value of 2.4 ± 0.6%.

The results of Mewaldt and Webber (1990) depend upon the nuclear fragmentation cross sections and the energy dependence of the propagation process. The latter is traced by the (Sc+Ti+V)/Fe ratio, and the calculations are required to reproduce this data. For cross sections, the new results of Webber, Kish and Schrier (1990) were employed. These are based on a series of recent accelerator experiments. To the extent that there are no systematic effects between Sc and Fe in the cross sections, the tracer approach should yield valid results.

At still higher energies, the CRN experiment, which flew on Spacelab-2, has reported results up to 1 TeV/nucleon (Swordy et al., 1990; Grunsfeld et al., 1988; 1990). This experiment combined gas Cherenkov counters with transition radiation detectors to obtain measurements over a large energy interval for $Z \geq 5$ nuclei. The surprising result from this experiment is that the observed spectra of the primary elements do not all have the same shape. While C and O had spectra with exponents $\gamma \sim 2.7$, in agreement with the Helium spectrum, Neon, Magnesium and, particularly, Silicon showed significantly larger indices. In fact for Silicon, no events were observed around 1 TeV/nucleon where several would have been expected. The iron group nuclei showed consistently flatter spectra than Carbon or Oxygen. The CRN data have now been analyzed in a leaky-box propagation calculation with a source spectrum of the form $E^{-2.1 \pm 0.1}$ and an escape length varying as $E^{-0.6}$. The calculated spectra agree well with the CRN measurements up to several hundred GeV/nucleon, and up to ~1 TeV/nucleon for C, O, Ne, Mg and the Fe group. The calculations, of course, do not fit the highest energy silicon point. With the exception of Silicon, however, the CRN results are consistent with the lower energy HEAO data and indicate that the source composition is about the same up to ~1 TeV/nucleon. Resolution of the question of the apparent differences in the spectra for Ne, Mg and Si will require additional experiments.

The CRN experiment also measured the energy dependence of the secondary to primary ratio, B/C, and of the mixed (secondary + primary) ratio N/O. Their B/C results are shown in Figure 4 as filled, vertical rectangles above 70 GeV/nucleon. The highest energy point is an upper limit. There is no evidence for a flattening of the B/C ratio at least up to 200 GeV/nucleon. This implies that the matter traversed continues falling with energy down to 1-2 g/cm^2 of material (Swordy et al., 1990). The current data, however, cannot exclude a flattening at or below this level, and further experiments are needed to extend the results to higher energies.

2.3 VERY HIGH ENERGIES

Measurements at still higher energies (>1 TeV/nucleon) have the potential to provide confirmation of the results at lower energies. In this very high energy region, the data on individual particles comes mainly from emulsion chambers in which the particles must interact. The interaction produces π^o's which decay into gamma rays that produce an electromagnetic shower in the calorimeter portion of the chamber. The total energy in the shower is a measure of the particle's incident energy. The charge of each event is measured in the upper layers of the chamber prior to the point of interaction. Emulsion chambers are small and compact and have a large solid angle acceptance. Being passive detectors, they are relatively easy to fly on balloons and can accumulate a large exposure factor. This experimental approach has been developed by the JACEE collaboration (Burnett et al., 1990a; 1990b; 1990c). Additional emulsion chamber investigations have been reported by Zatsepin et al. (1990) and Kawamura et al. (1990).

An alternative approach is to use a large scintillator based, ionization calorimeter combined with Cherenkov counters. Such systems have been flown on COSMOS Earth-orbiting satellites by the Moscow State University group. New results have been reported by Grigorov (1990) and by Ivanenko et al. (1990).

Figure 6 shows the differential energy spectra presented by the JACEE collaboration from measurements made on six separate balloon flights. Even with this large exposure, the statistical sample is small, and above Helium the results are presented in charge groups: C-O, Ne-S and the Fe group ($Z \geq 25$). The dashed lines show the extrapolations of spectra measured at lower energies into this very high energy region.

The Hydrogen and Helium spectra are determined most reliably. The proton events show a continuous spectrum which extends smoothly from the lower energy results up to at least 50 TeV/nucleon. Above this energy the data are consistent with either a continuation of the spectrum or with a transition ("break") to a steeper spectrum. The JACEE results are inconsistent with the proton spectrum reported by Grigorov (1990), which shows a break at a few TeV, but are in agreement with the data reported by Ivanenko et al. (1990) and Kawamura et al. (1990). The spectral indices reported for the different proton spectral measurements are:

$$\gamma = 2.76 \pm 0.09 \quad (E>6 \text{ TeV}) \quad \text{Burnett et al. (1990c)}$$
$$\gamma = 2.67 \pm 0.10 \quad (E>2.5 \text{ TeV}) \quad \text{Ivanenko et al. (1990)}$$
$$\gamma = 3.01 \pm 0.35 \quad (E>10 \text{ TeV}) \quad \text{Ivanenko et al. (1990)}$$
$$\gamma = 3.1 \pm 0.15 \quad (E>10.5 \text{ TeV}) \quad \text{Zatsepin et al. (1990) -- x-ray film alone}$$
$$\gamma = 2.93 \pm 0.15 \quad (E>20 \text{ TeV}) \quad \text{Zatsepin et al. (1990) -- x-ray + emulsion}$$
$$\gamma \sim 2.7 \text{ (est.)} \quad (E \geq 4 \text{ TeV}) \quad \text{Kawamura et al. (1990)}$$
$$\gamma = 3.08 \pm 0.15 \quad (E>4 \text{ TeV}) \quad \text{Grigorov (1990)}$$

For Helium, the JACEE results show a spectrum that is slightly steeper than for Hydrogen with an absolute intensity significantly larger than predicted by the extrapolation of lower energy data. These results are consistent with the measurements of Kawamura et al. (1990) and Ivanenko et al. (1990) who also find an increased intensity of helium. In addition, the JACEE group has analyzed H and He from a new long duration balloon flight (150 hour duration), and the new data also show an increased helium flux. This gives a p/α ratio of 12 ± 3 at 10 TeV/nucleon compared to a value of 24 ± 2 measured at 50-100 GeV/nucleon by Ryan et al. (1972). The origin of this high helium flux is still unknown. If this represents the true high energy ratio, then the source abundance of Helium, relative to protons, should be increased by a factor of ~2.

For the groups of heavier nuclei, Figure 6 shows two (dot-dash) lines extrapolated from lower energy. These are the range of extrapolations based upon the

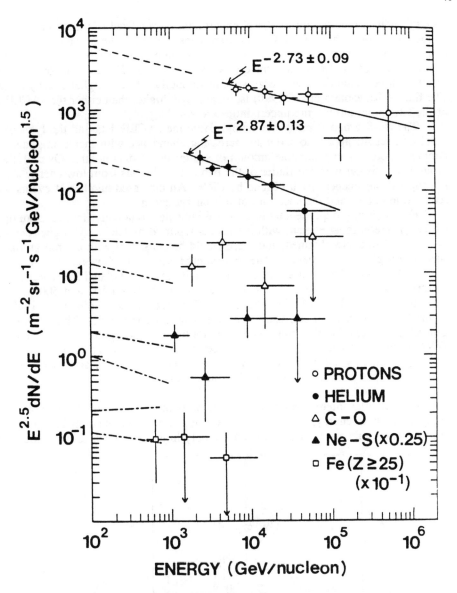

Figure 6. Differential energy spectra of the major primary components, protons, Helium, (C-O), (Ne-S), and Fe (Z ≥ 25) from the JACEE experiments. Upper (protons) and lower (helium) dashed lines denote the extrapolation of the spectra of Ryan et al. (1972). Three pairs of dash-dot lines represent the low-energy boundaries of the spectra, derived from the spectral indices of O, Mg, and Fe-group (25 ≤ Z ≤ 27) reported by Grunsfeld et al. (1988), with a normalization of (C-O), (Ne-S) and (Z ≥ 25) at 25-50 GeV/nucleon.

spectral indices reported by the CRN experiment, normalized to measurements at 25-50 GeV/nucleon. The JACEE C-O data are consistent with the low energy extrapolations. Kawamura et al. (1990) and Ivanenko et al. (1990) studied a slightly lower energy region, from a few hundred GeV/nucleon to ~20 TeV/nucleon, and obtain results that continue the low energy spectra smoothly into the higher energy region. The flux of Kawamura et al. (1990) is, on average, higher than either the JACEE data or the extrapolation, but the uncertainties are still large.

The Ne-S group is most interesting. Here the JACEE data and the Ivanenko et al. (1990) results appear to show an increasing abundance with increasing energy, although there is a considerable amount of scatter in the data points. Overall, this group is consistent with the flatter of the two extrapolations from low energy and does not support the steeper spectra found by CRN. An increased number of events will be required to understand the spectrum of this charge group.

For the iron group, the data in Figure 6 indicate a relatively flat spectrum up to ~1 TeV/nucleon in agreement with the results reported by CRN. At higher energies, only upper limits are obtained, and these would be consistent with an iron group spectrum beginning to steepen. The iron points reported by Kawamura et al. (1990) at ~200 and 500 GeV/nucleon are in agreement with the extrapolated low energy spectrum as are the results of Ivanenko et al. (1990) between 100 and 500 GeV/nucleon. At slightly higher energy, 1-2 TeV/nucleon, Zatsepin et al. (1990) report VH group spectra consistent with the other measurements. Thus, there is general agreement that the iron spectrum is flatter than the lighter elements up to 1-2 TeV/nucleon. The evolution of the iron spectrum (above a few TeV/nucleon), i.e. whether it remains flat with spectral index $\gamma \sim 2.55$ or steepens to an index $\gamma \sim 2.7$, remains an open question. Considerably increased exposures will be needed to answer this question.

Of particular interest in this energy region is the variation of the average composition with energy, since the average composition can be compared to air shower measurements extending to considerably higher energies. Such a comparison

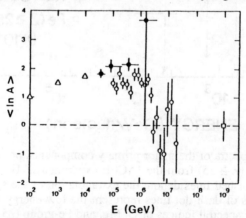

Figure 7. Comparison of the mean mass <ln A> measured by the JACEE experiments (●) with previous results (Watson 1985) for lower energy balloon data (△) and air shower analyses (O , □).

is shown in Figure 7 from Burnett et al. (1990c) where the mean atomic weight is plotted versus total particle energy for the JACEE data compared to previous results. (The highest energy solid point is based on the observation of a single event of $Z = 20$ at an energy of ~4×10^{15} eV.) The very high energy balloon results are consistent with the lower energy balloon data and extend the direct composition measurements to near 10^{15} eV total energy. In the $10^{14} - 10^{15}$ eV region, the balloon data is slightly higher than the estimates from air showers. At higher energies the air shower results indicate an apparent change at ~5×10^{15} eV to a proton dominated composition. Considerably larger balloon (or space) exposures will be required to bridge this energy gap and extend the direct composition measurements into the region of the apparent change.

3. Source Abundances

The cosmic ray source abundances provide information on the nucleosynthetic history of the cosmic ray matter and give clues to the "sites" of cosmic ray origin. Determining source abundances involves unfolding the propagation effects, particularly secondary nuclei, from the measured composition. Table I presents three sets of source abundances determined in 1975, 1983 and 1989, all normalized to silicon. Comparing entries along a row gives an idea of the "progress" that has been achieved in the past 15 years. Note that for the major primary elements, C, O, Ne, Mg, S and Fe, the values of the source abundances have not changed drastically, but the uncertainty assigned to the values has decreased. This is due both to better measurements and to more refined models for propagation in the ISM, particularly the nuclear cross sections that are used in the propagation calculations.

For the mixed elements, Na, Al, P, Cl-Ca, the early results were, often, only estimates. Improved data and propagation models in recent years have led to much better source abundances for many of these elements between S and Fe. Yet, there is still much work to be done in refining and improving these values.

For Hydrogen there is a considerable uncertainty depending upon whether the hydrogen and helium are considered as a function of rigidity or as a function of energy. This has led to large differences in the source abundance assigned to hydrogen.

From the recent results considered in this "update," there have been refinements to the source abundances which are noted in the fifth column of the table. The increased He source abundance, shown in parenthesis, is the inference of the decreased p/α ratio reported by JACEE at very high energies. It is still very uncertain, and an energy dependence for H and He between 50 GeV/nucleon and about 10 TeV/nucleon is difficult to reconcile with current models for cosmic ray propagation in the ISM.

For Nitrogen, the revised source abundance comes from the ^{14}N/O source ratios reported by Krombel and Wiedenbeck (1988) -- 3.7 ± 1.7% -- and Gupta and Webber (1989) -- 3.8 ± 1.0%. The data which has been analyzed by these groups consists of both the N/O elemental ratio and the isotopic ratios ^{14}N/O and ^{15}N/O with the latter acting as a "tracer" of the propagation process. This new Nitrogen source ratio is considerably smaller than the previous (1989) estimate.

The improved source abundance estimates for Ar, Ca, Cr, Mn and Ni come from the work of Mewaldt and Webber (1990) discussed previously. Both Ar and Ca are

TABLE I. COSMIC RAY SOURCE ABUNDANCES

Element	1975 (a)	1983 (b)	1989 (c)	1990 update	Local Galactic (d)
H	$2.4 \pm 0.3 \times 10^5$		$8.9 \pm 2.2 \times 10^4$		$2.7 \pm 0.3 \times 10^6$
He	$1.2 \pm 0.2 \times 10^4$		$1.2 \pm 0.1 \times 10^4$	(2.4×10^4)	$2.6 \pm 0.7 \times 10^5$
C	480 ± 70	444 ± 57	431 ± 34		1260 ± 330
N	38 ± 11	31 ± 7	31 ± 12	19 ± 9	225 ± 90
O	529 ± 76	513 ± 66	511 ± 20	$\equiv 511$	2250 ± 560
F		<5	<2.5		0.09 ± 0.06
Ne	71 ± 14	61 ± 10	64 ± 8		325 ± 160
Na	4.3 ± 2.0	10 ± 2	6 ± 4		5.5 ± 1.0
Mg	114 ± 19	109 ± 15	106 ± 6		105 ± 3
Al	11 ± 5	14 ± 2	10 ± 4		8.4 ± 0.4
Si	$\equiv 100$	$\equiv 100$	$\equiv 100$		$\equiv 100$
P	1^{+2}_{-1}	2.2 ± 0.5	<2.5		0.9 ± 0.2
S	14 ± 3	12.6 ± 2.0	12.6 ± 2.0		43 ± 15
Cl	$0.5^{+2.5}_{-0.5}$	1.0 ± 0.5	<1.6		0.5 ± 0.3
Ar	3.8 ± 2.4	<2.1	3.0 ± 0.7	1.8 ± 0.6	11 ± 5
K	$0.5^{+2.5}_{-0.5}$	<1.5	<1.9		0.3 ± 0.1
Ca	11 ± 4	5.6 ± 2.2	6.0 ± 1.8	5.1 ± 0.9	6.2 ± 0.9
Sc		<1.0	<0.8		$3.5 \pm 0.5 \times 10^{-3}$
Ti	$0.5^{+2.5}_{-0.5}$	<2.6	<2.4		0.27 ± 0.04
V		<2.1	<1.1		0.026 ± 0.005
Cr	1.9 ± 1.5	<3.6	<2.9	2.2 ± 0.6	1.3 ± 0.1
Mn	$0.5^{+2.5}_{-0.5}$	$1.5^{+2.1}_{-0.6}$	<3.7	1.7 ± 1.7	0.8 ± 0.2
Fe	105 ± 21	85 ± 18	93 ± 6	$\equiv 93$	88 ± 6
Co		<0.7	0.32 ± 0.12		0.21 ± 0.03
Ni	3.8 ± 1.1	4.3 ± 0.8	5.1 ± 0.9	5.1 ± 0.5	4.8 ± 0.6
Cu			0.06 ± 0.01		0.06 ± 0.03
Zn			0.07 ± 0.01		0.10 ± 0.02
Ga			$5.6 \pm 2.8 \times 10^{-3}$		$\sim 3.7 \times 10^{-3}$
Ge			$6.4 \pm 2.8 \times 10^{-3}$	$7.4 \pm 1.0 \times 10^{-3}$	$\sim 11.4 \times 10^{-3}$

a) Shapiro, Silberberg and Tsao (1975)
b) Simpson (1983)
c) Lund (1989)
d) Meyer (1985)

reduced from previous estimates, while Cr now has an assigned value with a much reduced uncertainty. The source abundance of Ni confirms the previous value and gives a reduced uncertainty. For Mn, the source component is still consistent with zero. The difficulty here is the isotope ^{54}Mn whose half-life for beta decay has not been measured with sufficient precision (see Grove et al., 1990a; Norman et al., 1990 for details).

The final column of Table I gives the "Local Galactic" abundances determined by Meyer (1985) from a consideration of solar system material plus nearby stars and the interstellar medium. This local galactic composition is a reference to which the cosmic ray source composition can be compared. It is immediately obvious that the elements up through Neon are considerably underabundant in cosmic ray source matter compared to the local galactic sample. Above Ne there are notable underabundances at S and Ar and a possible overabundance of Cr, based upon the 1990 update results.

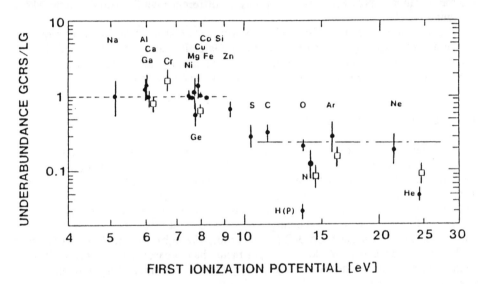

Figure 8. The ratio of the Galactic Cosmic Ray Source abundance to the Local Galactic abundance as a function of the first ionization potential of the elements (adapted from Lund, 1989). Open squares show changes from this "update."

It has been known for many years that this underabundance in the cosmic ray source is correlated with an atomic property of the elements, most often the first ionization potential, FIP (see Silberberg et al., 1991, this volume for a discussion). This dependence is illustrated in Figure 8 where the solid points indicate the ratio using the 1989 source abundances from Table I, and the open points show the modifications induced by the 1990 update column (Mn and Ni are not plotted). The H and He remain far off the two correlation lines as has been reported previously. It is interesting to note that the updated Nitrogen, Argon and Calcium points all moved farther away from the correlation lines, while the new (preliminary) point for Cr appears to be definitely above the low FIP line.

The interpretation of Figure 8 is in terms of the ionization state of the matter in the cosmic ray source regions. Below ~10 eV ionization potential, the elements are sufficiently ionized so that, essentially, the local galactic composition is preserved after acceleration. For elements with FIP above ~10 eV, there is a suppression of the relative abundances by almost a factor of 5. In this interpretation, H, He and N must be treated separately to explain their very low abundances.

The new data presented in this "update" does not qualitatively change this overall picture. However, Ar may have to be added to the list of elements to be "treated separately" and the high Cr abundance, if confirmed, would be another problem. Note that Ge is already a similar problem, falling below the correlation line (but see Secton 4). Alternatively, the FIP may not be the correct parameter to order the source abundances (see Sakurai, 1991, this volume) or the functional form of the underabundance versus FIP correlation may be different than the simple model shown in Figure 8.

In any case, what Figure 8 does demonstrate is that most of the cosmic ray source abundances can be derived from Local Galactic matter. What is needed is a model that yields a selection based upon first ionization potential (or some other atomic property of the elements) and a site for the acceleration.

4.   UH Cosmic Rays (Z>30)

The ultra-heavy (UH) cosmic rays encompass the upper 2/3 of the periodic table and provide a new dimension to the study of cosmic rays. The difficulty is that these nuclei are extremely rare. The relative abundances of UH cosmic rays fall by seven order of magnitude at the actinides (Z≥90) compared to the iron peak. Nevertheless, it has been possible to measure the elemental composition of the UH component using detectors of extremely large collecting power. The most recent of these were two space experiments on the HEAO-C (Binns et al., 1989a,b) and the Ariel-VI (Fowler et al., 1987) spacecraft. While both experiments have ceased returning new data, continuing analysis of the two datasets has yielded some interesting new results (Garrard et al., 1990).

The elements beyond the iron peak show a direct signature of the processes of nucleosynthesis that form UH nuclei. Whereas elements through the iron peak are formed mainly by fusion reactions, beyond the iron peak the elements are formed by neutron capture nucleosynthesis. Looking at the solar system abundances (e.g. Anders and Ebihara, 1982), two distinct components can be identified and ascribed to slow (s-process) and rapid (r-process) neutron capture nucleosynthesis. In the s-process, the time between neutron captures is long compared to the beta decay lifetime. A nucleus captures a neutron to form a stable or radioactive isotope. If radioactive, this isotope decays, in most cases, before the next neutron capture. Thus, the s-process "walks up" the valley of beta stability forming isotopes up to the Lead peak. Beyond Bismuth, there are no stable isotopes, so the s-process terminates at Pb-Bi.

In the classical r-process, on-the-other-hand, the neutrons are added in a burst, allowing no time for beta decay. Each "seed" nucleus captures as many neutrons as possible, i.e. it moves to the neutron drip line, and subsequently decays back to the valley of beta stability. These nuclei end at the first beta stable isotope that they encounter, populating the most neutron rich stable isotopes for each element. In contrast, the s-process populates the isotopes near the center of the distribution of stable isotopes. Note that the r-process nuclei can decay through the radioactive region above Bi and form the Actinide elements, $Z \geq 90$.

Each stable isotope in the UH region can be assigned an s-process and/or an r-process component. Looking at the elements, there are charge groups that are primarily s-process, groups that are primarily r-process and groups that are mixed. The important regions are (a) $Z \leq 40$ where $Z = 37$ (Rb) is predominantly r-process while $Z = 38$ (Sr) is an s-process element, (b) $50 \leq Z \leq 60$ where Te-Xe ($Z = 52$-54) are mainly r-process while Ba-Ce ($Z = 56$-58) are s-process dominated, (c) $75 \leq Z \leq 83$ where the "Pt peak", Re-Au, is r-process while the "Pb peak", Tl-Bi, is s-process, and (d) $Z \geq 90$ which is pure r-process. Interpretations of the UH cosmic ray data have focused on these four regions in order to search for differences between cosmic ray source matter and local galactic (solar system) material. Such differences would shed light on the question of the sites of cosmic ray acceleration since s- and r-process nucleosynthesis occur in very different astrophysical environments.

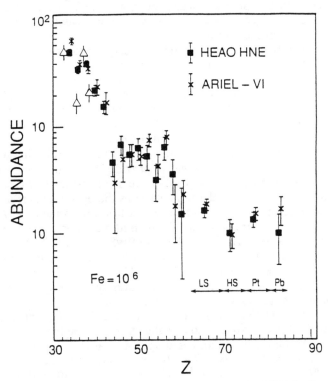

Figure 9. Comparison of the UH abundances measured by HEAO-C and Ariel-VI, normalized to the widths of the charge bins. The open triangles represent the recent analysis by Garrard et al. (1990) for $33 \leq Z \leq 40$.

Figure 9 shows a comparison of the HEAO-C and Ariel-Vl measurements, normalized to Fe = 10^6 (Binns et al., 1989b). Overall, there is reasonably good agreement between the two experiments. Note that element pairs (odd + even Z) are plotted up to Z = 60 while above Z = 60 the results are summed into charge groups. No actinide elements are shown in Figure 9 since the HEAO-C experiment saw none. However, Ariel-Vl did report an actinide abundance based upon a few events.

The overall agreement between the HEAO-C and Ariel-Vl measurements has led to their being combined into a single set of measured UHGCR relative abundances which have been the subject of detailed propagation studies using a variety of source compositions. The overall results of these investigations may be summarized as follows:

(i)   FIP effects are highly significant and need to be included in the analysis.

(ii)   Considering the total region $32 \leq Z \leq 60$, the data are well represented by a solar system abundance distribution at the cosmic ray source. This interpretation is, however, dominated by the abundant elements Ge and Se.

(iii)   Restricting the analysis to $35 \leq Z \leq 60$, the best fit source could have a small r-process enhancement.

(iv)   Above Z = 60, the "Pt peak" is pronounced and the "Pb peak" is underabundant. This implies a strong r-process enhancement; a pure r-process source would fit reasonably well. The observation of several actinide events by Ariel-VI is also indicative of an r-process enhancement.

(v)   A standard leaky-box propagation model is adequate to explain the observed abundances of secondary nuclei in the UH region.

Overall, the conclusion is that standard local galactic matter can <u>not</u> be the source composition for the UH cosmic rays, at least above Z = 60, even including FIP dependent enhancements in the source distribution. An additional component of r-process enriched material is required to explain the heaviest nuclei.

Garrard et al. (1990) re-analyzed the $32 \leq Z \leq 40$ interval selecting datasets with the highest charge resolution. The goal was to provide "best estimates" for the odd-Z nuclei abundances and to analyze the s- and r-process contributions at Z < 40. This high resolution data is compared to the full dataset as the open triangles in Figure 9. Note that the abundance of Z = 35+36 is reduced significantly while Z = 37+38 is enhanced. The uncertainties are larger for the revised measurements since only a subset of the data is analyzed. However, the ratio Rb/Sr = 0.24 ± 0.12 is lower than would be expected from solar system material with FIP fractionation. This is possible evidence for an s-process enhancement at Z < 40. Thus, it may be that the neutron capture history of cosmic ray matter differs from that of the solar system both at high charge and in the region just above the iron peak.

One of the interesting elements in this region is Ge (Z = 32), which was listed in Table I. Binns et al. (1989b) extract a source abundance for Ge from the combined UHGCR dataset of 80 (unfractionated), based upon a measured abundance of 91^{+12}_{-8}. This source abundance corresponds to 7.4×10^{-3} on a scale where Fe $\equiv$ 93, and is so entered in the 1990 update column of Table I. Note that in Figure 8, this "update" moves the point closer to the correlation line and reduces the uncertainty. The reanalysis by Garrard et al. (1990) gives a Ge abundance of 95.5 ± 9.2, about 5% larger than the measurement used to obtain the "update" value in Table I. Using the relative uncertainty on the measurement, the Ge underabundance becomes 0.68 ± 0.07, compared to 0.56 ± 0.25 for the 1989 column of Table I. The increased Ge abundance does not remove the discrepancy with the FIP correlation, and, moreover, the reduced uncertainty makes the discrepancy more significant.

Garrard et al. (1990) analyzed two subsets of the data, corresponding to a low energy subset and a high rigidity subset. For Ge, there was a significant difference between these two subsets with the low energy data showing a Ge abundance of 107 ± 13.5. If this is scaled to a source abundance, then the underabundance ratio becomes 0.76 ± 0.10, much closer to the correlation line at 1.0. The origin of the difference between the low energy and high rigidity subsets is not known; it may be merely a statistical fluctuation or it might indicate a propagation effect.

Thus, the Ge abundance remains a "key" problem (although perhaps not as large a problem?) for the FIP correlation models. A larger statistics experiment with good charge and energy resolution will be needed to fully resolve this question. However, the overall indication from analysis of the UHGCR data is that a FIP (or a related atomic property of the element) fractionation is needed in the cosmic ray source regions.

5. Isotopic Composition

The isotopes of the different elements in the cosmic rays may be an even more sensitive indicator of composition differences between cosmic rays and local galactic matter. Over the past ~2 decades, instrumentation has been developed with the capability to separate the isotopes of elements up to the iron peak. However, experimental opportunities have been lacking, and results are available for only a few of the primary elements.

There are, as well, numerous secondary isotopes available for study (which will not be reviewed here -- see Mewaldt, 1989; Wefel, 1988), and these provide information on the confinement and propagation of the particles. The isotopes ^2H and ^3He trace the propagation history of Helium, while $^{6,7}Li$, $^{7,9}Be$, and $^{10,11}B$ indicate the history of the Carbon-Oxygen primaries. Similarly, ^{15}N allows the secondary component of ^{14}N to be determined and thereby obtain a measurement of the $^{14}N/O$ source abundance, as discussed in Section 3. The isotopes ^{17}O and ^{21}Ne play analogous roles for the isotopic composition of the elements Oxygen and Neon.

Of special importance among the secondary isotopes are ^{10}Be, ^{26}Al, ^{36}Cl and ^{54}Mn all of which are radioactive with relatively long half-lives. Their relative abundance among the cosmic rays indicates the "age" or confinement time for the particles (see Ptuskin, 1991, this volume or Simpson and Garcia-Munoz, 1988).

A summary of current isotope results for primary or mixed isotopes is given in Figure 10 as the "underabundance" ratio with respect to solar system composition (c.f. Figure 8). The most striking result is the large overabundance (factor of 3-4) of the neutron rich isotope ^{22}Ne in the cosmic ray source, a result that has been confirmed by a number of measurements, both satellite and balloon experiments. Smaller enhancements (factor of ~1.4) have been reported for the neutron rich isotopes $^{25,26}Mg$ and $^{29,30}Si$. In the latter case, the enhancement must be regarded as only tentative since some experiments have observed it while others have not. For example, preliminary results from the ALICE balloon experiment show an

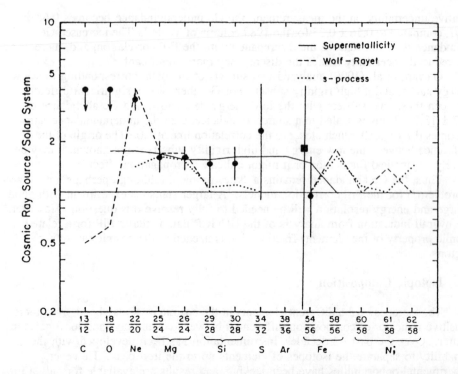

Figure 10. Cosmic ray source isotopic ratios as determined by recent measurements, normalized to solar system composition. The curves show predictions of models which attempt to explain the observations. Adapted from Spillantini and Basini (1989) with the addition of solid square from Grove et al. (1990b).

enhancement of ^{29}Si but not of ^{30}Si. Beyond Silicon, the data have not been of sufficient quantity or quality to confirm any departures from solar system composition.

A recent example is the work on the iron isotopes reported by Grove et al. (1990b) and shown as the solid square in Figure 10. This balloon investigation used the Cherenkov-Energy technique and obtained less than three dozen iron nuclei for which mass analysis was reported. The low statistics lead to the large uncertainty shown in the figure. An additional problem in determining the source abundance of ^{54}Fe is the contribution to ^{54}Fe from ^{54}Mn decay. The beta decay lifetime of ^{54}Mn is not well known, as discussed in Section 3, making the correction for ^{54}Mn decay very uncertain.

The curves in Figure 10 indicated the predictions of several models that were advanced to explain these departures from solar system composition (Woosley and Weaver, 1981; Prantzos et al., 1985; see also Silberberg et al., 1991, this volume). The only model that explains the large enhancement of ^{22}Ne is the Wolf-Rayet (WR) picture which assumes that the galactic cosmic ray source matter is a mixture of local galactic matter with material from evolved massive stars such as WR stars, whose strong stellar winds are invoked to remove material from the outer layers of the star and mix it to form the source composition. Note that this model can also explain the underabundance of nitrogen discussed in Section 3. The WR model predicts an underabundance of ^{13}C and ^{18}O, no appreciable enhancement of ^{29,30}Si and possible enhancements of ^{58}Fe and ^{61}Ni. These predictions are "testable" with the next generation of isotope experiments that will be performed during the 1990's. Similar "predictions" are indicated for the other models.

It is interesting that the low-Z isotopes, ^{13}C and ^{18}O, may play a crucial role in deciding between the models. Current results for these isotopes are shown as upper limits. This is due not to problems with the experimental data but to the difficulty in unfolding the secondary components to these mixed isotopes. The production cross sections for ^{13}C and ^{18}O from heavier cosmic ray species are not known with sufficient precision to subtract the fragmentation contributions accurately. This is an example of an astrophysical interpretation being limited by a lack of nuclear physics parameters, and points out the important connection between nuclear fragmentation experiments at particle accelerators and the interpretation of cosmic ray data. Current experimental programs at heavy ion machines are attempting to address this situation (see e.g. Guzik, 1990).

The isotopic data in Figure 10 do indicate, however, that there are major differences in the composition of cosmic ray source matter and local galactic matter. The ^{22}Ne enhancement and the smaller enhancement of ^{25,26}Mg appear well established and cannot be explained by propagation effects or by uncertainties in nuclear fragmentation cross sections. Such differences may well have their origin in nucleosynthesis processes which contribute differently to cosmic ray source matter than to local galactic material.

6. Summary

The cosmic rays are, indeed, a "unique" sample of galactic matter! The elemental composition for $Z \leq 30$ reflects the local galactic (solar system) composition after FIP dependent fractionation is taken into account. However, there are notable exceptions; H, He, N and, possibly, Ar, Cr and Ge. The UH ($Z > 30$) cosmic rays also require a FIP fractionation, but even with fractionation the source composition is not the same as the solar system. The r-process elements are strongly enhanced above $Z = 60$, and there may be an s-process enhancement in the $Z \leq 40$ region. The isotopic composition, however, is not affected by FIP fractionation. Here, the large overabundance of ^{22}Ne and the smaller enhancements of ^{25,26}Mg in the cosmic ray source represent major departures from solar system composition.

The cosmic rays may be a sample of interstellar matter from elsewhere in the galaxy. If so, the ISM in the regions of the cosmic ray sources has undergone a different history of nucleosynthesis compared to our local region of the galaxy. Alternatively, the cosmic rays may themselves be a mixture of freshly synthesized matter from massive stars or supernovae with local interstellar matter. Determining the sites for such a source remains an intriguing question. In either case, the study of composition holds a major "key" to understanding the origin and acceleration of the cosmic radiation.

52

7. Acknowledgements

Thanks are due to the Ettore Majorana Centre for their superb hospitality and to Gay Sutton for excellent assistance with the manuscript. This work was supported, in part, by NASA grant NAGW-1027, DOE grant DE-FG05-84ER40147, ONR grant N00014-90-J-1466 and NSF grant PHY-8907660.

8. References

Anders, E. and Ebihara, M., 1982, Geochim. Cosmochim. Acta, 46, 2362.

Binns, W. R., Garrard, T. L., Israel, M. H., Jones, M. D., Kamionkowski, M. P., Klarmann, J., Stone, E. C. and Waddington, C. J.,1988, Astrophys. J., 324, 1106.

Binns, W. R., Garrard, T. L., Israel, M. H., Klarmann, J., Stone, E. C., and Waddington, C. J., 1989a, in Cosmic Abundances of Matter, ed. C. J. Waddington, AIP Conf. Proc. 183, (New York, 1989, American Institute of Physics), p. 147.

Binns, W. R., Garrard, T. L., Gibner, P. S., Israel, M. H., Kertzman, M. P., Klarmann, J., Newport, B. J., Stone, E. C. and Waddington, C. J., 1989b, Astrophys. J., 346, 997.

Biswas, S., Durgaprasad, N., Mitra, B., Singh, R. K., Dutta, A. and Goswami, J. N., 1990, in 21st ICR Conference Papers, ed. R. J. Protheroe, (Australia, 1990, University of Adelaide), 3, 23.

Biswas, S., Durgaprasad, N., Mitra, B., Singh, R. K., Vahia, M. N., Dutta, A. and Goswami, J. N., 1989, Adv. Space Research, 9, 25.

Blanford, G. E., Jr., Freidlander, M. W., Klarmann, J., Pomeroy, S. S., Walker, R. M. and Wefel, J. P., 1972, J. Geophys. Res., 77, 6037.

Burnett, T. H., Dake, S., Derrickson, J. H., Fountain, W. F., Fuki, M., Gregory, J. C., Hayashi, T., Holynski, R., Iwai, J., Jones, W. V., Jurak, A., Lord, J. J., Miyamura, O., Oda, H., Ogata, T., Parnell, T. A., Roberts, F. E., Shibata, T., Strausz, S., Tabuki, T., Takahashi, Y., Tominaga, T., Watts, J. W., Wefel, J. P., Wilczynska, B., Wilczynski, H., Wilkes, R. J., Wolter, W. and Wosiek, B., 1990a, in 21st ICR Conference Papers, ed. R. J. Protheroe, (Australia, 1990, University of Adelaide), 3, 97.

Burnett, T. H. et al., 1990b, Ibid, 3, 101.

Burnett, T. H. et al., 1990c, Astrophys. J. Letters, 349, L25.

Durgaprasad, N., Mitra, B., Singh, R. K., Biswas, S., Dutta, A. and Goswami, J. N., 1990, in 21st ICR Conference Papers, ed. R. J. Protheroe, (Australia, 1990, University of Adelaide), 3, 389.

Durgaprasad, N. and Biswas, S., 1988, Astrophys. and Space Sci., 149, 163.

Dwyer, R. D. and Meyer, P., 1985, Astrophys. J., 294, 441.

Engelman, J. J., Goret, P., Juliusson, E., Koch-Miramond, L., Masse, P., Soutoul, A., Byrnak, B., Lund, N., Peters, B., Rasmussen, I. L., Rotenberg, M. and Westergaard, N. J., 1983, in 18th ICR Conference Papers, eds. N. Durgaprasad, S. Ramadurai, P. V. Ramana Murthy, M. V. S. Rao and K. Sivaprasad, (Bombay, 1983, Tata Institute of Fund. Res.), 2, 17.

Ferrando, P., Lal, N., McDonald, F. B. and Webber, W. R., 1990, in 21st ICR Conference Papers, ed. R. J. Protheroe, (Australia, 1990, University of Adelaide), 3, 40.

Fowler, P. H., Walker, R. N. F., Masheder, M. R. W., Moses, R. T., Worley, A. and Gay, A. M., 1987, Astrophys. J., 314, 739.

Gagarin, Yu. F., Dvoryanchikov, Ya. V., Lyaguchin, V. I., Ovchinnikova, A. Yu., Solovyev, A. V. and Khilyuta, I. G., 1990, in 21st ICR Conference Papers, ed. R. J. Protheroe, (Australia, 1990, University of Adelaide), 3, 11.

Garcia-Munoz, M., Guzik, T. G., Simpson, J. A. and Wefel, J. P., 1981, in 17th ICR Conference Papers, (Paris, 1981, CEN Saclay), 2, 192.

Garcia-Munoz, M., Guzik, T. G., Simpson, J. A. and Wefel, J. P., 1984, Astrophys. J. Letters, 280, L13.

Garcia-Munoz, M., Simpson, J. A., Guzik, T. G., Wefel, J. P. and Margolis, S. H., 1987, Astrophys. J. Suppl., 64, 269.

Garrard, T. L., Israel, M. H., Klarmann, J., Stone, E. C., Waddington, C. J. and Binns, W. R., 1990, 21st ICR Conference Papers, ed. R. J. Protheroe, (Australia, 1990, University of Adelaide), 3, 61.

Grigorov, N. L., 1990, Ibid, 3, 73.

Grove, J. E., Hayes, B. T., Mewaldt, R. A. and Webber, W. R., 1990a, Ibid, 3, 397.

Grove, J. E., Christian, E. R., Mewaldt, R. A., Schindler, S. M., Stone, E. C., Buffington, A. and Rasmussen, I., 1990b, Ibid, 3, 53.

Grunsfeld, J. M., L'Heureux, J., Meyer, P., Muller, D. and Swordy, S., 1988, Astrophys. J. Letters, 327, L31.

Grunsfeld et al., 1990, in 21st ICR Conference Papers, ed. R. J. Protheroe, (Australia, 1990, University of Adelaide), 3, 69.

Gupta, M. and Webber, W. R., 1989, Astrophys. J., 340, 1124.

Guzik, T. G., 1990, in Particle Astrophysics, eds. W. V. Jones, F. J. Kerr and J. F. Ormes, AIP Conf. Proc. 203, (New York, 1990, American Institute of Physics), p. 275.

Guzik, T. G. and Wefel, J. P., 1984, Adv. Space Research, 4, 215.

Henkel, M., Acharya, B. S., Heinbach, U., Heinrich, W., Hesse, A., Koch, Ch., Luzietti, B., Noll, A., Simon, M., Tittel, H. O., Esposito, J. A., Streitmatter, R. E., Ormes, J. F., Balasubrahmanyan, V. K., Christian, E. R., and Barbier, L. M., 1990, in 21st ICR Conference Papers, ed. R. J. Protheroe, (Australia, 1990, University of Adelaide), 3, 15.

Ivanenko, I. P., Rapoport, I. D., Shes-toperov, V. Ya., Basina, Yu. V., Vakulov, P. V., Vasiliev, Yu. Ya., Golinskaya, R., Gordeev, Yu. P., Grigorieva, L. B., Kazakova, A. E., Kozlov, V. D., Kumpan, I. P., Mischenko, L. G., Nikanorov, V. M., Papina, L. P., Platonov, V. V., Samonov, G. A., Smolensky, L. G., Sobinyakov, V. A., Tambovtsev, G. E., Trigubov, Yu. V., Fateeva, I. M., Fedorov, A. N., Hein, L. A., Chikova, L. O., Shiryaeva, V. Ya., Yakovlev, B. M. and Yashin, I. V., 1990, Ibid, 3, 77.

Kawamura, T., Matsutani, H., Nanjyo, H., Saito, M., Teraoka, K., Toda, K., Watanabe, Z., Ichimura, M., Kamioka, E., Kirii, K., Kobayashi, T., Shibata, T., Shibuta, K., Yoshizumi, Y., Sugimoto, H. and Nakazawa, K., 1990, Ibid, 3, 89.

Krombel, K. E. and Wiedenbeck, M. E., 1988, Astrophys. J., 328, 940.

54

Leske, R. A. and Wiedenbeck, M. E., 1990, in 21st ICR Conference Papers, ed. R. J. Protheroe, (Australia, 1990, University of Adelaide), 3, 57.

Lezniak, J. A. and Webber, W. R., 1978, Astrophys. J., 223, 676.

Lezniak, J. A. and Webber, W. R., 1979, Astrophys. Space Sci., 63, 35.

Lund, N., 1989, in Cosmic Abundances of Matter, ed. C. J. Waddington, AIP Conf. Proc. 183, (New York, 1989, American Institute of Physics), p. 111.

Maehl, R. C., Ormes, J. F., Fisher, A. J. and Hagen, F. A., 1977, Astrophys. Space Sci., 47, 163.

Mewaldt, R. A., 1983, Rev. Geophys. and Space Phys., 21, 295.

Mewaldt, R. A., 1989, in Cosmic Abundances of Matter, ed. C. J. Waddington, AIP Conf. Proc. 183, (New York, 1989, American Institute of Physics), p. 124.

Mewaldt, R. A. and Webber, W. R., 1990, in 21st ICR Conference Papers, ed. R. J. Protheroe, (Australia, 1990, University of Adelaide), 3, 432.

Meyer, J. P., 1985, Astrophys. J. Suppl., 57, 173.

Norman, E. B., Sur, B., Vogel, K. R., Lesko, K. T., Larimer, R. M. and Browne, E., 1990, in 21st ICR Conference Papers, ed. R. J. Protheroe, (Australia, 1990, University of Adelaide), 3, 401.

Osborne, J. L. and Ptuskin, V. S., 1988, Soviet Astron. Letters, 14, 132.

Prantzos, N., Arnould, M., Arcoragi, J. P. and Casse, M., 1985, in 19th ICR Conference Papers, (Washington, DC, 1985, National Aeronautics and Space Administration), 3, 167.

Ryan, M. J., Ormes, J. F. and Balasubrahmanyan, V. K., 1972, Phys. Rev. Letters, 28, 985.

Shapiro, M. M. and Silberberg, R., 1970, Ann. Rev. Nucl. Sci., 20, 323.

Shapiro, M. M. and Wefel, J. P., eds. Cosmic Gamma Rays, Neutrinos and Related Astrophysics, NATO ASI Series C, Volume 270 (Dordrecht, 1989, Kluwer Academic Publishers), 692 p.

Shapiro, M. M. and Wefel, J. P., eds. Genesis and Propagation of Cosmic Rays, NATO ASI Series C, Volume 220 (Dordrecht, 1988, D. Reidel Publ. Co.), 476 p.

Shapiro, M. M., ed. Cosmic Radiation in Contemporary Astrophysics, NATO ASI Series C, Volume 162 (Dordrecht, 1986, D. Reidel Publ. Co.), 274 p.

Shapiro, M. M., ed. Composition and Origin of Cosmic Rays, NATO ASI Series C, Volume 107 (Dordrecht, 1983, D. Reidel Publ. Co.), 414 p.

Shapiro, M. M., Silberberg, R. and Tsao, C. H., 1975, in 14th ICR Conference Papers, (Munich, 1975, Max-Planck-Institute), 2, 532.

Silberberg, R. and Tsao, C. H., 1990, Physics Reports, 191, 352.

Simpson, J. A., 1983, Ann. Rev. Nucl. Part. Sci., 33, 323.

Simpson, J. A. and Garcia-Munoz, M., 1988, Space Sci. Reviews, 46, 205.

Soutoul, A., Engelmann, J. J., Ferrando, P. H., Koch-Miramond, L., Masse, P. and Webber, W. R., 1985, in 19th ICR Conference Papers, (Washington, DC, 1985 National Aeronautics and Space Administration), 2, 8.

Soutoul, A., Ferrando, P. and Webber, W. R., 1990, in 21st ICR Conference Papers, ed. R. J. Protheroe, (Australia, 1990, University of Adelaide), 3, 337.

Spillantini, P. and Basini, G., 1989, in Physics and Astrophysics in the Space Station Era, eds. P. L. Bernacca and R. Ruffini, Conf. Proc. Vol. 17, (Bologna, 1989, Italian Physical Society), p. 17.

Stephens, S. A. and Golden, R. L., 1987, Space Sci. Reviews, 46, 31.

Stephens, S. A. and Golden, R. L., 1988, Astron. Astrophys., 202, 1.

Swordy, S. P., Muller, D., Meyer, P., L'Heureux, J. and Grunsfeld, J. M., 1990, in 21st ICR Conference Papers, ed. R. J. Protheroe, (Australia, 1990,. University of Adelaide), 3, 93.

Vylet, V., Waddington, C. J., Binns, W. R., Garrard, T. L., Israel, M. H., Klarmann, J. and Metzger, M., 1990, Ibid, 3, 19.

Waddington, C. J., 1988, in Origin and Distribution of the Elements, ed. G. J. Mathews, (Singapore, 1988, World Scientific), p. 294.

Watson, A. A., 1985, in 19th ICR Conference Papers, (Washington, DC, 1985, National Aeronautics and Space Administration), 9, 111.

Webber, W. R., 1982, Astrophys. J., 252, 386.

Webber, W. R., Kish, J. C. and Schrier, D. A., 1990, Phys. Rev., C41, 520.

Wefel, J. P., 1988, in Genesis and Propagation of Cosmic Rays, eds. M. M. Shapiro and J. P. Wefel, NATO ASI Series C, Volume 220 (Dordrecht, 1988, D. Reidel Publ. Co.), p. 1.

Woosley, S. E. and Weaver, T. A., 1981, Astrophys. J., 243, 561.

Young, J. S., Freier, P. S., Waddington, C. J., Brewster, N. C. and Fickle, R. K., 1981, Astrophys. J., 246, 1014.

Zatsepin, V. I., Zamchalova, E. A., Varkovitskaya, A. Ya., Sokolskaya, N. V., Sazhina, G. P., Ryabova, N. G. and Mandritskaya, K. V., 1990, in 21st ICR Conference Papers, ed. R. J. Protheroe, (Australia, 1990, University of Adelaide), 3, 81.

INTERSTELLAR DUST-GAS RELATIONSHIPS

J. Mayo Greenberg
Laboratory Astrophysics, Department of Astronomy and Physics,
Huygens Laboratory, Leiden University, P.O.Box 9504, 2300 RA
Leiden, The Netherlands

ABSTRACT. The evolutionary chemical and morphological properties of
interstellar dust are shown to provide a basis for varying the
correlation factor between dust, hydrogen and CO.

1. Introduction

The questioning of the mass of molecular hydrogen in the galaxy has
come into prominence partly as a result of the reduced estimates made
by the group of Wolfendale (1,2,3) based on cosmic gamma-ray methods.
Since the dust is generally assumed to be well coupled to the gas this
raises a further question about the amount of dust assuming that the
dust is constrained by the local "cosmic" abundance of the heavy (so-
called condensable) elements. In the neighbourhood of the sun this
abundance ratio is assumed to be very similar to that in the solar
system. In the galactic center there are reasons, both observational
and theoretical, to expect higher abundances of heavy elements. The aim
of this paper is to discuss the intertellar dust consistency or
inconsistency with derived values of the molecular hydrogen density. In
particlular whether there is a lower limit on the value of the ratio of
the column density of hydrogen to the integrated CO intensity, $X =
N(H_2)/I_{CO}$, for providing the observed dust density and the required
molecular (other than H_2) densities.

2. Interstellar dust and cosmic abundance constraints.

2.1 Interstellar dust.
Currently we have knowledge of a wide variety of material constituents
of the dust. Some of these are volatiles in the form of frozen ices,
the others being relatively non-volatile or refractory. However even
the refractories have varying degrees of volatility. The major refractory components which have been observed may be characterized as silicates and organics.
The core-mantle model of interstellar dust is the basis for explaining
many of the observed properties of the solid particles in the space
between the stars (4,5). The silicate cores are formed in the
atmospheres of cool evolved stars and, from their infrared absorption
spectra, are deduced to be in an amorphous form. After being ejected
from the stars these particles undergo a series of cyclic processes.
First, they accrete mantles of molecular ices —predominantly H_2O and CO
in dense molecular clouds. The CO is actually accreted while the H_2O is
predominantly formed by surface reaction on the grain surface. The
"dirty ice" mantles containing other molecules as well (but in
generally lower abundance) are subjected to the ultraviolet photons
which are present in adequate abundance even in the shielded region of

57

M. M. Shapiro et al. (eds.), Cosmic Rays, Supernovae and the Interstellar Medium, 57–68.
© 1991 Kluwer Academic Publishers. Printed in the Netherlands.

dense clouds to produce chemical modifications. Simple molecules are broken and recombination between the fragments lead to new and generally more complex molecules. During the molecular cloud phase, the more volatile molecules are explosively desorbed about every 10^5 years as a result of triggered reactions among the ultraviolet produced radicals. The subsequently reaccreted molecules are again subjected to photoprocessing along with the less volatile (H_2O) molecules. The result of this recurring accretion, desorption, accretion and photoprocessing is creation of a layer of complex organic molecules (organic refractories). When the molecular cloud is dispersed after about 5×10^7 years, the grains are sent into the low-density diffuse medium where all the volatiles are removed by various destructive processes from which the grains have been shielded in the molecular cloud phase. The resulting grains then consist of silicate cores with organic refractory mantles. These organic mantles are further subjected to ultraviolet photoprocessing in the harsh ultraviolet environment of the diffuse medium leading to partial dehydrogenation and reduction in the abundance of O and, to a lesser extent N, with respect to C. Such grains are later swept up again into molecular clouds and the accretion/photoprocessing of ice mantles is repeated. In the mean one diffuse/molecular cloud cycle takes about 10^8 years. Ultimately, a grain is consumed (totally destroyed) by being incorporated into a new star; i.e., the interstellar gas and dust is cycled through stars every 5×10^9 years by star formation. This is then the maximum mean lifetime for a core-mantle grain which has undergone of the order of 50 complete diffuse/molecular cloud cycles of volatile mantle formation and destruction.

It is primarily from infrared absorption that we are made aware of the molecular constituents of the dust whereas the molecular constitutents of the gas are observed in the radio region. Just as the identifications of molecular constituents in the gas are based on laboratory measurements, so the identifications of the molecular constituents of the dust are based on laboratory spectra. It has been possible to recreate in the laboratory the physical conditions leading to the chemical evolution of interstellar dust - low temperature, high vacuum, vacuum ultraviolet radiation. Laboratory infrared absorption spectra of various ice mixtures, photoprocessed as well as unirradiated have provided the basic data. In fact, the photoprocessing of interstellar type ices was studied in the laboratory by infrared and other analytical techniques before many of the observations were made (6,7). A major prediction of the laboratory analog studies was the presence of organic residues with a 3.4 μm absorption feature. Among other facts it has been established that all interstellar ice mantles are amorphous and that only in regions near newly forming stars or in the atmospheres of certain cool types of stars can this ice be crystalline. In the latter case one may say that the dust is not truly interstellar.

Among the many cases in which not all the dust is consumed by star formation there is the one in which the dense cloud collapses to a disk out of which the planets and comets are formed around the star - as was the case 4.5 Gyr ago around the sun. The dust in this protoplanetary disk, if it has not been raised to too high a temperature, will resemble the dust in dense molecular clouds. In fact, the process of gas accretion may proceed unchecked in the final stage of contraction if the desorption process is sufficiently reduced. The time scale for accretion is $\tau_{acc} = (2 \; 10^9 / n_0)$ yr where n_0 is the hydrogen density.

TABLE 1   Molecules Directly Observed in Inter-
stellar Grains and/or Strongly Inferred from
Laboratory Spectra and Theories of Grain Mantle
Evolution.

Molecule	Comment *	
H_2O	O	M2
CO	O	M2
H_2S	O	M2
NH_3	O	M2
H_2CO	O	M2
$(H_2CO)_n$	I	M2
OCN^-	O	M2
$NH4^+$	O	M2
CH_3OH	O	M2
OCS	O	M2
CO_2	O	M2
CH_4	I	M2
S_2	I	M2
complex organic	O	M1
"Silicate"	O	C
"Carbonaceous"	(O,I)	B
PAH's	(O,I)	B

*: O=observed, M1=inner mantle, M2=outer mantle
   B=small bare, I=inferred, C=core

Even at the *moderately* dense contraction phase of $n_0 = 10^7$ cm^{-3} the accretion time is only 100 yr whereas the photoprocessing time needed to create and store the approximately 1% radical concentration required for explosive desorption to be effective is at least 10^4 yr (8). Note that along with the molecular accretion the small particles and large molecules will be trapped in the outermost mantle.

Table 1 contains a listing of the present information on the chemical composition of interstellar dust. These identifications have come mainly from comparing laboratory with interstellar infrared spectra (9,10). However, even though the complex organic component has been noted as a residue of photoprocessed low temperature laboratory ices for many years (11,12), it has not been completely identified. Since the organic refractory grain mantles must resemble the laboratory residues, at least in part, a substantial effort has gone into chemical and physical analysis of the laboratory residue. Normally we find that the residues constitute mixtures of many different species and we see evidence for polymerization of aliphatic as well as aromatic molecules. The more soluble part of the laboratory photoproduced organic refractory samples is being analysed by the group of Prof. J. Ferris at the R.P.I. (Troy, N.Y.) by GCMS (Gas Chromatography - Mass Spectrometry) and HPLC (High Pressure Liquid Chromatography). A summary of the results of these analyses are shown in Table 2. For details of these analysis, see e.g. Agarwal *et al* (13) and Schutte (14). It is interesting to note that one of these compounds (Hexamethylene Tetramine) involves some of the most basic units in prebiotic chemistry.

TABLE 2 Products Resulting from the Simulation of Interstellar Grain Photolysis ($H_2O:CO:NH_3 = 5:5:1$) (from (13,14)).

Name	Formula
Glycolic Acid	HCH_2COOH
3-Hydroxy-propionic acid	$HOCH_2CH_2COOH$
Formamidine	$HNCHNH_2$
2-Hydroxy-acetamide	$HOCH_2CONH_2$
Hexamethylene Tetramine	$C_6H_{12}N_4$
Urea	H_2NCONH_2
Biuret	$H_2NCONHCONH_2$
Oxamic Acid	$H_2NCOCOOH$
Ethanolamine	$H_2NCH_2CH_2OH$
Gycerol	$HOCH_2CHOHCH_2OH$
Glycine	H_2NCH_2COOH
Oxamide	$H_2NHCOCONH_2$
Glyceric Acid	$HOCH_2CHOHCOOH$
Glyceramide	$HOCH_2CHOHCONH_2$

Element		Abundance (%)
Carbon	(C)	0.21
Oxygen	(O)	0.27
Nitrogen	(N)	0.05
Hydrogen	(H)	0.47

We see that a starting mixture with O:C = 2 leads to a mixture with O:C = 1. For the more refractory organics this ratio is still further reduced and subjecting the materials to more ultraviolet radiation leads to less and less O and H compared to C.

The less soluble part is analysed, among other methods (see e.g. (15)), by electron impact mass spectrometry (EI-MS) at the FOM-Institute in Amsterdam. All the samples consist of compounds of very high molecular weight – many with mass peaks of more than 500 AMU (see figure 1) well above the background noise level. In order to check whether these big molecules do not come from contamination (e.g. pump oil in the system), we labelled some of the samples and compared their spectra with the ones of unlabelled samples. It was found that the peaks shifted, and thus the peaks are real and do not come from contamination. We also checked whether the peaks were reproducible or not, and we found they were, i.e. two different samples with the same parent gas mixture and irradiation time, gave the same main peaks.

Although not yet completely characterized, we can say that the non-soluble part of the O.R. consists of a very complex mixture of hydrocarbon chains since a significant number of main peaks are separated by mass number 14 (CH_2 groups) and, following a main peak, decrease in intensity with increasing fragment weight. The complexity of the spectra would arise from there being many different isomers within homologous series, and from being a mixture of too many different molecules. The most prominent fragment ions (m/z = 68, 82, 96, 110, 124, ...) belong to a $C_nH_{2n}CN$ series (Alkyl cyanides, cycloalkenyl, bicycloamines (16)). There is also evidence (17) for aliphatic hydrocarbons (C_nH_{2n-1} series) like those of the Murchison Meteorite. Another interesting thing found in these studies is that of the different volatilities at which the different compounds come off. See for example fig. 2.

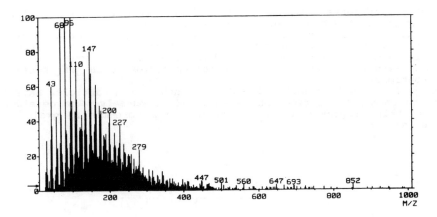

Fig. 1. EI-mass spectra of UV-irradiated H₂O:CO:NH₃ = 5:5:1. The arrow indicates the **maximum** signal level on the blank.

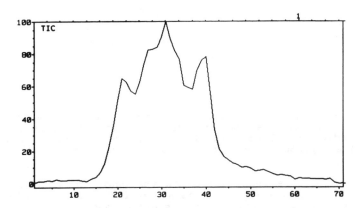

Fig. 2. Total ionization current. It starts at 200°C and finishes at 800°C, almost linearly. Various peaks correspond to different degrees of volatility.

2.2 Grain model calculation.
The average interstellar extinction as shown in Fig. 3 has three distinct regions. The first, up to $\lambda^{-1} = 3 \ \mu m^{-1}$, is characteristic of the tenth micron size particles. The second is the absorption band at 4.6 μm^{-1} which is most likely produced by carbonaceous particles of size 0.01 μm. The last is the far ultraviolet (FUV), upward curvature whose source is not yet definitely identified but which may be caused by very large molecules - the suggestion being that these may be polycyclic aromatic hydrocarbons (PAH's). There is a fourth feature of

62

the extinction curve which is not so evident. This is a linear slope starting at about 3-4 μm^{-1} and extending into the FUV (34). So far no clear identification exists for the cause of this contribution except that it is so clearly correlated with the visual extinction ("large") particles that one may conjecture that it is due to some directly related aspect of the tenth micron particles such as surface perturbations..

Although it is well established that the tenth micron particles have a size and chemical distribution we shall limit ourselves to consider them as being represented by an average size core-mantle grain in diffuse clouds.

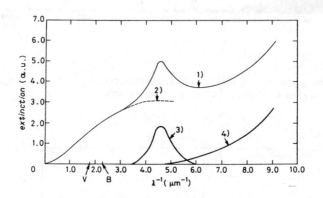

Fig. 3. Schematic representation of the mean extinction curve (1)). The "visual" portion (2)) is the contribution made by classical-size particles (radius ~ 0.1 μm). The hump (3)) and the far-ultraviolet portion (4)) are produced by much smaller particles ($\leq 0.01 \mu m$).

A simplified model has been derived on the basis of simultaneously satisfying the polarization and visual extinction. A single size spheroidal particle with semi-minor axis 0.1 μm and elongation 2:1 is taken to represent the mean interstellar characteristics. The volume ratio of the organic refractory mantles to the silicate core is 2:1 (mass ratio about 1:1).

The abundances of the atoms, molecules and dust in the interstellar medium are intercoupled by the absolute and relative abundances of the elements. It is generally accepted that gas molecular density (represented by the total hydrogen content, n (H I) + 2n (H$_2$) + n (H$^+$) is correlated with the dust. We will consider mostly regions where the hydrogen is unionized and is either dominated by neutral or molecular hydrogen. The observations which lead us to believe in a correlation of dust and gas are limited to regions in which atomic hydrogen is dominant - diffuse clouds. The correlation is here expressed in terms of the ratio of the extinction, actually the difference in extinction at B and V = A(B) - A(V) = E(B-V) to the column density of hydrogen. The current accepted value for this as given by Spitzer (18)

$$\frac{N(H)}{E(B-V)} = 5.9 \times 10^{21} \text{ cm}^{-2} \tag{1}$$

or $\quad N(H)/A(V) = 1.9 \times 10^{21} \text{ cm}^{-2}$ (2)

is derived by comparing extinctions with 21cm neutral hydrogen column densities. The second form makes the assumption that the extinction curve is uniform everywhere and that the ratio of total to selective extinction, $R = A(V)/E(B-V) = $ constant.
The assumption is that, given a cloud whose color excess $E(B-V)$ can be determined, a value of the column density of hydrogen may be derived even if the hydrogen is in its unobservable molecular form. There are two basic implied assumptions underlying this assumption:
1)   the number density of the dust particles which produce the visual extinction is correlated with the number density of hydrogen in all forms ($N(H) = n(HI) + 2n(H_2)$));
2)   the dust which produces the visual extinciton is the same in molecular clouds as it is in diffuse clouds.

The first assumption would be violated if dust could coagulate in clouds or if the dust and gas can be decoupled by some radiation pressure effects. Although the former does occur in protoplanetary regions -vis a vis comets - it is probably not significant in normal high density clouds ($n(H) = 10^{7-8}$ cm-3). The latter may occur in highly specialized regions such as near very hot young stars, but is probably not significant in general. The second assumption is known to be violated as shown by the presence of accreted mantles in molecular clouds. It turns out that if one strictly uses $E(B-V)$ in equation 1 as the measure of the dust extinction this does not have so strong an influence on the result. But, if one uses star counts or galaxy counts to determine the total extinction, then one must use equation 2 which is only valid on the average in diffuse clouds. Since the ratio of total to selective extinction $R = A(V)/E(B-V)$ may be higher in molecular clouds by as much as 60 - 70% than in diffuse clouds the number density implied by Eq.(2) may be substantially higher than it actually is.

2.3 Cosmic abundance constraints.
The relative abundances of the most abundant elements in space which constitute the dust (i.e., are condensable and form solids at low temperatures) are shown in Table 3. These ratios are presumend to be fairly uniform within the galaxy (possibly except in the galactic center).

Table 3. Relative cosmic (solar system) abundances of the most common elements

	(a)	(b)	(c)	(d)
H	1	1	1	1
He	0.069	0.068	0.081	0.079
C	3.71(-4)	4.17(-4)	4.45(-4)	4.90(-4)
N	1.18(-4)	0.87(-4)	0.91(-4)	0.98(-4)
O	6.76(-4)	6.92(-4)	7.40(-4)	8.13(-4)
Mg	0.32(-4)	0.399(-4)	0.396(-4)	0.380(-4)
Si	0.32(-4)	0.376(-4)	0.368(-4)	0.355(-4)
S	0.16(-4)	0.188(-4)	0.189(-4)	0.162(-4)
Fe	0.25(-4)	0.338(-4)	0.331(-4)	0.467(-4)

(a)   (19) A.G.W. Cameron (1973) Sp. Science Reviews 15, 121–146.

(b)   (20) A.G.W. Cameron (1982) in "Elements and Nuclide Abundances in the Solar System", ed. C. Barnes, R.N. Clayton and D.N. Schramm (Cambridge, Cambridge Univ. Press), 23.

(c)   (21) E. Anders and Mitsuru Ebihara (1982), Geochimica & Cosmochimica Acta 46, 2363–2380.

(d)   (22) N. Grevesse (1984), Physica Scripta T8, 49–58.

We are here primarily interested in the carbon and oxygen depletion on the dust. This may be derived from the mass of the material per unit extinction. The extinction per particle (2:1 spheroid) (in the model above) is $A_V = 1.086 \; 2 \; \pi a^2 \; Q_V$ where Q_V is the extinction efficiency and a is the semiminor axis. The mass of the organic mantle is ~ 1/2 the total mass, $m_{OR} = 2/3 \; \pi a^3$. Applying equation 1 to obtain N_H from A_V, we get

$$\frac{m_{OR}}{N_H m_H} = 0.36 \times 10^{-2} \tag{3}$$

For the organic refractory material we have no simple molecular representations. However, we know, from the previous section, that it must be carbon rich. As a representative we use _relative_ atomic abundances in the molecular mixtures given by C:O:H:N = 3:1:6:0.5. From this we deduce from Eq. 3 (and see Table 3),

$$(N_C/N_H)_{OR} = 1.66 \times 10^{-4} = 0.4 \; (N_C/N_H)_{C.A.}$$

Similarly, for the core and mantle we find oxygen depletion

$$(N_O/N_H)_{sil} = 0.13 \; (N_O/N_H)_{C.A.}$$

$$(N_O/N_H)_{OR} = 0.08 \; (N_O/N_H)_{C.A.}$$

We must still consider the depletions of carbon caused by the hump and the FUV particles. Models of these components are still in the development stage but they are likely to be

$$(N_C/N_H)_h + (N_C/N_H)_{FUV} \geq 0.2 \ (N_C/N_H)_{C.A.}$$

In fact, according to those grain models which use graphite to produce the hump, the hump alone accounts for about 0.25 of the carbon depletion, so that we are here assuming a rather high estimate of the 4.6 μm^{-1} absorption efficiency per unit mass of carbonaceous material. The FUV particles have been estimated as requiring the value of 0.10 of the available carbon if they are PAH's.

Thus our <u>base</u> depletions of oxygen and carbon by the dust in the diffuse clouds are $\delta_0 = 0.21$, $\delta_c \geq 0.6$. For general purposes we will assume the lower limit of the dust carbon depletion.

3. <u>Dust: CO - hydrogen correlations.</u>

The mass of a large fraction of the interstellar medium can not be deduced from the dust extinction because it becomes impossible or difficult to measure A_v when it gets too large as it often does in dense clouds. The appeal then is to the CO abundance where it has to be assumed that some general relation exists between CO and the number of hydrogens expressed as either a ratio of column densities of hydrogen to CO or as $n(H_2)/I_{CO} = X$ in units of molecules cm^{-2} (K km s^{-1})$^{-1}$ where $I_{CO} = \int T(^{12}CO)dV$. There has arisen some controversy of the values of the conversion factor X (23,24) in which the dust properties must play a role. However, I shall not here attempt to *resolve* the questions but rather, as simply as possible, to show some of the ways in which dust evolution in molecular clouds or differences in dust properties in different galactic regions may provide some additonal insight into the correlation factors.

There have been extensive studies of the abundances of CO and comparison with hydrogen column densities. Theoretical models of the molecular abundances may be derived for regions with specific characteristic ranging from diffuse or translucent clouds where the hydrogen ($n_H \leq 10^3$ cm^{-3}) to dense clouds which contain most of the molecular hydrogen. Where CO is most abundant it is most probable that it is observed also as a solid component of the dust. The presence of CO in the dust is a strong indicator of the presence of a substantial mantle of ices dominated by oxygen. The observation of the gaseous CO column density in general are compared with the visual extinction in the cloud (25,26,27) and, in fact, because ^{12}CO is saturated at high extinction the quantity directly evaluated is the ^{13}CO-Av relation. In order to derive the hydrogen column density one assumes a given $^{13}CO/^{12}CO$ ratio and then a "standard" $N(H_2)/Av$ ratio. Because the ice grain mantles are likely to be thicker in <u>just</u> those cases where the ^{12}CO is saturated, the effect on the $N(H_2)/Av$ relation is obvious. Since the dust correlation is a <u>number</u> correlation, we assume the same number of dust grains per hydrogen, but each dust grain has a higher extinction the thicker the grain mantle. In dense clouds the mantle may easily add an extra 20% to the mean grain diameter so that the area per grain may be increased by as much as 50%. This leads to a drecrease in the $N(H_2)/Av$ ratio from 0.95 x 10^{21} to 0.6 x 10^{21} cm^{-2}. Subsequent conversion to the value of X involves the knowledge of the linewidth (velocity dispersion) and the excitation temperatures. Frerking et al. (25) found that, in the range 12 > Av > 4 mag, X = 1.8 x 10^{20} cm^{-2} (K km/s)$^{-1}$ which they suggested was reasonable for large warm molecular cloud structures but noted that this value should be used with considerable caution. We note that, given the effect of grain mantles alone the value of X is brought down to 1.2 x 10^{20} which happens to be rather like the value championed by Wolfendale and his colleagues (see Wolfendale, this volume). I don't want to overemphasize this correspondence by this example but it serves to show that factors of as much as 2 are already inherent in use of the dust-hydrogen correlation.

A further fact worth noting is that according to the theories of grain evolution and including gas-dust interactions, the amount of CO in the gas is possibly matched by the amount of CO in the grain mantles. In fact, it is probably only because of explosive dust mantle desorption mechanisms that any of the CO remains in the gas (28,29). However, where the dust is substantially heated, as in the neighborhood of protostars or hot young stars within the dense molecular cloud complexes, the total CO may be in the gas. This may produce a local superabundance of CO relative to H_2. Here, the mantles would be depleted, but the increased value of the CO density would again lead to a lower value of X. Thus, there are at least two reasons why the X values are less than if one considers "standard" dust-gas relations.

With regard to global differences in the galactic value of X; for example, the possible gradient with galactocentric radius, this too may be attributed to dust properties. The evidence for an increased abundance of heavy elements towards the galactic center may be inferred from the higher values of the core and mantle absorptions (at 9.7 and 3.4 μm) relative to the visual extinction. The ratio of both these absorptions per unit extinction is about twice as high towards the galactic center as they are towards the object Cyg OB2 # 12 (30,31). Insofar as the 9.7 μm absorption alone it has long been recognized that it is at least two times higher than the local average (32). In fact, using the known column density of hydrogen to the G.C. the silicon abundance required is about twice the cosmic abundance value. While the increased value of X toward the galactic center may be, in part, attributed to higher excitation temperatures, there is also, from the dust, an independent reason to expect it to be reduced by virtue of the higher dust-gas ratio.

Another factor which must be taken into account is the conversion form ^{13}CO to ^{12}CO. Apparently this, too, varies with galactocentric distance, $^{12}C/^{13}C$ being smaller by a factor of as much as 2 or more in the galactic center than at the solar distance (33). Thus unqualified use of "standard" $^{12}C/^{13}C$ ratios would, towards the galactic center, leads to too high H_2 abundances, just as the assumption of standard dust to gas ratios based on "standard" cosmic abundances of condensable atoms.

The amount of carbon in the dust places a constraint on the column density of CO. Assuming diffuse cloud dust with no icy mantles, and therefore no CO on the grains, the absolute maximum ^{12}CO to the ratio is

$$N_{CO}/N_H \leq (1 - 0.6) \times 4.17 \times 10^{-4} = 1.7 \times 10^{-4}$$

or equivalently, where all H is as H_2

$$CO/H_2 \leq 3.4 \times 10^{-4} .$$

In the Orion -KL shock we expect no solid CO and, indeed, one finds (27) $CO/H_2 = 1.2 \times 10^{-4}$ which is substantially less than the maximum. In the ρ Oph complex the ratio $^{13}CO/A_V = 2.6 \times 10^{15}$ (26) when combined with $^{12}CO/^{13}CO = 60$ (33) gives (for the "standard" dust-gas ratio) $CO/H_2 = 1.4 \times 10^{-4}$. However, using an increased value of the total to selective extinction ($R = A_V/E(B-V) = 4-5$ instead of 3) increases this to $CO/H_2 = 2.1 \times 10^{-4}$. Although this is still well within the cosmic abundance limit it does not take into account the solid CO implied by the thick mantles. If the solid CO is of the same order as the gaseous component (29,35) (as it is in some clouds) the total amount of CO may approach (and even exceed) this limit.

The conclusion would appear to be that factors of two differences in the derived values of $N(H_2)/I_{CO}$ are inherent in the assumptions and their uncertainties.

REFERENCES

1. Bhat, C.L., Mayer, C.J., Wolfendale, A.W., 1986, Phil.Trans. R. Soc. London A319, 249.
2. Wolfendale, A.W., 1988, in: Molecular clouds in the milky way and external galaxies, eds. R. Dickman, R.Sneel, J. Young, Heidelberg, Springer, p. 76.
3. MacLaren, I., Richardson, K.M., Wolfendale, A.W., 1989, Cosmic rays and the masses of giant molecular clouds, J.Phys. G: Nucl.Part. 15, 1305-1321.
4. Greenberg, J.M., 1989, Interstellar dust: an overview of physical and chemical evolution, in: Evolution of interstellar dust and related topics, eds. A. Bonetti, J.M. Greenberg and S. Aiello, North Holland, 7-51.
5. G. Chlewicki and J.M. Greenberg, 1990, Interstellar circular polarization and the dielectric nature of dust grains, Astrophys. J. 365, 230-238.
6. J.M. Greenberg, 1978, Physics and astrophysics of interstellar dust, in: *Infrared Astronomy*, eds. G. Setti and G. Fazzio, Dordrecht, Reidel, 51-95.
7. Hagen, W., Allamandola, L.J. and Greenberg, J.M., 1979, *Interstellar molecule formation in grain mantles: the laboratory analog experiments*, Astrophys. Sp. Sc. 65, 215-240.
8. Greenberg, J.M., 1979, Grain mantle photolysis; a connection between the grain size distribution function and the abundance of complex interstellar molecules, in *Stars and Star Systems*, ed. B.E. Westerlund, Dordrecht, Reidel, 173-193.
9. d'Hendecourt, L.B. and Allamandola, L.J., *1986*, Astr. Ap. Supp. 64, 453.
10. Allamandola, L.J., Greenberg, J.M., Norman, C.A. and Hagen, W., 1980, The Chemical identification of grain mantles by infrared spectroscopy, in *Proc. IAU Symposium no. 87 on Interstellar Molecules*, ed. Andrew, B.H., Reidel Publ. Co., 373-380.
11. Greenberg, J.M., 1973, Chemical and physical properties of interstellar dust, in Molecules in the galactic environment, eds. M.A. Gordon, and L.E. Snyder, John Wiley, 94-124.
12. Greenberg, J.M. and Schutte, W., 1985, Infrared spectral identification of complex organic molecules in interstellar grains, in Search for extraterrestrial life, IAU Symposium 112, Reidel, 145-150.
13. Agarwal, V.K., Schutte, W., Greenberg, J.M., Ferris, J.P., Briggs, R., Connor, S., van de Bult, C.P.E.M. and Baas, F., 1985, Origins of Life 16, 21-40.
14. Schutte, W.A., *1988, The Evolution of Interstellar Grain Mantles*, Ph.D. Thesis, Univ. of Leiden, The Netherlands.
15. Mendoza-Gómez, C.X. and Greenberg, J.M., G.B. Eijkel and J.J. Boon, 1991, Astromacromolecules: Formation of very large molecules in interstellar space, in Chemistry in Space, eds. J.M. Greenberg and V. Pirronello, Dordrecht, Kluwer, 455-457, .
16. Mc.Lafferty, F.W., *1980, Interpretation of Mass Spectra*, 3rd. edition, University Science Books.
17. Mendoza-Gómez, C.X. and Greenberg, J.M., 1992, *Proceedings of the IAU colloquium 126, Origins and evolution of interplanetary dust*, in press.
18. L.J. Spitzer, 1978, Physical processes in the interste;llar medium, New York, Wiley.
19. A.G.W. Cameron, 1973, Sp. Science Reviews 15, 121-146.

20. A.G.W. Cameron, 1982, in "Elements and Nuclide Abundances in the Solar System", ed. C. Barnes, R.N. Clayton and D.N. Schramm (Cambridge, Cambridge Univ. Press), 23.
21. E. Anders and Mitsuru Ebihara, 1982, Geochimica & Cosmochimica Acta 46, 2363-2380.
22. N. Grevesse, 1984, Physica Scripta T8, 49-58.
23. Bloemen, H., 1989, Diffuse galactic gamma-ray emission. Ann.Rev. Astron. Astrophys. 29, 469-516.
24. Maloney, P., 1990, Mass determination from CO observations, in: The interstellar medium in galaxies, eds. H.A. Thronson Jr. and J.M. Shull, Kluwer, 493-523.
25. Frerking, M.A., Langer, W.D. and Wilson, R.W., 1982, The relationship between carbon monoxide and visual extinction in interstellar clouds, Astrophys. J. 262, 590.
26. Dickman, R.L. and Herbst, W., 1990, The $^{13}CO-A_v$ relation at high extinction: The ρ Oph complex, Astroph. J. 357, 531-538.
27. Van Dishoeck, E.F. and Black, J.H., 1987, The abundances of interstellar CO, in: Physical processes in interstellar clouds, eds. G.E. Morfill and M. Scholer, Dordrecht, Kluwer, 241.
28. d'Hendecourt, L.B., Allamandola, L.J., Greenberg, J.M., 1985, Time dependent chemistry in dense molecular clouds, I: grain surface reactions, gas/grain interactions and infrared spectroscopy, Astron. Astrophys. 152, 130-150.
29. d'Hendecourt, L.B., Allamandola, L.J., Baas, F., Greenberg, J.M., 1982, Interstellar grain explosions: Molecule cycling between gas and dust, Astron.Astrophys. 109, L12-L14.
30. Butchart, I., McFadzean, A.D., Whittet, D.C.B., Geballe, T.R. and Greenberg, J.M., 1986, The 3.4μm absorption towards the galactic center, Astron.Astrophys. 154, 15.
31. Adamson, A.J., Whittet, D.C.B. and Duley, W.W., 1990, The 3.4μm interstellar absorption feature in Cyg OB2 no. 12, M.N. R.Astr.Soc. 243, 400-404.
32. Greenberg, J.M., Hong, S.S., 1974, Dust in the galactic centre, in: HII regions and the galactic centre, ed. A.F.M. Moorwood, ESRO-SP 105, 221-225.
33. Langer, W.D., and Penzias, A.A., 1990, $^{12}C/^{13}C$ isotope ratio across the galaxy from observations of $^{13}C^{18}O$ in molecular clouds, Astrophys. J. 357, 457-493.
34. Fitzpatrick, E.L.. and Massa, D., 1988, An analysis of the shapes of ultraviolet extinction curves, II: the far-UV extinction. Astrophys. J. 328, 734-746.
35. Whittet, D.C.B., and Duley, W.W., 1991, Carbon monoxide frosts in the interstellar medium. The Astron. and Astrophys. Rev., in press.

DUST, GAS AND COSMIC RAYS IN THE INTERSTELLAR MEDIUM

A.W.WOLFENDALE
Physics Department
University of Durham
South Road
Durham DH1 3LE
UK.

ABSTRACT. The case is made for supernova remnants being the source of the energy of the bulk of the cosmic radiation below 10^{10}eV - and perhaps to higher energies too. An analysis of the inter-relation of the cosmic ray particle flux, the ISM and the cosmic gamma radiation leads to the claim that the mass of molecular hydrogen in the ISM is much less than commonly thought. The inter-relation of gas and dust allows conclusions to be drawn about the latter, too. It is concluded that, with certain provisos, the mass of cold dust in the Galaxy is less than sometimes claimed.

1 Introduction

The interaction between the entities considered in the present paper can be seen by reference to Figure 1.

Thus supernovae (SN) produce remnants (SNR) which in turn are thought to accelerate cosmic rays (CR). The CR interact with the gas and gamma rays are produced, the study of which relates to the product of CR intensity and gas density. An alternative estimate of gas density can then be derived. Insofar as the uncertain, but important, molecular hydrogen component of the ISM is largely confined to dust clouds, the studies also give (indirect) information about the dust.

2 Supernovae, SNR and Cosmic Rays.

2.1 THE COSMIC RAY GRADIENT

The best evidence favouring Galactic sources of any kind for the CR component is probably what we termed 'the cosmic ray gradient' (Wolfendale and Young, 1977 - see Ramana Murthy and Wolfendale, 1986, for a further treatment of this topic). The situation is shown in Figure 2. An earlier scare from the Cos B group (Bloemen et al., 1984) that there was

M. M. Shapiro et al. (eds.), Cosmic Rays, Supernovae and the Interstellar Medium, 69–79.
© 1991 *Kluwer Academic Publishers. Printed in the Netherlands.*

70

no gradient at the highest gamma ray energies, for which the primaries are mainly protons, has gone away. At low gamma ray energies the primary particles responsible are electrons (of energy in the region of hundreds of MeV) and the gradient is quite marked; the gradient may be a little smaller for protons - the progenitors of the highest energy gamma rays - but this is understandable in terms of an energy-dependent diffusion coefficient for the transport of particles through the ISM. In fact, however, the conclusion about energy dependent diffusion is suspect because of the possibility of different radial distributions of electrons and protons of different energies near their sources.

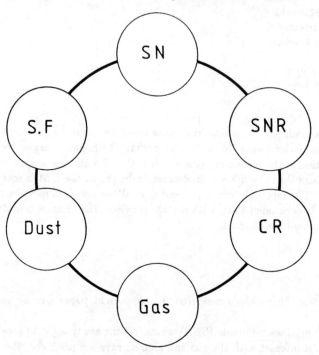

Figure 1. The inter-relation of the topics under consideration.

2.2 THE SOURCES OF GALACTIC COSMIC RAYS : SNR

There is no shortage of types of Galactic sources (see, e.g. Wolfendale, 1983); however, the case for SNR is quite strong. The work of Bhat et al. (1985) showed a distinct excess CR emissivity from an analysis of the SASII gamma ray results towards Loop I for energies in the range 35-100 MeV where electrons are the progenitors, Lebrun and Paul (1985) came to the same conclusion. Loop I is usually considered to delineate an SNR (a detailed consideration of the remnant will be given later). It is well known that there is electron-

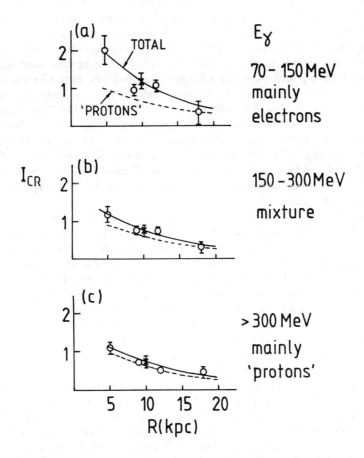

Figure 2. The cosmic ray gradient : the fall of cosmic ray intensity I_{CR}, with increasing Galactocentric radius, R. It can be inferred that the cosmic rays responsible for the gamma rays are produced in our Galaxy as distinct from being incident on it from outside, viz. that the sources are Galactic.

synchrotron radiation coming from SNR but there is the standard problem that the strength of the magnetic field is not known with any accuracy. The gamma ray technique has the advantage that it is the gas density inside the remnant, as distinct from the field, that is needed and this quantity is (hopefully) better known.

More recent analyses have used the CosB data, at both low energies (electrons) and high energies (protons) and our results are shown in Figure 3 (Van der Walt and Wolfendale, 1988). It is claimed that there are excesses for Loop III and round the Vela region as well as for Loop I but it must be remarked that these results are not universally accepted. Results from the GAMMA-1 and GRO satellites should solve this problem.

Before comparing observation with expectation the cosmogenic data will be examined in a little detail. Figure 4 shows a composite of data reported by Kocharov et al. (1990) on cosmogenic ^{10}Be and ^{14}C; the sources are in fact 3 independent groups : Raisbeck et al. (1987) and Vogel et al. (1983) as well as the work of the Leningrad group.

In what follows, a brief summary of the recent analysis by Szabelska et al. (1990) will be given. A rather strong case can be made for the SNR shock being associated with Loop I, the solar system having been passed by a bulge in the SNR conditioned by the well known fact that the density of the ISM is much lower locally than on average thereby giving a higher shock velocity. A similar situation appears to pertain for the Cygnus Loop where the remnant is expanding asymmetrically and producing a bulge in a low density region (Green, 1984). A set of parameters which appear to fit the data are as follows : distance to SN : 80 pc, age of SN 7 x 10^{4}y, velocity of shock at time of arrival 600 kms^{-1} for E^{-2} spectrum. The half thickness of the shock at the time it passed the earth was $\sim$ 5% of the radius, a value not inconsistent with the apparent width of the Loop I spur as currently seen in synchrotron radiation.

Supporting evidence, at least to some extent, that the Loop I SNR has passed the earth is the fact that the local wind in the ISM is blowing from the general direction of the SN (the velocity has been determined by Crutcher, 1982, Bzowski, 1988 and others). There is other evidence favouring a "recent" SN locally such as the need to explain the ^{26}Al gamma ray results (Clayton, 1984) and the presence of soft x-ray emission from the local region. However, it cannot be claimed that there is agreement about the local, recent SN; estimates of age and distance vary by a factor $\simeq$10! (see Frisch and York, 1986).

In Figure 3 both derived CR energies are indicated. It is interesting to note that the upper value, which is more reasonable in view of the fact that the spectral shape of particles in the shock should be E^{-2}, is close to the average line through the other experimental points. We recommend further attention to these interesting cosmogenic results.

Figure 3 indicates that the CR energy content of the SNR shocks is $\sim$ 50% of that predicted. The question of what fraction of the CR energy escapes into the general ISM depends, of course, on the age of the the SNR at which it itself merges into the ISM. More specifically, presumably there is a merging of weak SNR shocks so that the whole Galaxy can be considered as full of shocks at some level. The weak shocks are indeed postulated as the source of reacceleration (eg. Simon et al., 1986 Giler et al, 1988) and as we have shown, such reacceleration can contribute rather a large fraction of the total energy ($\simeq$ 30%). Returning to Figure 3 the primary SNR shocks probably merge, locally, at R $\approx$ 150 pc so that the effective energy is $\sim$ 30% of the initial SN energy. Such a value is not unreasonable from the theoretical standpoint (Drury, 1990). The energetics for the Galaxy as a whole can be written down in a simple fashion:

$$(\varepsilon_{CR})_{SNR} = \eta E_{SN}.V_G^{-1}\tau.F_{SN}$$

where $(\varepsilon_{CR})_{SNR}$ is the cosmic ray energy density, averaged over the Galaxy, η is the efficiency of SNR for generated CR, V_G is the Galactic volume, τ is the mean lifetime of CR in the Galaxy and F_{SN} is the frequency of SN of the type in question. There is uncertainty about each and every one of the quantities but we can take 'typical' values, as follows: $E_{SN} = 10^{51}$erg (for Type II SN) $V_G = 4$ x $10^{67}h_k$ cm^3, where h_k is the halo scale height in kpc, $\tau = 3.10^{14}\tau_7$s where τ_7 is the mean lifetime in units of 10^7y, and $F_{SN} = (100y)^{-1} = 3.10^{-10}$

s^{-1}. The result is $(\varepsilon_{CR})_{SNR} \sim 1.7\ \eta\tau_7/h_k$. Clearly, many combinations of η, τ_7 and h_k

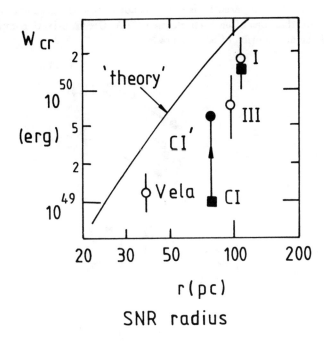

Figure 3. Total cosmic ray energy as estimated for the SNR indicated (see Van der Walt and Wolfendale, 1988, for details). The points marked CI and CI^1 relate to our interpretation of recently reported data on cosmogenic nuclei at earth which are tentatively attributed to the passage of an SNR shock from the Loop I SN having passed the earth about 30,000 years ago (see text). The solid line is an average line through a number of theoretical predictions (principally by Blandford and Cowie, 1982).

can be chosen which will give $(\varepsilon_{CR})_{SNR} \approx 0.5$, or less if it is desired to have continuous acceleration play a role. A not unreasonable combination would be $\eta = 0.3$, $\tau_7 = 7$, $h_k = 10$ yielding $(\varepsilon_{CR})_{SNR} \simeq 0.36$ eV cm^{-3}. All that can be said from the energetics standpoint is that the energetics are 'reasonable'; however, it cannot be disproved that SNR contribute only a few percent of the CR energy budget.

It is interesting to consider the relationship between the SNR energetics and the radial gradient of Figure 2. Of the quantities in the expression, η and F_{SN} are certainly functions of Galactocentric radius, R. Strictly the expression should be reformulated under these conditions, and diffusion properties should be introduced, nevertheless an approximate analysis can be made. It can be seen that although $F_{SN}(R)$ is falling with R, $\eta(R)$ will certainly rise with increasing R due to intersecting shocks being less common and our termination point in Figure 3 being higher at larger R. It is therefore not unreasonable to find $\varepsilon_{CR}(R)$ falling slowly with increasing R. This problem has worried others, eg Dogiel (this volume), who postulates diffusion in a large halo to reduce the slope of $\varepsilon_{CR}(R)$. This is not to say that a large halo is absent - it probably exists - but it does not seem to be required by such arguments. In parenthesis it can be added that the gradient of SNR in the Galaxy is less certain than has often been claimed (D.A. Green, private communication). A new analysis of the distribution of SNR is needed.

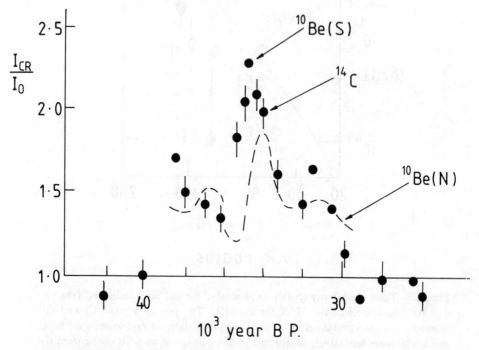

Figure 4. Inferred relative cosmic ray intensity as a function of time from studies of cosmogenic nuclei (after Kocharov et al., 1990). It is tempting to interpret the results in terms of a supernova remnant having passed the earth about 30,000y ago.

Before concluding this discussion of the evidence for SNR acceleration of CR attention can be drawn to the situation for electrons. Cavallo et al. (1981) has examined some 64 old SNR remnants in the Galaxy and, although the results are dependent upon the ubiquitous problem of the strength of the magnetic field in the remnants, the conclusion is that remnants of radius $\sim$ 150 pc have a cosmic ray electron energy content of $\sim 10^{49}$erg (in agreement with the low energy gamma ray analysis of Bhat et al., 1985); this is $\simeq$ 3% of the energy content of cosmic ray protons and it is tempting to explain the well-known 3% e/p ratio in the ambient CR flux along these lines.

3 DUST AND GAS IN THE INTERSTELLAR MEDIUM

3.1 GAMMA RAYS AND GAS

The information about gas (and the associated dust) in the ISM by way of the cosmic gamma ray technique is well documented (eg Wolfendale 1990). The importance of the topic of gas and dust in the ISM in this and other galaxies cannot be overstressed. The whole area of interstellar chemistry is involved as are such apparently diverse topics as the relevance of the masses of giant molecular clouds (GMC) to the velocity dispersion of stars, the stability of the Oort Cloud of comets and the efficiency of star formation (Fig. 1)

Figure 5 shows the present situation with regard to determinations of the mass of molecular gas in the Galaxy (it will be appreciated that this is the uncertain component, the atomic hydrogen, HI, being much easier to study using the 21cm technique). The early observations of the strong 2.6mm line from CO were interpreted in terms of vast quantities of molecular hydrogen, which is supposed to excite the CO by impact and is essentially non- observable in dense dust clouds. Very largely through the insistence of gamma ray astronomers the estimates have come down - to the levels shown in Figure 5; however, we contend that most estimates are still too high. The basis of the gamma ray method is straightforward - if the cosmic ray intensity in a GMC is known then the measured gamma ray flux gives the total gas mass directly (the clouds are almost certainly penetrable by the cosmic rays in question). The gamma ray technique is not without its own problems, however, most notably the presence of discrete sources of gamma rays in (some) GMC and the lack of certainty about the general CR intensity, particularly away from the solar system. Indeed, the hope was - and still is - that the gas masses would be known from other considerations and that the gamma ray data could be used to examine the distribution of the cosmic ray intensity - protons and electrons - over the Galaxy, and beyond.

In our own work (eg Bhat et al, 1986., MacLaren et al, 1988., MacLaren et al, 1990) we have used a variety of techniques to study this problem: X-rays, virial theorem and far infra-red. All appear to give consistent results and the value marked D in Figure 5.

We argue that the upper values (SSS and CSS) are too high because of misapplication of the virial theorem and of the visual extinction technique. Turning to the set marked 'B' these refer to CO observations by the Columbia group (Bronfman et al, 1988) which were used with different values of the conversion factor, X, to give the total H_2 mass. Bloemen et al (1986) derived the Columbia-related value $X_c = 2.8$ but later work by Strong et al (1988) using the same (CosB) gamma ray data yielded $X_c = 2.3$. Use of this value still gives an upper limit to 'X', however, because of the undoubted presence of unresolved gamma ray sources in the detected gamma ray flux from the Inner Galaxy. There is some argument as to what this value should be but we find it hard to believe that it is less than 30%. Using this value drops X_c to 1.6 and the mass indicated in Figure 5. Turning to our own value (D), our often quoted X for the Inner Galaxy is unity. However, this relates to the Stony-Brook CO data (ie $X_s = 1$); there is a difference in absolute CO intensity between the two sets of results by a factor of 30% and our result corresponds to $X_c \simeq 1.3$. The difference between the X_c values, 1.3 and 1.6, is not significant and the masses are equally close. We see no reason to doubt our estimate of 60% for $M(H_2)/M(HI)$ in the Inner Galaxy.

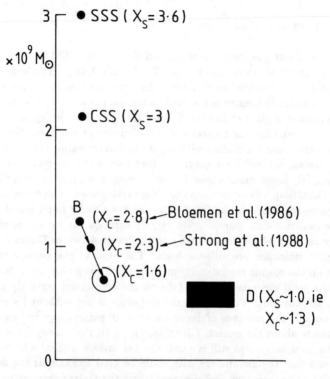

Figure 5. Mass of molecular gas in the Inner Galaxy (R:2-10 kpc) from various authors. D denotes the Durham value (see text). The arrows are recommended corrections by us. We conclude that there is no significant difference between the (corrected) estimate of Bloemen et al (1986) - using the gamma ray technique - and our own using a range of techniques ('D').

3.2   THE DUST PROBLEM

It is generally accepted that gas and dust are reasonably well mixed in the ISM although there are almost certainly gradients in the dust to gas ratio (eg Issa et al, 1990). Dust can be studied using the far infra-red surveys (eg Hauser etal, 1984, IRAS) so that an alternative approach is afforded. A number of workers have followed this path, Sodroski et al (1987) and Bloemen ct al (1990) derive 'low' values for the gas mass but then correct them upwards in view of the claimed presence of unseen cold dust. It is true that cold dust

(T$\stackrel{\sim}{<}$ 15K) would not be seen in the IRAS 60μ and 100μ surveys but it should have been observed in our analysis which also used results at 150 and 250μ (from Hauser et al, 1984). The situation is indicated in Figure 6.

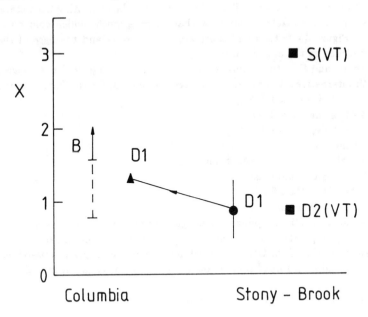

B : Bloemen et al. (1990)

D1 : 'Durham' ≡ Broadbent et al. (1988,9)

D2 : 'Durham' = Maclaren et al. (1989)

S : Scoville et al. (1987)

Figure 6. X-values derived from the far infra-red and virial techniques. We argue that the virial theorem technique appropriately applied gives a low value of X and that the 'lower limit' of Bloemen et al (1990) is in fact close to the actual value.

It is undoubtedly true that the interiors of some dust clouds are very cold but we argue that <u>most</u> of the dust in the Galaxy is at modest optical depths from quite strong sources of radiation. The nearby Taurus and Orion can be taken as examples. Taurus appears to be a comparatively inert cloud and our application of the FIR technique indicates that the median depth is only $A_v \simeq 1.3$ and that its FIR emission at 100μ is some 40% low, because of the absorption of the external UV which heats the cloud. Orion on the other hand, a more massive and dense cloud, has a median A_v of $\simeq 3$ but the embedded stars compensate for the undoubted absorption and the 100μ emission is roughtly as would be expected for no absorption and no heating (MacLaren and Wolfendale, 1990). It is true that many of the GMC in the Inner Galaxy are more massive than those locally therefore there will be more absorption; however, there will also be a higher ambient heating from stars and from cosmic rays and it is unlikely in our view that there is much hidden cold dust. Our D1 (Columbia) - Figure 6 - is thus still considered appropriate and the base of the B arrow should be regarded as the upper limit.

To be specific, and thus to encourage the proponents of large cold dust masses to come forward with alternatives, the estimated masses are quoted, for the Inner Galaxy:

HI, $< T > \sim$ 23K, $\sim 1 \times 10^9$ M$_\odot$
  (30 - 40% of the 100μ flux)
H$_2$, $< T > \sim$ 20K, $\sim 0.6 \times 10^9$ M$_\odot$
  (40% of the 100μ flux)
  with less than $\sim 0.1 \times 10^9$ M$_\odot$ below 15K.
HII, $< T > \sim$ 38K, small mass
  (20 - 30% of the 100μ flux)
  (all from Broadbent et al, 1989).

It is appreciated that the coupling between gas and dust is not complete from the thermal standpoint - the temperatures indicated are those determined from an analysis of the 60μ - 250μ data already referred to. Other essential ingredients are the grain emissivities of Draine and Lee (1984) and an assumed proportionality of the dust to gas ratio with metallicity.

3.3 IMPLICATIONS OF LOW GAS MASSES

There are a number of interesting implications of the low gas masses, and associated subleties, which can be 'credited' to the initial cosmic gamma ray work.

1. There will be variations in CO - H$_2$ calibration from place to place in the Galaxy and from galaxy to galaxy.

2. In our Galaxy, although the GMC in the Inner Galaxy are less massive than previously thought those in the Outer Galaxy (and in such galaxies as have low temperatures and low metallicities) are more massive than presently thought.

3. There will have been less loss of initial Oort cloud comets in the lifetime of the solar system.

4. The efficiency of star formation (mass of new stars/mass of molecular gas from which they have formed) is greater than thought.

5. The role of GMC in providing the velocity spread of stars is less important than thought hitherto.

4 CONCLUSIONS

Briefly, the case for SNR acceleration of cosmic rays below 10 GeV is strengthening and the gamma ray astronomy technique - inspired reanalysis of the amount of molecular gas and dust in the Galaxy deserves to be taken seriously.

5 ACKNOWLEDGEMENTS

The author is grateful to Professors M.M. Shapiro and J.P. Wefel for the opportunity to attend another excellent International School of Cosmic Ray Astrophysics at Erice. Discussions with both Faculty and Students were very rewarding. Particular thanks are due to Prof. J.M. Greenberg and Drs. D.A. Green and M. Bzowski for helpful remarks.

REFERENCES

Bhat, C.L., Mayer, C.J. and Wolfendale, A.W., 1986, Phil. Trans. R. Soc. Lond. 319, 249.

Broadbent, A., MacLaren, I. and Wolfendale, A.W., 1989, Mon. Not. R. astr. Soc., 237, 1075.

Bloemen, J.B.G.M. et al, 1984, Astron. Astrophys. 139, 37; 1988, Acta Astronomica, 38, 443; 1990, Astron. Astrophys. (in press).

Bzowski, M., 1988, Acta Astronomica, 38, 443.

Cavallo, G., Palumbo, G.G.C. and Vettolani, G., 1981, Proc. 17th Int. Cosmic Ray Conf., Paris, 9, 230.

Clayton, D.D., 1984, Astrophys. J., 280, 144.

Crutcher, R.M., 1982, Astrophys. J., 254, 82.

Draine, B.T. and Lee, H.M., 1984, Astrophys. J., 285, 74.

Drury, L. O'C., 1990. Proc. 21st Int. Cosmic Ray Conf., Adelaide, (in press).

Frisch, P.C. and York, D.G., 1986, 'The Galaxy and the Solar System', eds. R. Smoluchowski, J.N. Bahcall and M. Matthews (Univ. Arizona Press, Tucson Ariz.).

Giler, M., Szabelska, B., Wdowczyk, J. and Wolfendale, A.W., 1987, Proc. 20th Int. Cosmic Ray Conf., Moscow, 2, 211.

Giler, M., Wdowczyk, J. and Wolfendale, A.W., 1988, Astron. Astrophys. 196, 44.

Green, D.A., 1984, Mon. Not. R. Astron. Soc., 211, 433.

Hauser, M.G. et al., 1984, Astrophys. J., 285, 74.

Issa, M.R., MacLaren, I. and Wolfendale, A.W., 1990. Astron. Astrophys. (in press).

MacLaren, I., Richardson, K.M. and Wolfendale, A.W., 1989, Astrophys. J., 333, 821.

Kocharov, G.E., Konstantinov, A.N. and Levchenko, V.A., 1990, Proc. 21st Int. Cosmic Ray Conf., Adelaide, 7, 120.

Raisbeck, G.M. and Yiou, F., 1985, Ann. Glaciology, 7, 138.

Simon, M., Heinrich, W. and Mathis, K.D., 1986, Astrophys. J., 300, 32.

Sodroski, T.J., Dwek, E., Hauser, M.G. and Kerr, F.J., 1987, Astrophys. J., 322, 101.

Strong, A.W. et al., 1987 Proc. 20th Int. Cosmic Ray Conf., Moscow, 1, 125.

Szabelska, B., Szabelski, J. and Wolfendale, A.W., 1990. (to be published).

Vogel, J.C., 1983, Radiocarbon, 25, 213.

Wolfendale, A.W. and Young, E.C.M., 1977, Proc. 12th ESLAB Symp. Frascati (ESA SP-124 July 1977), 157.

Wolfendale, A.W., 1990, 7th Man. Conf. on Mol. Clouds, (Camb. Univ. Press, in press).

COMPARISON BETWEEN GREENBERG AND MATHIS MODELS OF GRAINS FOR THE H_2 FORMATION INDUCED BY COSMIC RAYS

D. Averna[1], V. Pirronello[1], W.L. Brown[3], L.J. Lanzerotti[3]

[1]Istituto di Astronomia, Universita' di Catania, Italy
[2]Dipartimento di Fisica, Universita' della Calabria, Italy
[3]AT&T Bell Laboratories, Murray Hill, New Jersey, USA

ABSTRACT. The formation of molecular hydrogen in dense clouds is evaluated by means of a Monte Carlo simulation of the bombardment of cosmic protons and helium ions (E< 1 GeV) on interstellar dust grains of the Greenberg type. A comparison with results obtained for the Mathis model is given.

1. The Grain Models

A major problem in studying either physical or chemical processes involving interstellar dust stands in the choice of the model of grains. In fact, ever since the presence of the dust in interstellar medium was firmly established, several models have been proposed in order to interpret extinction curves and polarization of star light.

In a previous evaluation of H_2 production in dense clouds (Pirronello and Averna, 1988) we considered the model proposed by Mathis, Rumpl and Nordsieck in 1977 (hereafter called the Mathis model). According to this model, a grain in a diffuse cloud is composed of graphite or silicates and follows a size distribution that varies as "$a^{-3.5}$", where "a" is the radius of the grain; if, during its life, the grain enters in a dense region it can accrete a layer of ices, by slow deposition from the gas phase. It is then covered by an amorphous mantle, the so called "dirty ice mantle". The limits of the size distribution we considered were from 400 A to 4000 A in radius.

Here we should like to extend the evaluation of the H_2 formation rate in molecular clouds to a model that is very interesting for its evolutionary meaning: that of Greenberg (Greenberg, 1979). He proposed that a grain in a

81

M. M. Shapiro et al. (eds.), Cosmic Rays, Supernovae and the Interstellar Medium, 81–85.
© 1991 *Kluwer Academic Publishers. Printed in the Netherlands.*

diffuse cloud is composed of a "core" of refractory material surrounded by an organic refractory mantle that is the highly photoprocessed residue of a icy layer that the grain accreted during a stage when it was in a dense region. Greenberg derived a size distribution function of the form

$$n(a) = n_d \, f_o \exp \, [-5((a-a_c)/a_i)^3]$$

where

n_d = total number density of grains

f_o = normalization factor = $(0.5222 \, a_i)^{-1}$

a = radius of the grain

a_c = core radius

a_i = the maximum mantle dimension consistent with cosmic abundance (0.21 μm).

For this model we assumed a radius of 500 A for the core, a thickness between 600 A and 2400 A for the organic refractory mantle, and a thickness of a few hundred Angstroms for the external icy layer.

In all cases, the silicate used for the core is assumed to be of an Olivine type and the icy mantle considered is made of pure water. We tentatively represent this intermediate mantle by a material having an average abundance ratio between "heavy atoms" (N+C+O) and hydrogen of about 1:2 at the beginning of the period the grains spend in a dense cloud.

We use the two grain models in our Monte Carlo simulation of the interaction between low energy cosmic rays and interstellar grains. These cosmic rays are taken to be essentially protons and helium ions with E< 1GeV and with an energy spectrum deduced from Morfill, Volk and Lee (1976).

We will present, in section 2, a brief description of the process investigated and, in section 3, the results obtained.

2. The Simulation

The interstellar location chosen for the study of cosmic ray-grain interaction is a small, spherical dense cloud without internal sources, such as that proposed by Boland and de Jong (1984).Cosmic rays are assumed injected from the outside of the cloud with random directions.

For both grain models an impact parameter is pseudorandomly chosen and defines the ion path inside the grain, establishing whether the ion traverses only a mantle or also a core. Whenever a cosmic ray crosses either the icy or the organic refractory mantle the energy the particle loses is calculated. From this, the amount of H_2 it produces is evaluated.

We have used a value of the yield of H_2 from pure water ice by 1.5 MeV He^+ bombardment of:

$$Y(H_2) \cong 0.2$$

taken from Brown et al. (1982).

When we consider the intermediate organic refractory mantle of the Greenberg model we have deduced the yield of molecular hydrogen per impinging ion at a given energy from the experimental work of Lanzerotti et al. (1985, 1987). We have deduced the differential yield of H_2 released per incident ion from a film initially composed of 3×10^{17} CD_4 molecules cm^{-2} but after an impinging fluence such that the film has a D\C ratio of 2 (we assume the material at this ratio represents the organic refractory inner mantle in the Greenberg grain model). At these conditions:

$$Y(H_2) \cong 85$$

To estimate the production rate of molecular hydrogen per unit volume and per second at various depths in the cloud we use the expression:

$$R(H_2) = 4\pi^2 \int_{a_{min}}^{a_{max}} \int_0^{E_{max}} Y(E') \, (dJ'/dE') \, n_g \, a^2 \, dE' \, da$$

where
a_{min} = minimum value of the radius of the grain size distribution of the two models
a_{max} = maximum value of the radius used for the size distribution of the two models
E_{max} = 1 GeV, maximum energy of cosmic rays considered in the simulation
E' = residual energy of cosmic rays after interacting with the gas inside the dense cloud
dJ'/dE' = energy spectrum of cosmic rays impinging on grains

Details of the simulation have been published in 1988 (Pirronello and Averna, 1988) and the reader is referred to that paper.

3. Results

Results of the simulation, in terms of the production rate of molecular hydrogen "$R(H_2)$" in mol. cm^{-3} s^{-1}, are shown in TABLE 1 as a function of the depth measured in magnitudes inside the cloud (Column 1) for both grain models considered.

Column 2 is the rate of molecular hydrogen production obtained using Greenberg's model with only the organic refractory mantle, as a ratio of the H_2 production using the Mathis model.

TABLE 1. Comparison between the two production rates

$d(A_v)$	$R_0(G)/R_0(M)$
2	2.9×10^3
4	3.1×10^3
6	3.2×10^3
8	3.1×10^3

It is evident that the rate of formation and release of molecular hydrogen, at all depths in the clouds, is more than three orders of magnitude higher using the model of Greenberg compared to that of Mathis.

This difference depends principally on the presence of the organic refractory mantle in the Greenberg model.

An interesting fact associated with the formation of molecular hydrogen from any organic refractory material is that the production by cosmic ray bombardment can occur even in regions where physical conditions do not allow the existence of icy mantles, such as at the edge of dense clouds or in the diffuse medium.

4. References

Boland, W., de Jong, T.: 1984, Astron. Astrophys., 134, 87-98

Brown, W.L., Augustyniak, W.M., Simmons, E., Marcantonio, K.K., Lanzerotti L.J., Johnson, R.E., Boring, J.W., Reimann, C.T., Foti, G., Pirronello, V.: 1982 Nucl. Inst. Meth., 198, 1-8

Greenberg, J.,M.: 1979, "Stars and Star Systems", B.E. Westerlund ed., p. 173-193, Reidel Publishing Company, Dordrecht

Lanzerotti, L.J., Brown, W.L., Johnson, R.E: 1985, in "Ices in the Solar System", J. Klinger, D. Benest, A. Dollfus and R. Smoluchowski eds., p. 316-325, Reidel Publ. Co., Dordrecht

Lanzerotti, L.J., Brown, W.L., Marcantonio, K.,J.: 1987, Astrophys. J., 313, 910-919

Mathis, J.S., Rumpl, W., Nordsiek, K.H.: 1977, Astrophys. J., 217, 425-433

Morfill, G., Volk, H., Lee, M.,A.: 1976, J.G.R., 181, 584

Pirronello, V., Averna, D.: 1988, Astron. Astrophys., 196, 201-206

SHOCK ACCELERATION OF COSMIC RAYS

L. O'C. Drury
Dublin Institute for Advanced Studies
School of Cosmic Physics
5 Merrion Square
Dublin 2
Ireland

ABSTRACT. The basic concepts of diffusive shock acceleration are reviewed and the mechanism, applied to the shocks bounding Galactic supernova remnants, is considered as a possible source for the Galactic cosmic rays.

1. Introduction

The idea that shocks might have some connection with particle acceleration is quite an old one; among the many references in the older literature some of the more interesting are Hoyle (1960), Parker (1958), Hudson (1965), Schatzman (1963), Jokipii (1966) and Fisk (1971). However the definitive formulation of what is now generally called diffusive shock acceleration first appeared in four independent publications by Krymsky (1977), Axford Leer and Skadron (1977), Bell (1978a) and Blandford and Ostriker (1978). The crucial point of these papers is that they all identify a specific form of Fermi acceleration operative at shocks which naturally produces power-law spectra. Two recent reviews which can be consulted for further details, additional background and slightly different viewpoints on the subject of this talk are those by Blandford and Eichler (1987) and Berezhko and Krymsky (1988).

1.1. SHOCKS

Before progressing to the details of this acceleration process it is probably worth spending a little time on the physical significance of shocks and some of their elementary properties (for more detail I recommend Zeldovich and Raizer, 1966). An isolated system containing interacting particles will generally tend (excluding selfgravitating systems and those with phase changes) to a spatially uniform state. The paradigm motivating this whole discussion, and indeed the theory of shocks, is a volume filled with gas (*i.e.* the particles interact only through two-body collisions) which indeed, as is a matter of common experience, tends to a state of uniform density and pressure (unless the scales are such that selfgravity is important, or the gas is condensing to the liquid or solid phases, or strong external body forces are imposed). If this uniform state is then disturbed locally, for example the density or pressure is increased by injecting mass or energy, information about this local excess spreads out as the system relaxes back to a uniform state. If inertial effects are unimportant this propagation is typically diffusive, the linear extent of the region affected by the disturbance increasing as the square root of the time since the

87

M. M. Shapiro et al. (eds.), Cosmic Rays, Supernovae and the Interstellar Medium, 87–96.
© *1991 Kluwer Academic Publishers. Printed in the Netherlands.*

disturbance was applied. However if inertial effects are important the disturbance typically propagates as one or more waves with characteristic velocities, so that the linear extent of the region affected is directly proportional to the time. In the case of gas dynamics this is simply the sound speed and information about the local excess of pressure is communicated to the rest of the system by the propagation of sound waves through the gas.

In a tenuous plasma containing magnetic fields, such as the interstellar or interplanetary medium, two body collisions are relatively unimportant modes of interaction between the particles. However a similar rôle is played by the collective interaction of the particles with the electromagnetic field, so that the plasma behaves as if the particles were coupled together on scales much smaller than the two-body mean free path, down indeed to scales of order a few ion gyro-radii. Disturbances in the plasma can propagate *via* a large number of plasma modes, but for scales substantially larger than the ion gyro-radius the only important ones are the Alfvén and associated magneto-sonic modes (for a recent survey see Quest, 1988).

The crucial point giving rise to the formation of shocks is that these characteristic wave velocities with which disturbances propagate are not constant (in mathematical terms the wave modes are governed by *nonlinear* hyperbolic partial differential equations). Let us suppose that, as is usually the case, the propagation speed increases as the system is compressed and consider a model system consisting of a tube closed at one end by a piston. If we now start to compress the contents of the tube by smoothly pushing the piston into the tube, it is clear that the initial disturbance produced by the piston starting to move will travel at a slower speed than the subsequent disturbances which it produces (which are propagating in an already compressed medium). It follows that the front of the compressional disturbance moving ahead of the piston will become steeper and steeper until at some point the waves all pile up and the local gradients become very steep. This concentration of the entire disturbance into a very thin layer is what is termed a shock wave, or shock front, or simply a *shock*.

If, as we have assumed, the propagation speed increases when the system is compressed, a shock is a thin layer in which the medium through which the shock is propagating is suddenly compressed. Locally we can approximate the shock as a plane surface into which the medium flows with uniform velocity U_1 and density ρ_1 and emerges with velocity U_2 and denisty ρ_2. Clearly mass conservation requires $\rho_1 U_1 = \rho_2 U_2$, so that if the shock compression ratio is $r = \rho_2/\rho_1$ then $U_1 = rU_2$ and the kinetic energy flux going into the shock, $\frac{1}{2}\rho_1 U_1^3$, is a factor of r^2 larger than that coming out. Thus in the shock a substantial amount of mechanical energy can be dissipated in a small volume.

The extent of the compression is determined by momentum and energy conservation across the shock. If we consider the limiting case of a very strong shock, *i.e.* where the kinetic energy density is much larger than the internal energy density upstream and the ram pressure much larger than the internal pressure, then the three conservation equations are

$$\rho_1 U_1 = \rho_2 U_2$$
$$\rho_1 U_1^2 = \rho_2 U_2^2 + P_2$$
$$\frac{1}{2}\rho_1 U_1^3 = \frac{1}{2}\rho_2 U_2^3 + U_2(E_2 + P_2)$$

where P_2 is the downstream pressure and E_2 the internal energy density. It is a matter of elementary algebra to deduce that the compression ratio

$$r = \frac{U_1}{U_2} = 1 + 2\frac{E_2}{P_2}.$$

If the particles constituting the gas or plasma system are nonrelativistic and have no internal degrees of freedom (ideal gas limit) then $P = 2/3E$ and the maximum compression in a strong shock is 4. It is important to note however that if the energy dissipated in the shock is used for anything other than increasing the random motion of the particles, or if any of these particles start to become relativistic, then the compression will be greater than four. In this sense four is the minimum maximum compression a shock can have.

1.2. PARTICLE PROPAGATION

Finally, before turning to the question of acceleration, it is necessary to discuss briefly the propagation of energetic charged particles. Extraterrestrial plasmas usually contain significant numbers of charged particles with energies well above typical thermal energies. These are coupled to the bulk plasma by the ambient magnetic field, in particular they are scattered by irregularities in the magnetic field with length scales comparable to their gyroradii (resonant scattering), and because their inertia is (usually) negligible the resulting random walk of the energetic particles through the plasma can be well described as a diffusion process in space. The energy of the scattered particle is conserved in the rest frame of the scattering structure. In general these structures will have some random velocity dispersion which will give rise to some classical second order Fermi acceleration, however we will ignore this and assume that the scatterers are effectively frozen into the plasma. Then if we measure a particle's energy, or equivalently the magnitude of its momentum $p = |\mathbf{p}|$, in the local plasma frame the distribution function will be very close to isotropy, $f(\mathbf{p}) \approx f(p)$, and the propagation can be described by the diffusion equation

$$\frac{\partial f}{\partial t} = \nabla \kappa \nabla f$$

where κ is the diffusion tensor.

This assumes that the plasma rest frame does not vary from point to point, in other words that there is no relative motion within the plasma. While it is not too hard to derive the transport equation for the case where there is relative motion, this is unnecessary for the application to shock acceleration where we can treat the upstream and downstream media as spatially uniform.

2. Diffusive shock acceleration

Let us now consider a shock with energetic particles scattering in the upstream and downstream media. We assume that the particles are sufficiently energetic for their gyroradii to be substantially larger than the thickness of the shock front so that they do not interact with the complicated electromagnetic fields in the shock itself and only see it as a sudden transition between the upstream and downstream states. (For protons and heavier ions this amounts to saying that the particles must have more than a few times the energy of a downstream thermal ion, however for electrons it is a much more severe constraint.)

Let the plasma flow into the shock with (vector) velocity U_1 and leave with U_2 downstream. Although the particles do not interact with the shock directly, on crossing the shock they go from a region where where we have agreed to measure energy in the frame which, seen from the shock, is moving at velocity U_1 to one where we have agreed to use the frame moving at velocity U_2 or *vice versa*. There is thus a change of energy or momentum which, on expanding the Lorentz transformation to first order, is easily found to be for a particle of momentum p

$$\Delta p = \frac{\mathbf{p} \cdot \Delta \mathbf{U}}{v}$$

where v is the particle speed corresponding to the momentum p and $\Delta \mathbf{U}$ is the velocity jump seen by the particle. Integrating over all directions in which the particle can cross the shock we obtain a total flux of particles through the reference momentum level p of

$$\Phi(p) = \int \frac{\mathbf{p} \cdot (\mathbf{U}_1 - \mathbf{U}_2)}{v} \mathbf{v} \cdot \mathbf{n} p^2 f(\mathbf{p}) d\Omega$$

where $\mathbf{n}$ is the unit normal to the shock front. This is the rate, per unit area of the shock front, at which particles cross the front with an initial momentum below p and a final momentum above p as measured in the respective local frames.

If the distribution function can be assumed to be close to isotropy it is straightforward to evaluate this flux;

$$\Phi(p) = p^2 f(p) \int \frac{\mathbf{p} \cdot (\mathbf{U}_1 - \mathbf{U}_2)}{v} \mathbf{v} \cdot \mathbf{n} d\Omega$$

and the integral is clearly a rotationally invariant linear function of the two vectors $\mathbf{n}$ and $\mathbf{U}_1 - \mathbf{U}_2$. It must therefore be proportional to the scalar product and the constant of proportionality can be evaluated in any convenient case, say that in which both vectors are parallel. Thus

$$\Phi(p) = \frac{4\pi}{3} p^3 f(p) \mathbf{n} \cdot (\mathbf{U}_1 - \mathbf{U}_2).$$

(In a general magnetohydrodynamic shock $\mathbf{U}_1 - \mathbf{U}_2$ and $\mathbf{n}$ will be exactly parallel only if the magnetic field is itself aligned with the shock normal or the field is so weak that it is dynamically insignificant.)

Essentially this result says that because of the compression in the shock there is an associated flux of particles upwards in momentum (or energy) at a rate proportional to the number density of particles at that momentum, $p^3 f(p)$, and to the rate at which plasma is being compressed in the shock, $\mathbf{n} \cdot (\mathbf{U}_1 - \mathbf{U}_2)$.

We have not however said anything about where the particles come from. Clearly one obvious source of particles is the upstream plasma; any pre-existing energetic particles in the upstream medium will be carried into the shock and can then participate in this process. Another potential source is the shock itself. Unlike the two-body collisions responsible for the dissipation in gas shocks, the collective plasma processes responsible for the fine-scale structure of collisionless plasma shocks need not produce exactly Maxwellian distributions downstream. Indeed observations (of interplanetary shocks) and computer simulations show that there is usually a high-energy tail to the downstream ion distribution. Some of these suprathermal ions will have sufficient energy to be regarded as energetic particles and their subsequent acceleration can then be described by the simple model outlined above.

If now we look for a steady spectrum of particles accelerated by the shock we must balance the spatial flux of particles into and out of the the the shock against the injection of particles at the shock and the divergence of the upward flux in momentum space associated with the shock. Noting that, as is easily seen by examining the diffusion equation, in a steady state the downstream distribution function must be spatially uniform and equal to its value at the shock we can write down the particle conservation equation

$$\frac{\partial \Phi}{\partial p} - \mathbf{n} \cdot \mathbf{U}_1 4\pi p^2 f_1(p) + \mathbf{n} \cdot \mathbf{U}_2 4\pi p^2 f_2(p) = Q(p)$$

where Q is the source term representing direct injection at the shock, f_1 is the far upstream distribution function advected into the shock and f_2 is the downstream distribution advected out of the shock. Noting that at the shock $f = f_2$ and substituting for Φ this simplifies to

$$\frac{1}{3}\mathbf{n} \cdot (\mathbf{U}_1 - \mathbf{U}_2) p \frac{\partial f_2(p)}{\partial p} + \mathbf{n} \cdot \mathbf{U}_1 f_2(p) = Q(p) + \mathbf{n} \cdot \mathbf{U}_1 f_1(p).$$

This is a simple first order homogeneous differential equation relating the output, f_2, to the total input, $Q(p) + \mathbf{n} \cdot \mathbf{U}_1 f_1(p)$ and the general solution is trivially found to be

$$f_2(p) = p^{-q} \int_0^p (Q(p') + \mathbf{n} \cdot \mathbf{U}_1 f_1(p')) p'^{q-1} dp'$$

where

$$q = \frac{3\mathbf{n} \cdot \mathbf{U}_1}{\mathbf{n} \cdot (\mathbf{U}_1 - \mathbf{U}_2)} = \frac{3r}{r-1}.$$

The essential points to note about this result are, firstly, that the process is a pure acceleration; the output, $f_2(p)$, depends only on the input at momenta below p. Secondly if the input is predominantly at low energies the output, at energies above the input energy, is a power-law spectrum with slope q determined only by the compression in the shock; in particular for a compression ratio close to 4 the predicted output is $f_2(p) \propto p^{-4}$ corresponding to a differential energy spectrum of E^{-2}. This should be contrasted with classical Fermi acceleration which is better described as diffusion in momentum space than as acceleration and which only produces power-law spectra with rather unnatural fine-tuning.

A final important point to note is that in all this we have ignored the reaction of the accelerated particles on the shock structure. This is clearly inconsistent with high efficiencies. However despite much work over the last decade our understanding of the nonlinear aspects of shock acceleration is, in my view, very unsatisfactory. The interested reader will find extensive discussions in the literature cited; here I will simply note that a problem exists, and that the reaction effects, if they are important, will almost certainly destroy the exact power-law form of the spectrum predicted by elementary theory.

3. Observational constraints

Observations show (as discussed extensively in this volume) that, after correction at energies below a few GeV for the effects of solar modulation, all the nuclear components of the cosmic radiation have very similar power-law spectra from about 1 GeV/n over about six decades in energy. There is then a feature, usually called the 'knee' in the total energy spectrum after which the spectrum steepens somewhat and continues to at least 10^{19} eV with perhaps a hint of an 'ankle' near 10^{20} eV. The differential energy spectra of the main nuclear species in the region below the 'knee' have exponents in the range 2.6–2.7, *i.e.* the intensity per unit area per second per steradian $J(E) \propto E^{-2.65\pm0.05}$. This corresponds for an isotropic distribution (and the observed anisotropy is only of order 10^{-4}) to a phase space density $f(p) \propto p^{-4.65\pm0.05}$. However this is the observed flux; to deduce the production spectrum we must correct for Galactic propagation effects.

The key here is provided by the secondary spallation nuclei for which we know the production spectrum. Ignoring fine details associated with the energy variation of spallation cross-sections the production spectrum of the secondary nuclei should be a power-law with the same exponent as the observed primary spectrum. But in the energy range where accurate composition data are available (roughly 0.1 GeV to 100 GeV) observations of the secondary to primary ratios show that the secondary nuclei have spectra which are steeper by a factor of roughly 0.6 in the exponent. Thus propagation effects, whether due to energy dependent escape or to reacceleration or to some other process, have steepened the secondary spectra and have presumably had the same effect on the primary spectra. If we apply a similar correction of 0.6 to the primary spectra we deduce that the source spectrum should be more like $f(p) \propto p^{-4.05\pm0.05}$ which is in remarkable agreement with what we expect from strong shocks.

However the observed primary power-law extends over some six decades and the compositional data on which this propagation correction is based is derived from observations in only the first two of these decades. There is an obvious danger in extrapolating over four decades in energy, but until we have high-energy composition measurements there is little else we can do. One argument which makes it somewhat more reasonable is to note that the only natural way to produce a good power-law spectrum is to start with a power-law and apply a power-law correction; otherwise one must suppose that non-power-law behaviour in the propagation has almost exactly cancelled a non-power-law form of the source spectrum. As we are discussing the possible application of shock acceleration to cosmic rays let us proceed on the assumption that the cosmic ray source spectrum is roughly

$$Q(p) = Q_0 \left(\frac{p}{mc}\right)^{-4} \qquad 10^{-2} < p/mc < 10^6,$$

(the reasons for the upper and lower limits will be discussed later) and see where this takes us. It is then a relatively straightforward task, given the observed near-Earth cosmic ray intensity and a propagation model, to deduce a value for Q_0 and then by integration derive estimates for the cosmic ray acceleration power and the particle injection rate (for details see Drury, 1990).

If we do this for a simple leaky box model the results are conveniently stated *per interstellar atom* because all the loss terms in the propagation model are proportional to the mean interstellar number density. For the acceleration power in the solar neighbourhood I get 1.3×10^{-14} eV s^{-1} atom^{-1}. Assuming a total ISM mass of about 5×10^9 M$_\odot$ or 6×10^{66} atoms this implies a total power of 1.3×10^{41} erg s^{-1} for the Galaxy as a whole. This is significantly higher than the 'canonical' estimate of 3×10^{40} erg s^{-1} usually quoted, mainly because of the assumption of a hard $f(p) \propto p^{-4}$ source.

The injection rate is rather strongly dependent on the lower cut-off to the source spectrum, p_{min}, and of order $10^{-24}(mc/p_{min})$ s^{-1} atom^{-1}. However for injection from the ISM the ratio mc/p_{min} must be smaller than 10^4, corresponding to almost thermal velocities for the injected particles, and greater than 1, corresponding to injection at relativistic energies. A value of $10^{2\pm1}$ seems reasonable, giving an injection rate of $10^{-22\pm1}$ s^{-1} atom^{-1} or for the whole Galaxy $6 \times 10^{44\pm1}$ s^{-1}.

3.1. SUPERNOVA REMNANT SHOCKS

The major source of strong shock waves in the Galaxy is thought to be the explosion of supernovae leading to the formation of large expanding supernova remnants (SNRs) bounded by strong shocks. The canonical figures are a rate of roughly one supernova every 30 years in the Galaxy releasing about 10^{51} erg of mechanical energy. This represents a power input of 10^{42} erg s^{-1} so that SNRs could generate the Galactic cosmic ray power if the acceleration efficiency is of order 13%.

What about the injection? Let us suppose that a fraction η of the ions passing through the shock become energetic particles. A typical point in the interstellar medium should be hit by a SNR shock of radius $\leq R$ on average every

$$\frac{3V_{Gal}}{4\pi R^3} t_{SN} \approx 6 \times 10^{15} \left(\frac{30\text{pc}}{R}\right)^3 \text{ s}$$

where V_{Gal} is the volume of the Galactic disc and $t_{SN} \approx 30$ y is the interval between Galactic SNae. If cosmic ray production takes place in SNRs of radius R (probably around 30 pc) in a phase of the ISM with density n, then

$$1.6 \times 10^{-16} \left(\frac{R}{30\,\text{pc}} \right)^3 \eta n \approx 10^{-22\pm 1} \langle n \rangle$$

where $\langle n \rangle$ is the average ISM density. Thus

$$\eta \approx 10^{-6\pm 1} \left(\frac{30\,\text{pc}}{R} \right)^3 \frac{\langle n \rangle}{n}$$

which, allowing for the fact that SNRs probably expand in a low density phase of the interstellar medium, suggests that η in the range 10^{-5} to 10^{-4} is what is required. This certainly seems possible.

An interesting consequence of this estimate is that the reacceleration of ambient cosmic rays advected into the shock is not a very significant source of particles. The number density of cosmic rays in interstellar space is only of order $10^{-10}\,\text{cm}^{-3}$. Thus for a mean interstellar number density of $1\,\text{cm}^{-3}$ the ratio of freshly injected cosmic ray particles to reaccelerated ambient cosmic rays is $10^{4\pm1}(30\,\text{pc}/R)^3$. This limit on reacceleration by strong shocks is consistent with that derived from consideration of the effects on the secondary to primary ratios; it should not of course be taken to imply that there is no reacceleration by *weak* shocks.

3.1.1 *Maximum energy* In a shock of finite size and age the acceleration process cannot of course accelerate particles to arbitrarily high energies; detailed studies show that the steady spectrum is established up to a cut-off momentum, determined in the case of SNR shocks mainly by the finite age of the shock, and then falls off very rapidly. The cut-off momentum has been estimated in several papers and the general consensus is that it is impossible, using conventional values for SNR shock parameters, to accelerate protons beyond a few $10^{14}\,\text{eV}$. Fig. 1 shows my 'best guess' (Drury, 1990) estimate of the proton spectrum one expects from acceleration in strong SNR shocks propagating in the interstellar medium. The cut-off is a cut-off in rigidity, *i.e.* momentum per unit charge, so that the spectra of heavier nuclei should show similar cut-offs, but at correspondingly higher momenta. Thus Iron (with $Z = 26$) could be accelerated to an energy per nucleus of $10^{16}\,\text{eV}$, but there is no way of producing the spectrum beyond the 'knee', say in the range $10^{16}\,\text{eV}$ to $10^{18}\,\text{eV}$ with conventional SNR shocks. One interesting possibility for reaching higher energies is to use the strong magnetic fields which may be present in the stellar wind bubble produced by the pre-supernova star (Völk and Biermann, 1988).

3.1.2 *Reaction effects* A major worry in the application of diffusive shock acceleration theory to SNR shocks is the extent to which the shock structure is modified by reaction effects. The main success of the theory, the power-law spectrum, appears to depend on the shocks not being significantly modified; yet the energy arguments indicate that efficiencies averaging 10%, which implies peak efficiencies more like 30%, are required. Current indications are that reaction effects are not as serious as earlier studies suggested, if due account is taken of all the effects which complicate expanding spherical SNR models (Drury *et al*, 1989). Improved numerical models should help to answer some of these questions.

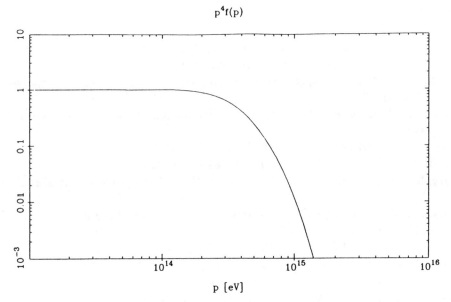

Fig. 1   *The upper cut-off expected for SNR shock accelerated protons.*

4. Conclusion

Diffusive shock acceleration in SNR shocks can explain the intensity of the Galactic cosmic rays, the spectrum below about 10^{14} eV and the general nature of the composition (although the FIP correlation is not explained, the tendency to an overabundance of heavier nuclei, otherwise very remarkable, is what one naturally expects from direct injection at the shock; Eichler, 1979).

However the particles in and above the 'knee' have to be made, in this picture, by some other source and it is then rather remarkable that the spectrum goes smoothly through the 'knee' region. Also, although there are tantalizing hints in the gamma ray data (Bhat et al, 1985; Lebrun and Paul, 1985) there is no strong evidence yet for the acceleration of nuclei, as distinct from electrons, in SNRs. And in the case of electrons the range of radio synchrotron spectral indices is quite large although the average is close to that expected from a strong shock, namely $\alpha = 0.5$. Also on the theoretical front it is not obvious why the injection parameter η should be of order 10^{-4}. Indeed heliospheric observations suggest much higher values (Ellison and Möbius, 1987; Ellison et al 1989).

Thus the situation is hopeful, but confused. There is still much work to be done on the injection process and its regulation, on the details of galactic propagation, and on the extent to which nonlinear effects modify the acceleration process. At least one aspect should soon become clear; with the next generation of gamma ray telescopes we should be able to determine whether cosmic ray nuclei really are enhanced (and have a harder spectrum) inside SNRs. If they turn out not to be we will have to look elsewhere for the source of the cosmic rays!

REFERENCES

Axford, W. I., Leer, E., and Skadron, G., (1977) *Proc 15th ICRC (Plovdiv)* **11** 132

Bell, A. R., (1978) *Mon. Not. Roy. astr. Soc.* **182** 147

Berezhko, E. G., and Krymsky, G. F., (1988) *Usp. Fiz. Nauk* **154** 49 (*Sov. Phys. Usp.* **31** 27)

Bhat, C. L., Issa, M. R., Mayer, C. J., and Wolfendale, A. W., (1985) *Nature* **314** 515

Blandford, R., and Eichler, D., (1987) *Phys. Rep.* **154** 1

Blandford, R. D., and Ostriker, J. P., (1978) *Ap. J.* **221** L29

Drury, L. O'C., Markiewicz, W. J. and Völk, H. J. (1989) *Astron. Astrophys.* **225** 179

Drury, L.O'C. (1990) *Proc 22 Int. Cosmic Ray Conf. (Adelaide)* in press

Eichler, D., (1979) *Ap. J.* **229** 419

Ellison, D. C., and Möbius, E., (1987) *Ap. J.* **318** 474

Ellison, D. C., Möbius, E., and Paschmann, G., (1990) *Ap. J.* **352** 376

Fisk, L. A., (1971) *J. Geophys. R.* **76** 16622

Hoyle, F., (1960), *Mon. Not. Roy. astr. Soc.* **120** 338

Hudson, P. D., (1965) *Mon. Not. Roy. astr. Soc.* **131** 23

Jokipii, J, R., (1966) *Ap. J.* **143** 961

Krymsky, G. F., (1977) *Dok. Akad. Nauk SSR* **234** 1306

Lebrun, F., and Paul, J., (1985) *Proc 19th Int. Cosmic Ray Conf. (La Jolla)* **1** 309

Parker, E. N., (1958) *Phys. Rev.* **109** 1328

Quest, K., (1988) *J. Geophys. Res.* **93** 9649

Schatzman, E, (1963) *Ann. Astrophys.* **26** 234

Völk, H. J., and Biermann, P. L., (1988) *Ap. J.* **333** L65

Zeldovich, Ya. B., and Raizer, Yu. P. (1966) *Physics of Shock Waves and High Temperature Phenomena* Academic Press, New York

SOURCE COMPOSITION, SITES OF ORIGIN AND ACCELERATION OF COSMIC RAYS

R. SILBERBERG and C.H. TSAO
E.O. Hulburt Center for Space Research
Naval Research Laboratory, Washington, DC 20375-5000

M.M. SHAPIRO
University of Maryland, College Park, MD 20472

and P.L. BIERMANN
Max-Planck Institut für Radioastronomie
Auf dem Hügel 69, D-5300 Bonn 1, Germany

ABSTRACT. The source composition of cosmic rays is deduced from the observed composition above the atmosphere by propagation (or nuclear transport) calculations. These calculations make corrections for the nuclear spallation reactions suffered by the cosmic-ray nuclei in the interstellar gas and clouds. To learn about the sites of origin, the source composition is compared with the general Galactic abundance of elements and isotopes, which is based on spectroscopic studies of the Sun and stars and composition of the C1 meteorites. (The composition of these meteorites is the least fractionated sampling of matter out of which the solar system condensed). While there are still alternative proposals on the sites and processes of cosmic-ray origin, we shall describe here our recent work which has yielded an agreement to 20% between the source composition derived from cosmic-ray observations, and those deduced from the general Galactic abundance of elements. It should be noted that the general Galactic abundances differ from the cosmic-ray source abundances by factors of up to 30. Hence, the agreement to 20% implies that the injection and nucleosynthetic processes we have postulated greatly improve the agreement between the source abundances derived from observations and those deduced from the general abundances.

1. Introduction

Cosmic rays constitute the only sample of matter from outside the solar system. The elemental and isotopic composition of cosmic rays contains important clues for testing ideas and models about nucleosynthesis in

97

M. M. Shapiro et al. (eds.), Cosmic Rays, Supernovae and the Interstellar Medium, 97–117.

stars, evolution of stars, and the interstellar medium. The solar and meteoritic composition is representative of the interstellar medium at the time the sun condensed from it, about 4.5×10^9 years ago. The early solar nebula may also have contained a small admixture of material from supernova(e) that preceded by a relatively short time the condensation of the solar system.

Cosmic rays play a significant role in Galactic dynamics. The energy densities of (1) cosmic rays, (2) the magnetic fields in the Galaxy, and (3) of the thermal gas in the ISM (interstellar medium) are about 1 eV/cm^3 each. The annual Galactic energy input is about 10^{60} eV/year, (calculated from the cosmic-ray energy density, the volume of the Galactic radio disk and the cosmic-ray confinement time in the Galaxy). The corresponding number of cosmic rays accelerated per year is about 10^{51}, with a mean energy near 10^9 eV. During the age of the Galaxy of 10^{10} years about 10^4 solar masses of Galactic particles have been accelerated to become cosmic rays.

In this paper the topic of cosmic-ray propagation will not be discussed explicitly, though it is important for deriving the source composition. We have explored the process of cosmic-ray propagation at the two preceding courses of the International School of Cosmic-Ray Astrophysics, (Silberberg et al. 1988, 1989). In Section 2 we compare the source composition of cosmic rays with the general Galactic composition. In Section 3 we discuss the processes that modify the general Galactic composition and sites where cosmic rays are injected and accelerated, including the contribution of nucleosynthesis products of highly evolved stars. This investigation is limited to nuclei with energies 0.1 to 10^3 GeV/nucleon. In Section 4 we <u>shall</u> explore the composition at higher energies, at 10^3 to 10^6 GeV/nucleon, and interpret it in terms of the composition of the stellar winds of pre-supernova stars that are accelerated by the shock waves of the supernova. In Section 5 we propose tests for the cosmic-ray reacceleration by the weak shock waves of old, greatly expanded supernova remnants.

2. The Source Composition of Cosmic Rays

About half of cosmic-ray nuclei heavier that helium have suffered nuclear collisions in the interstellar medium, breaking up into lighter nuclei. These collisions alter the cosmic-ray composition and mask the source composition. Many nuclides are dominated by the contributions of secondary nuclei. For example ^{14}N has a dominant contribution from the breakup of ^{16}O, and ^{23}Na from ^{24}Mg and ^{28}Si. To derive the source abundances, it is essential to know (or to be able to estimate) the nuclear spallation cross sections. E.g. for ^{14}N it is essential to know the cross sections of ^{16}O into ^{14}N, ^{14}O and ^{14}C; (the latter two nuclides decay into ^{14}N) and also for the tertiary process ^{16}O into ^{15}N into ^{14}N. Also the breakup cross sections of Ne, Mg and Si into ^{14}N are needed. Silberberg and Tsao (1973) constructed semiempirical cross sections for nuclear stripping, spallation, fission and fragmentation reactions that cover the whole periodic table of stable and radioactive isotopes with a precision of 30% for nuclei that are essential for cosmic-ray propagation calculations. Recently, Webber et al. (1990) have measured many cross sections with a high degree of precision, and constructed semiempirical equations that for a given set of product isotopes yield a fit to about 10%.

The observed composition and the source composition of cosmic rays was presented by Prof. Wefel at this Course. As was shown, the relative abundance of nearly pure secondary elements (like Li, Be, B) to primary elements (like C, O) yield the path length of material traversed and permits one to disentangle the secondary and source-component contributions to nuclides that have significant fractions of both components (like ^{14}N and ^{23}Na).

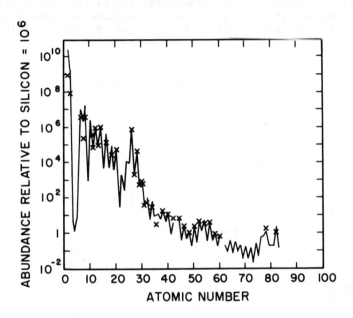

Figure 1: The general abundance of elements in nature with a comparison of cosmic-ray source abundances normalized at 10^6 for silicon.

We shall next explore the similarities and differences of the cosmic-ray source composition and the general Galactic composition of elements and isotopes. Figure 1 illustrates the striking similarity of cosmic-ray source abundances to the general abundances. This figure was presented at Erice two years ago by Silberberg et al. (1989). The line represents the general abundances, which reflect the nucleosynthetic processes in various stars and in supernovae. We note the large abundances of H and He, the very low values of Li, Be and B that burn readily into heavier elements, the even-odd element effect, with large abundances for C, O, Ne, Mg and Si, and the high peak at the very stable nucleus Fe, with atomic number Z = 26. The general abundances are taken from Cameron (1982), which are rather similar to those of Anders and Ebihara (1982), Meyer (1985), and the recent values of Grevesse and Anders (1989). For the abundant elements with $Z \leq 26$, Grevesse and Anders (1989) agree with Cameron (1982) to within 10%, only H, C and N differ by 20%. Grevesse and Anders in their Table 2 estimate that for the abundant elements with $Z \leq 28$ the standard deviation for both the photospheric and meteoritic abundances is about 10%, though the solar value of Fe exceeds the meteoritic by 1.5. The cosmic-ray source abundances in Figure 1 are illustrated by the symbol X. These values are taken from Lund (1989) for $Z \leq 30$, for heavier ones from Binns et al. (1989) and for N, the mean of Krombel and Wiedenbeck (1988), Gupta and Webber (1989) and Engelmann et al. (1990). This value for N/O at sources is 0.04 ± 0.01. We note in Figure 1 that while the general abundances and cosmic-ray source abundances vary by about 10 orders of magnitude, the cosmic-ray abundances agree with the general abundances remarkably; only H, He and N differ by factors larger than 10.

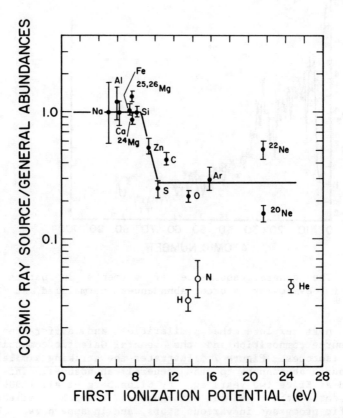

Figure 2: The ratio of cosmic-ray source abundances to general abundances. The calculated values of Table 1 (not plotted in avoid cluttering) are within the error bars shown, or close to it.

The differences between the cosmic-ray source and the general abundances are displayed in Figure 2, which shows the ratios of cosmic-ray source abundances to general abundances. The ratio is normalized to unity at Si. These ratios are plotted as a function of the first ionization potential. In the next section we shall explore the significance of the first ionization potential.

3. Processes at Sites of Origin of Cosmic Rays

3.1. FIRST IONIZATION POTENTIAL

Here we explore which processes at the sites of origin cause the cosmic-ray source composition to differ from the general abundances. Figure 2 suggests that there is a partial correlation with the first ionization potential. Elements whose first ionization potential exceeds 10 eV are about 4 times less abundant in cosmic rays. The physical meaning of the first ionization potential is: if the energy input to an atom equals the first ionization potential, the atom can be stripped of an electron from its outermost filled energy level, producing a singly ionized atom. The temperature at which such ionization occurs is like that of the photosphere of a normal star like the sun. Atoms with a first ionization potential (FIP) < 10 eV are those of Na, Mg, Al, Si, Ca, Fe, Ni; actually most elements belong to this group. The list with FIP > 10 is much shorter to enumerate: the noble gases He, Ne, Ar, Kr, and Xe, and the relatively light elements H, C, N and O, the halogens F, Cl, Br and I, and P, S and Hg, i.e. the non-metallic elements except Hg. The solar coronal composition (like that of the cosmic rays) displays a dearth by a factor of 4 of elements whose first ionization potential exceeds 10 eV. The solar wind particles and solar flare particles are derived from the corona, and hence have a composition more similar to the cosmic-ray source particles than the solar photosphere; this was noted by Webber (1975) and Meyer (1985). The FIP-dependent suppression of certain elements was first proposed by Havnes (1971); a detailed investigation was carried out by Cassè, Goret and Cesarsky (1975). The difference between the photospheric and coronal composition is suggestive of diffusion from the photosphere into the corona, with easier diffusion for the singly ionized nuclei than for the neutral nuclei, possibly along magnetic field lines. Meyer (1985) points out that a further stage of injection (stellar flare particles near the shock waves of supernova remnants) at energies near 1 MeV is plausible, as relative ionization loss effects on particle range and the composition cancel due to the effective charges of atoms near energies of 1 MeV/n. Shapiro (1990) presents several strong arguments that the very numerous flare stars are likely to be injectors of cosmic rays.

We suggest a model of three stages of acceleration, and two "filters". The first stage of acceleration brings the particles from stellar photospheres (energies near 1 eV) to the corona (energies near 10^3 eV), with the first FIP-dependent "filter" acting on the elemental composition. The second stage of acceleration energizes some coronal particles ($\sim 10^3$ eV/n) to flare particles ($\sim 10^6$ eV/n or 1 MeV/n). The second "filter" proposed by Silberberg and Tsao (1990) suppresses the lighter nuclei ($Z \leq 10$) prior to acceleration to cosmic-ray energies. We shall now explore the second "filter" and the physical processes giving rise to it.

3.2. RIGIDITY-DEPENDENT SUPPRESSION OF LIGHT NUCLEI

A second difference between the cosmic-ray source composition and the general abundances is the underabundance of H, He, and N is cosmic rays, as seen in Figure 2. The explanation proposed here would also result in an underabundance of C and O. However, this is compensated by nucleosynthesis in WC stars, which is discussed in the next sub-section. The underabundance could be due to a rigidity cutoff or deceleration at the boundaries of astrospheres (analogous to the heliosphere) and interstellar space, due to the effective charge dependence of the rigidity. (Rigidity is proportional to the radius of curvature of a particle in a magnetic field). Near 1 MeV, multiple electron pickup, with $(Z_{eff}/Z) < 1$ becomes appreciable in the interval C to Mg. (The effective charge of a particle is the nuclear charge minus the number of electrons attached to the nucleus). In the discussion below we make use of the following relationship: rigidity = momentum/Z_{eff} = (momentum/nucleon) x (A/Z_{eff}). From Northcliffe and Schilling (1970; Table and eq. on page 236), one can deduce that the ratio of mass number to effective charge (near energies of 1 MeV per nucleon) A/Z_{eff} = 2.0 for He and 2.95 for Mg. Thus, if there is an effective rigidity cutoff R_0 near the boundary of the astrosphere, in the neighborhood of energies of 1 MeV/n, the momentum per nucleon at the cutoff = P_0 = R_0 x Z_{eff}/A = 0.5 R_0 for He and 0.339 R_0 for Mg, i.e., the momentum per nucleon at the cutoff is numerically less than the cutoff rigidity, expressed in same units, MV/c. Thus, a greater part of the momentum spectrum of Mg passes the cutoff than of the spectrum of He. If the exponent of the integral momentum spectrum of stellar flare particles is 5, i.e., $J(P > P_0)$ α P_0^{-5}, then He is suppressed relative to Mg by a factor of $(2.95/2)^5$ = 7. The exponent of the stellar flare spectra is chosen to be 5, to yield a suppression of He and N relative to Mg and Si by a factor of 7 or 8. The suppression of H relative to He probably has a velocity dependent component, as discussed by Silberberg and Tsao (1990).

The near-constancy of the ratio of the cosmic-ray source abundance to the general abundance above $Z \geq 12$ would require a "bending over" or a threshold in the momentum per nucleon spectrum of flare particles, so that nuclei with momentum per nucleon values smaller than those of $Z = 12$ at the astrospheric rigidity threshold are nearly excluded. (At the value near 1 MeV for flare particles the relative ionization loss effects on the range of particles nearly cancel due to pickup of electrons by the nuclei, as shown by Meyer, 1985).

We note from Figure 2 that in addition to H, He, and N, the nuclide ^{20}Ne can be interpreted as being affected by the process of suppression of light nuclei. This implies that C and O in the principal cosmic-ray source are affected. We also note a significant discrepancy in the ratio of the cosmic-ray abundances to the general abundances of C and

O, see Figure 2, (that is removed by the combined effects of light-ion suppression and Wolf-Rayet star contributions). The determination of the suppression factor from first principles would require detailed knowledge of the energy spectrum of stellar flares and of processes at the astrosphere boundary shocks. In the absence of such knowledge, we shall adopt an empirical factor $S(Z)$, where $0.12 \leq [S(Z) = 0.15 Z - 0.93] \leq 1.0$, i.e., $S(Z) = 0.12$ for $Z \leq 7$ and 1 for $Z \geq 13$. This factor explains the values of H, He, N, and ^{20}Ne in Figure 2. The ratio of cosmic-ray to general abundances is given by $I S(Z)$, except for the nuclides with a major component from Wolf-Rayet stars. The term $I = 0.27$ is the factor that represents the correction for FIP, if FIP ≥ 10.4 eV. $I = 1$ for FIP ≤ 8.4, and there is a transition region in between, shown by the line in Figure 2, and the element Zn.

3.3. CONTRIBUTION OF WOLF-RAYET STARS TO THE COMPOSITION OF COSMIC RAYS

A third difference between the cosmic-ray source composition and the general abundances is the enhancement of ^{22}Ne, ^{25}Mg, and ^{26}Mg. Meyer (1981) explained this in terms of a 2% contribution of Wolf-Rayet stars to the cosmic-ray source material. Prantzos et al. (1985) showed that the abundance ratio C/O in cosmic rays (about twice the solar one) can be explained in terms of Wolf-Rayet star contribution to carbon. (The winds of Wolf-Rayet stars are energetic, close to 0.1 MeV per nucleon, relatively close to the energies of flare particles. The acceleration of these wind particles thus is plausible). The Wolf-Rayet stars go through two phases: WN, when N produced in the CNO hydrogen-burning cycle is abundant at the stellar surface, and WC, when C, produced in helium burning is abundant at the surface, and ^{14}N burns into ^{22}Ne.

However, we suggest a modification of the calculations of Prantzos et al. (1985), that reduces the ratio of $^{22}Ne/(C + O)$, or enhances C and O, compensating for light-ion suppression. The calculated abundance (mass fraction) of ^{22}Ne of Prantzos et al. (1986) is 1.6 times higher than that of Maeder (1983, 1987) and Maeder and Meynet (1987). This is because Prantzos et al. (1986) assume the mass fraction $(Z > 2)/(Z \leq 2) = 0.03$, while the general solar system abundances of Grevesse and Anders (1989) yield 0.019 and of Cameron (1982) yield 0.018, in agreement with the latter. (The value of Prantzos et al. (1986) probably is good for the Galactic center region that has a higher metallicity and a large concentration of Wolf-Rayet stars). Hence the initial CNO abundances of Prantzos et al. (1986) should be reduced by $0.019/0.03 = 0.63$. Thus, the abundance of N for the WN phase calculations of Prantzos et al. should be reduced by 0.63, and also of ^{22}Ne and ^{25}Mg and ^{26}Mg during the WC phase. The abundances of C and O during the WC phase are not thus affected, since these are formed from He.

3.4. THE CALCULATION OF SOURCE ABUNDANCES AND COMPARISON WITH THE EXPERIMENTAL SOURCE ABUNDANCES

Based on the procedures discussed above, the calculated cosmic-ray source abundances (CR) are given by the equation

$$(CR) = 10^{-4}(G) \; I \; S + 2.1(10^4 \; A^{-1})[1.0 \; or \; 0.63](WC + aWN). \tag{1}$$

Here (G) is the general abundance of Grevesse and Anders (1989), normalized to 10^6 for Si. Hence multiplication by 10^{-4} changes it to Lund's normalization of 100 for Si. The first ionization potential factor I and light-ion suppression factor S have been defined above. WC and WN are the compositions of ejecta from the WC and WN stars, tabulated in Table 2 of Prantzos et al. (1986). The factor "a", also from Table 2, is the fraction of mass loss during the WN phase. Integrating over the initial mass function given by Prantzos et al. (1986), a = 0.5. Since the table is in mass fractions while cosmic-ray abundances are in numbers of nuclei, the mass number A is introduced for conversion. The factor 0.63 is the correction for metallicity, discussed in Section 3.3.; it applies, e.g., to nitrogen and for nuclei produced via nitrogen-burning in helium and nuclei heavier than ^{16}O in the Wolf-Rayet stars. For helium and for nuclei produced via He-burning (e.g., ^{12}C, ^{16}O, and ^4He), the factor 1.0 is used, as shown in Section 3.3. The factor 2.1×10^4 is for normalization.

A comparison of experimental cosmic-ray source abundances and those calculated from equation (1) is given in Table 1. The calculated and experimental values agree to within 20%. In the publication of Silberberg and Tsao (1990), the calculated value of N at the sources was 47% too high. Now, a new average value of N/O = 0.04 is used, based on Krombel and Wiedenbeck (1988), Gupta and Webber (1989) and Engelmann et al. (1990). Thus, the first change in the experimentally deduced source abundances yields appreciable improvement, providing a favorable test for the model.

Table 1. Comparison of Calculated and Observationally Deduced Cosmic-Ray Source Abundances (Normalized to Si=100)

Element or isotope	Source Obs.	Source Calc.	Element or isotope	Source Obs.	Source Calc.
H	8.9×10^4	9.0×10^4	^{24}Mg	79	73
He	1.2×10^4	1.3×10^4	$^{25,26}Mg$	27	23
C	431	490	Al	10.2	8.5
N	20	22	Si	100*	100*
O	511	469	S	12.6	13.9
^{17}O	<1+	0.3	Ar	3	2.7
^{20}Ne	46	47	Ca	6	6.1
^{22}Ne	18	21.3	Fe	93	90
Na	5.6	4.8	Ni	5.1	4.9

*Normalization
+Upper limit taken as 10% of measured abundance mainly secondary.

4.   Source Composition of Cosmic Rays at Energies 10^6 to 10^9 MeV/Nucleon

A model is developed for deriving the source composition of cosmic rays at energies 10^{12} to 10^{15} eV/nucleon from the composition of the stellar winds of the pre-supernova stars.   At energies ≥ 10 eV/nucleon, the source abundances are not yet well known.   But NASA-sponsored experiments during the next 10 years will explore this energy domain.

At energies near 10^{12} and 10^{13} eV/nucleon, the data of Burnett et al. (1989), Jones et al. (1985), Grunsfeld et al. (1988), Müller (1989) and Swordy (1989) imply differences from the composition at lower energies. The He/H ratio is larger by a factor of about 2, the (C,O)/H ratio by a factor of 5 $\pm$ 3, and Ar/Fe may be larger factor of about 2 $\pm$ 1.

4.1.   THE ACCELERATION MODEL

Several very young supernova remnants have strong radio emissions 0.1 to 10 years after the supernova outburst as observed by Weiler et al. (1986). Their Figure 8 shows that their power of radio emission exceeds by several orders of magnitude those of Galactic supernovae 300-1000 years old. Radio observations of star burst galaxies like M82 demonstrate with a very large sample of young supernova remnants, how efficient particle acceleration is in the early phases of remnant evolution [Unger et al. (1984), Kronberg et al. (1985), Kronberg and Sramek (1985) and Bartel et al. (1987)].

In the model adopted here, we consider the very high-energy particles at energies 10^{13} - 10^{15} eV/nucleon to be produced from the particles in the stellar wind cavities around the star that becomes the supernova, using the recent shock-wave acceleration model of Völk and Biermann (1988) in the immediate vicinity of the supernova. These very high-energy cosmic-rays thus would reflect the surface composition of the supernova precursors, the red and blue supergiants and the WR stars which display the effects of the CNO cycle and helium-burning nucleosynthesis on their surfaces. As the shock waves of the supernova remnant pass beyond the stellar wind domain, they become somewhat weaker and accelerate mainly the particles that end up in the energy interval 10^8 to 10^{12} eV/nucleon.

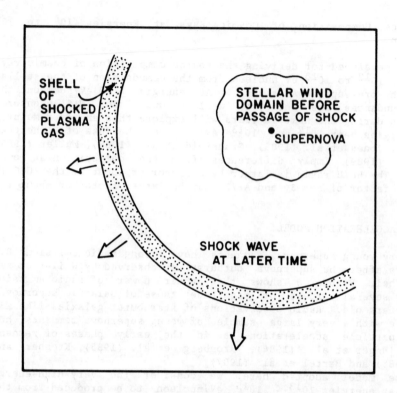

Figure 3: Illustration of the regions of acceleration of cosmic rays. First the very strong shock waves of the young supernova remnant accelerate the presupernova stellar wind particles. Later, energetic (flare) particles, possibly near 1 MeV/nucleon, are accelerated in interstellar space.

Figure 3 illustrates the respective acceleration regions, the stellar wind domain, and the outer acceleration region in which probably the flare particles of neighboring stars and higher-energy wind particles, such as those of Wolf-Rayet stars get accelerated. Figure 4, based on a review by Linsley (1983), and the recent review by Burnett et al. (1989), shows the energy spectrum of cosmic rays. In the present model, the strong shock waves in the immediate vicinity of the supernova generate the flatter region of energy spectrum near 10^5 and 10^6 GeV, and its dashed extension toward lower energies, while the steeper spectrum below about 10^4 GeV is attributed to the outer acceleration region shown in Figure 3. Correcting the spectra for rigidity-dependent leakage from the Galaxy yields flatter source spectra, with the respective exponents α of $dJ/dE = KE^{-\alpha}$ reduced from 2.75 to about 2.4, and from 2.50 to about 2.15 (without weak reacceleration, the reduction of α would be larger, about 0.5).

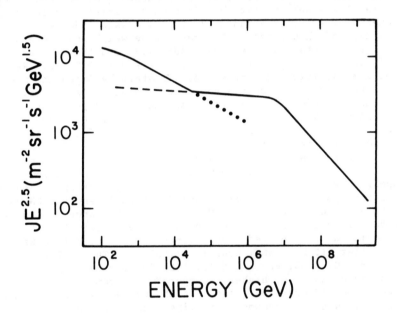

Figure 4: The energy spectrum of cosmic rays, multiplied by $E^{2.5}$ at energies 10^2 to 10^9 GeV, based on Linsley (1983) and Burnett et al. (1989). The significance of the slopes at 10^2 to 10^4 GeV and 10^4 to 10^6 GeV is discussed in the text.

4.2. SOURCE COMPOSITION, DEDUCED FROM PRESUPERNOVA STELLAR WIND

The composition of cosmic rays at energies 10^{12} to 10^{15} eV/n is taken to be that of the winds of presupernova stars, applying the acceleration model of Völk and Biermann (1988). These stars are the red supergiants (RSG), with initial masses about 9-23 $M_\odot$, blue supergiants (BSG), 23-25 $M_\odot$ and WN and WC stars of the Wolf-Rayet (WR) group with initial masses 35-100 $M_\odot$. (The latter groups also pass through the red supergiant phase). The boundary values of 23 and 35 $M_\odot$ are rough estimates, based on Maeder (1987), Maeder and Meynet (1987) and Vanbeveren (1987). Furthermore, the respective types of stars overlap across the boundaries, depending on initial composition and other properties. The contributions of these three mass groups are weighted by (a) the initial mass function from Humphreys and McElroy (1984), $\phi(M)$ dM α $M^{-2.5}$ dM, where $\phi(M)$ is expressed per log $(M/M_\odot)$ interval, and (b) the stellar mass loss function evaluated from Table 2 of Maeder and Meynet (1987). For stars with masses greater than 20 $M_\odot$, Vanbeveren (1984) was able to fit his data with initial mass functions having exponents of -2.2, -2.4 and -3.0. The value adopted here is close to the mean of this range. The respective weighting factors for the RSG, BSG, and WR stars adopted are: 530:43:17, and the stellar mass loss rates in units of $M_\odot$ per 10^5 years are 0.13:0.8:2.8. Recent estimates of stellar mass loss rates of WR stars by Smith and Maeder (1989) and Langer (1989) are consistent with the value used here. The respective combined weighting factors for the red supergiants, blue supergiants and Wolf-Rayet stars thus are: 1.45:0.72:1.0, where the WR contribution has been normalized to unity. The value for BSG is small because of the narrow mass interval of 23 to 35 $M_\odot$.

For the stellar wind composition, the general abundances of Grevesse and Anders (1989) were adopted and modified as follows: (1) for red supergiants, the suppression factor 0.25, dependent on the first ionization potential FIP, is assumed to apply and the CN cycle is assumed to have converted C into N, with the abundance of C on the stellar surface reduced to 0.5, while N is enhanced by 2.5. The surface composition of the red supergiants is adopted from Weaver, Woosley and Fuller (1985) and Schramm (1987). The FIP factor is applied to H, He, C, N, O, Ne, S and Ar. (2) For blue supergiants, the FIP is displaced due to higher temperature from 10 to 20 eV (alternatively, no FIP operates), and the CNO cycle has converted most C and O into N, with a composition like that of Fig. 4 of Maeder (1987). Thus, H is reduced by 1.8, He enhanced by 2, C reduced by 20, N enhanced by 9, and O reduced by 3. Furthermore, due to burning of ^{22}Ne, Na is probably enhanced by 5. Alternative calculations with the FIP factor 0.25 applied (or, alternatively not applied) to He and Ne were carried out. (3) In WC stars, the He-burning products ^{12}C, ^{16}O and ^{22}Ne are at the surface, with a composition like that of Prantzos et al. (1986), but adjusting the initial metallicity mass function Z = 0.03 to Z = 0.019 on the basis of Grevesse and Anders (1989). For WR stars, H is reduced to zero, He enhanced by 2.4, C by 65, N by 2, O by 25, ^{22}Ne by 75 and Na and ^{25}Mg and ^{26}Mg by 18.

The above values are theoretical ones based on nucleosynthesis calculations, stellar evolution and mass loss. They are in rather good agreement with actual observations by several investigators, summarized by Maeder (1983, 1987), which display the effects of carbon transformation into nitrogen in the CN cycle, and possibly also partial oxygen transformation into nitrogen, with the full CNO cycle. These observations are on 4 ON stars where the C/N ratio has been reduced to about 0.02, two red supergiants αOri and αSco (the former has C/N = 0.6), the supergiant ηCar, with C/N < 0.05 and O/N < 0.5, and several Wolf-Rayet stars of WN and WC types. The WN stars have C/N = 0.02, and WC stars have C/N > 100. In the latter ^{14}N has burned into ^{22}Ne, and some ^4He into ^{12}C.

Table 2. Abundances Predicted for the Component that Originates in Pre-Supernova Stellar Winds with Energies of 10^{13} - 10^{15} eV/nucleon

Element/ Isotope	F	GAF[a]	L[a]	GAF/L	Dominant Contributors
^1H	0.25	7×10^5	9×10^4	1[b]	BSG,RSG
^4He	1	2.7×10^5	1.2×10^4	3	WC,WN
^{12}C	20	2×10^4	431	6	WC
^{14}N	3	900	15	8	BSG,WN
^{16}O	8	2×10^4	511	5	WC
^{20}Ne	0.5	160	46	0.5	WC,RSG,BSG
^{22}Ne	23	900	18	6	WC
Ne	3	1000	64	2	WC
Na	6	35	5.6	0.8	WC,WN,BSG
$^{24,25,26}Mg$	2	200	106	0.3	RSG,WC,BSG
Si	1[b]	100[b]	100[b]	0.13	RSG,WC,BSG
S	0.65	34	12.6	0.4	WC,BSG
Ar	0.65	7	3	0.3	WC,BSG
Fe	1	90	93	0.13	RSG,WC,BSG

[a]If H is compared with others, one should note that in "L" a rigidity threshold or rigidity interval was used. Hence, for purpose of comparison, this was adopted also for "GAF".

[b]Normalization

Table 2 shows the relative abundances and enhancement factors of several nuclides and elements for the component that originates in pre-supernova stellar wind material. In our model, this component dominates at energies of 10^{13} to 10^{15} eV/n. F is the combined adjustment factor for elemental abundance, weighted over the red supergiant, blue supergiant and Wolf-Rayet stars. GA represents the general abundances of Grevesse and Anders (1989). The column GAF, i.e. GA x F, shows the expected relative cosmic-ray abundances at about 10^{13} to 10^{15} eV/nucleon. The composition of cosmic rays at energies < 1 TeV/nucleon, presumably representative of the composition of cosmic rays accelerated at old supernova remnants, is taken from Lund (1989). It is shown in column L. The column GAF/L shows the ratio of the cosmic-ray source abundances at 10^{13} to 10^{15} eV/nucleon to those at lower energies. This column is normalized to unity for hydrogen, because at high energies, the spectrum of hydrogen is the one best known. The last column shows the dominant contributors to the very high energy cosmic rays, if the model presented here is valid. If the FIP does not apply to the blue supergiants (BSG), then the abundance of He in Table 2 should be raised by 30%, while the effect on (^{20}Ne + ^{22}Ne) is negligible. WC and WN represent, respectively the carbon-rich and nitrogen-rich phases of the Wolf-Rayet stars. The burning of ^{22}Ne during the BSG phase, yielding Na, may increase the values of Na in Table 2 by about 20%.

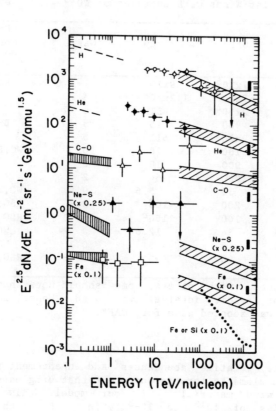

Figure 5: The experimental cosmic-ray spectra of Ryan et al. (1972) are shown by the dashed lines, those of Grunsfeld et al. (1988) are shown by the cross-hatched regions on the left, and those of Burnett et al. (1990) by the error bars. The calculations based on the present model are shown by the hatched regions between energies of 30 and 2,000 TeV/nucleon, and those based on acceleration at old supernova remnants

by the black vertical bars in the right margin. The dotted line for Fe
(and Si) at 100 to 2,000 TeV/nucleon illustrates the case in which
acceleration at old supernova remnants is reduced above 100
TeV/nucleon.

A cursory inspection of Table 2 would suggest that the source
abundance of Si and Fe could be low at energies near 10^{14} eV/nucleon.
However, we note from Figure 5 that the contribution of the component
with the steeper spectrum could still be significant at these energies,
and prevent the Fe/H or Si/H ratio from falling below about 0.5 of the
low-energy value of Lund (1989).

Figure 5 shows the experimental and calculated spectra for H, He,
the C-O group, the Ne-S group and Fe. The experimental data between
0.1 to 1 TeV/nucleon for H and He are from Ryan et al. (1972), and for
C to O, Ne to S, and Fe from Grunsfeld et al. (1988). At energies of
approximately 1 to 100 TeV/nucleon, the experimental data are from
Burnett et al. (1990). The calculated spectra shown by the hatched
regions at energies 30 to 2000 TeV/nucleon are based on the present
model. The values shown by the dark vertical bars at the right margin
of Figure 5 are based on extrapolating the data below 1 TeV/nucleon
that correspond to the model of acceleration at old supernova remnants.
The present model does not lead to any sharp discontinuities because of
the gradual transition in spectra between the "old" and "young"
supernova remnant models, as displayed in Figure 4.

Sharper discontinuities are expected if acceleration at old
supernova remnants becomes inefficient at say 10^{14} eV/nucleon. Then
the spectra of Si and Fe drop off, as shown by the dotted line in
Figure 5. In this case, enhancements should be observed in the ratios
Ar/Si, Ar/Fe, S/Si and S/Fe at 10^{15} eV/nucleon relative to those below
10^{12} eV/nucleon. However, if neutron star surface material is
accelerated to ultra-high energies $\geq 10^{15}$ eV/nucleon, then iron would
instead be enhanced near 10^{15} eV/nucleon. Observations of the
abundances of Si and Fe near 10^{15} eV/nucleon could show whether
acceleration at old supernova remnants becomes inefficient near 10^{14}
eV/nucleon, and/or neutron star surface material enhances the abundance
of Fe.

Some consequences of the acceleration model of wind particles
displayed in Figure 5 are these: (1) Since hydrogen is depleted during
the WC and WN stages, and reduced to ~ 1/2 in blue supergiants, the
H/He ratio is decreased by a factor of 2, in agreement with the data of
Burnett et al. (1989, 1990) near 10^{13} eV/nucleon. (2) C and O are
enhanced by a factor of 5 relative to H, due to helium burning into C
and O during the WC stage, in agreement with Burnett et al.
(1989,1990).

The reduction of Ne-to-S relative to C-to-O and He is supported by
the (C+O)/(Mg+Si) ratio of Grunsfeld et al. (1988), Müller (1989) and
Swordy (1989) near 1 TeV/nucleon, and by Burnett et al. (1990) near 3
TeV/nucleon. However, the data of Burnett et al. (1990) near 1 and 10
TeV/nucleon favor instead the model of acceleration at old supernova
remnants. The data of Burnett et al. (1990) for Fe have large error

bars, hence they are consistent with either model. The ratios Ne/C and Ne/O of Grunsfeld et al. (1988) are lower at 1 TeV/nucleon than at lower energies, i.e. consistent with the present model, as seen from the values 2:6 of Table 2, column GAF/L. However, the uncertainties are too large for using these data to support the present model.

Our model also makes predictions that can be tested in future experiments: (a) N/O would increase from the low-energy value of 0.04 to 0.65 due to the large N-abundance in blue supergiants and WN stars; (b) S/Fe should increase by a factor of 3, due to absence of the FIP effect in blue supergiants and WR stars, but this would be observable near 10^{15} eV/nucleon only if the contribution of Fe accelerated at old supernova remnants becomes minor; (c) most Ne should be ^{22}Ne, as a result of the contribution of WC stars, and ^{22}Ne/H should be enhanced by a factor of about 5; the ratio Ne/Si should become ≥ 2; (d) Na/Si should increase from 0.06 at 10^9 eV/nucleon to about 0.2 at 10^{15} eV/nucleon, due to nucleosynthesis in blue supergiants and WN and WC stars, as can be seen from Fig. 8b of Prantzos et al. (1986).

For particles well above 10^6 GeV, acceleration at supernova remnants fails, and a different acceleration mechanism is required, possibly at pulsars, or at accreting neutron stars in binary systems, or at the terminal shock of the Galactic wind. The composition at these energies is not explored in detail in this paper; it may have a major component from binary stellar companions (e.g. red giants) of accreting neutron stars. If the neutron stars contribute surface material, an iron-rich component may set in near 10^{15} eV/nucleon, and may contribute also at lower energies. However, the dense photon field near the neutron star can also produce lighter-than-iron photo-disintegration products.

5. Reacceleration of Cosmic Rays

Dr. Simon will soon discuss in detail the weak or modest reacceleration of cosmic rays, which probably occurs at very old, extended supernova remnants, with weakened shock waves, or by large scale magnetic turbulence.

Since the present article deals with the source composition of cosmic rays, it is important to point out that the deduction of the source composition from the measured elemental or isotopic abundances at low energies (a few hundred MeV per nucleon) is affected by reacceleration. This is particularly the case for elements that have a large contribution of secondary cosmic-ray products, if there is an appreciable energy dependence in the production cross sections. Such cases are N, Na, Al and P. These elements are largely produced from the abundant neighboring heavier elements O, Mg, Si and S via (p,pn) and (p,2p) reactions, which have a large energy dependence. The single-nucleon stripping cross sections peak at low energies, and with reacceleration the abundances of nuclides are enhanced and shifted to higher energies. If these enhanced values are used for estimating the source abundances, spuriously large values are assigned.

Finally, in this section we suggest some definitive tests for reacceleration that cannot be reproduced in the standard model, and permit the deduction of the parameters of the reacceleration model, after the energy dependences of isotopic abundances in cosmic rays are measured.

Earlier investigations of reacceleration have compared secondary-to-primary ratios as a function of energy, and explored cosmic-ray energy spectra. These ratios and spectra can be reproduced with reacceleration models, with a constant power law in momentum (with a possible exception for protons) and a constant exponent for the rigidity dependence of the mean path length of the leakage rate from the Galaxy. But these ratios and spectra can also be reproduced with the standard propagation model, if the energy or momentum spectra have exponents that vary with energy or momentum and the exponent of the rigidity dependence of the mean path length varies with rigidity.

We have developed tests for the presence or absence of reacceleration that do not suffer from the ambiguity discussed in the previous paragraph, and are suitable for NASA-sponsored experiments during the 1990-ies. Models with and without reacceleration predict a different energy dependence of the isotopic abundance ratios of the nuclides that decay by electron capture relative to its neighboring isotope or daughter product. Examples of secondary nuclides that decay by electron capture are ^{37}Ar, ^{41}Ca, ^{44}Ti, ^{49}V, ^{51}Cr, ^{53}Mn and ^{55}Fe. Data of Webber (1981) and Webber et al. (1985) on these isotopes measured near 600 MeV/n suggest that the effects of decay are present, as expected with the hypothesis of distributed acceleration. Table 3 presents these data.

Table 3. Ratios of observed to calculated abundances of nuclides (that decay by electron capture) at 600 MeV/nucleon, if no reacceleration had occurred.

Nuclide	^{37}Ar	^{41}Ca	^{49}V	^{51}Cr	^{53}Mn
Ratio	0.2 ± 0.2	0.7 ± 0.5	0.6 ± 0.2	0.4 ± 0.3	0.6 ± 0.3

We have calculated the energy spectrum of cosmic-ray ^{49}V, taking into account ionization losses, electron-capture decay and reacceleration. This spectrum is displayed in Figure 6. The degree of reacceleration is best determined by comparing the spectrum of a nuclide that decays by electron capture with one that does not.

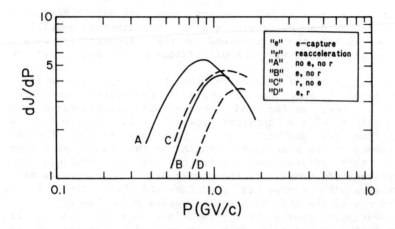

Figure 6: Momentum spectrum of ^{49}V with and without the effects of the electron capture and reacceleration.

Figure 7 shows such a comparison, the ratio $^{49}V/^{50}V$. A large enhancement of the effect of electron-decay is possible by comparing the energy dependence of the ratio of the electron-decay nuclide to that of its daughter product.

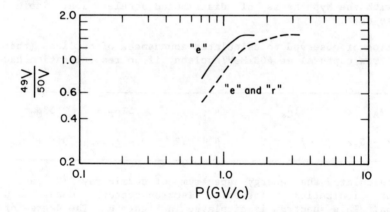

Figure 7: Ratio of $^{49}V/^{50}V$ as a function of momentum, with decay by electron capture and with both electron capture and reacceleration.

This is shown in Figure 8 which displays the ratio $^{49}V/^{59}Ti$. These calculations of the combined effects of electron capture and reacceleration (on suppressing the abundance of ^{49}V at low energies, and of the $^{49}V/^{50}V$ and $^{49}V/^{49}Ti$ ratios at low energies (at a few hundred MeV/n) were based on simplifying assumptions, decoupling reacceleration from spallation and ionization losses.

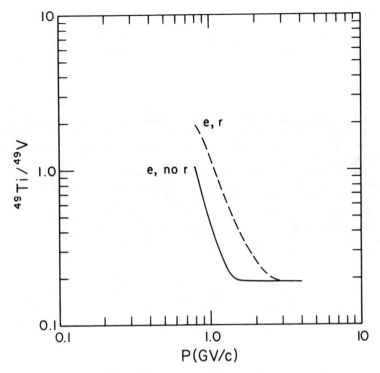

Figure 8: Ratio of ^{49}Ti/^{49}V as a function of momentum, with decay by electron capture and with both electron capture and reacceleration.

This corresponds to the nested leaky box model in which the inner box contributes a large part of the total path length (g/cm^2) at low energies, E $\leq$ 500 MeV/n, as proposed by Guzik et al. (1985). Reacceleration with this assumption is considered to occur predominantly later by the weakened shock waves of old supernova remnants in the low-density component of the interstellar medium.

An additional test for reacceleration is the shift of the energy dependence of the ratio of a product with large target-product mass difference ΔA, to that with a small ΔA. Such a ratio is (^{40}K + ^{41}K)/Cr. The corresponding ratio of cross sections from Fe, at 300 MeV/n, is 0.3 of that at 2 GeV/n, as shown in figure 16 of Webber et al. (1990). With reacceleration, the energy dependence of the above ratio will be shifted to higher energies. (The isotope ^{39}K is to be omitted, since much of ^{39}K comes from ^{40}Ca rather than ^{56}Fe). Giler et al. (1987) explored the ratio K/Cr, but data from experiments with isotopic resolution of K are needed.

Such tests with experiments during the new decade should establish the need for reacceleration and help to determine the reacceleration parameters.

ACKNOWLEDGEMENTS

M.M.S. and P.L.B. gratefully acknowledge a grant from the Scientific Affairs Division of NATO. R.S. and C.H.T. acknowledge the support of ONR.

REFERENCES

Anders, E. and Ebihara, M. 1982 Geochim. Cosmochim. Acta 46, 2363.

Bartel, N., Ratner, M.I., Rogers, A.E.E., Shapiro, I.I., Bonometti, R.J., Cohen, N.L., Gorenstein, M.V., Marcaide, J.M., and Preston, P.A. 1987 Ap.J. 323, 505.

Binns, W.R., Garrard, T.L., Israel, M.H., Klarmann, J., Stone, E.L. and Waddington, C.J., 1989 in "Cosmic Abundances of Matter" ed. C.J. Waddington (New York:AIP Conf. Proc. 185), p. 147.

Burnett, T.H., et al. 1989 Cosmic Abundances of Matter, ed. C.J. Waddington, (New York: AIP Conf. Proc. 183), p. 396.

Burnett, T.H. et al. 1990 Ap. J. (Letters), 349, L25.

Burnett, T.H., et al. 1990 21st Internat. Cosmic Ray Conf. (Adelaide) 3, 101.

Cameron, A.G.W. 1982 in "Essays of Nuclear Astrophysics", ed. C. Barnes, R.N. Clayton and D.N. Schramm, Cambridge Univ. Press, p. 23.

Cassè, M., Goret, P. and Cesarsky, C.J. 1975 14th Internat. Cosmic Ray Conf. (Munich) 2, 646.

Engelmann, J.J. et al., 1990 Astron. Ap. 233, 96.

Giler, M., Osborne, D.L., Szabelska, B., Wdowczyk, J. and Wolfendale, A.W. 1987 20th Internat. Cosmic Ray Conf. (Moscow), 2, 214.

Grevesse, N. and Anders, E. 1989 in "Cosmic Abundances of Matter", ed. C.J. Waddington (New York: AIP Conf. Proc. 183), p. 1.

Gupta, M. and Webber, W.R. 1989 Ap.J. 340, 1124.

Guzik, T.O., Wefel, J.P., Garcia-Munoz, M. and Simpson, J.A. 1985 19th Internat. Cosmic Ray Conf. (La Jolla), 2, 76.

Havnes, O. 1971 Nature 229, 548.

Humphreys, R.M. and McElroy, B. 1984 Ap. J. 284, 565.

Jones, M.D., et al. 1985 19th Internat. Cosmic Ray Conf. (La Jolla), 2, 28.

Krombel, K.E. and Wiedenbeck, M.E. 1988 Ap. J. 328, 940.

Kronberg, P.P., Biermann, P.L. and Schwab, F.R. 1985 Ap. J. 291, 693.

Kronberg, P.P., and Sramek, R.A. 1985 Science 227, 28.

Langer, N. 1989 Astron. Ap. 220, 135.

Linsley, J. 1983 Rapporteur Paper, 18th Internat. Cosmic Ray Conf. (Bangalore) 12, 135.

Lund, N. 1989 in "Cosmic Abundances of Matter", ed. C.J. Waddington (New York: AIP conf. Proc. 183), p. 111.

Maeder, A. 1983 Astron. Ap. 120, 113.

Maeder, A. 1987 Astron. Ap. 173, 247.

Maeder, A., and Meynet, G. 1987 Astron. Ap. 182, 243.

Mewaldt. R. 1989 in "Cosmic Abundances of Matter", ed. C.J. Waddington (New York: AIP Conf. Proc. 183), p. 124.

Meyer, J.P. 1981 17th Internat. Cosmic Ray Conf. (Paris) 2, 265.

Meyer, J.P. 1985 Ap.J. Suppl. 57, 173.

Müller, D. 1989 Adv. Space Res. 9, (12) 21.

Northcliffe, L.C. and Schilling, R.F. 1970 Nuclear Data Tables A7, 233.

Prantzos, N., Doom, C., Arnould, M. and de Loore, C. 1986 Ap. J. 304, 695.

Prantzos, N., Arnould, M., Arcoragi, J.P. and Cassè, M. 1985 19th Internat. Cosmic Ray Conf. (La Jolla) 3, 167.

Ryan, M.J., Balasubrahmanyan, V.K., and Ormes, J.F. 1972 Phys. Rev. Letters, 28, 1497.

Schramm, D.N. 1987 20th Internat. Cosmic Ray Conf. (Moscow), Invited Paper, 7, 155.

Shapiro, M.M. 1990 21st Internat. Cosmic Ray Conf. (Adelaide), 4, 8.

Silberberg, R. and Tsao, C.H. 1973 Ap. J. Suppl. 25, 315.

Silberberg, R. and Tsao, C.H. 1990 Ap. J. Letters, 352, L49.

Silberberg, R. Tsao, C.H., Letaw, J.R. and Shapiro, M.M. 1988 in "Genesis and Propagation of Cosmic Rays", ed. M.M. Shapiro and J.P. Wefel, Publ. by Reidel, Dordrecht, Holland, p. 41.

Silberberg, R., Tsao, C.H. and Letaw, J.R. 1988 in "Cosmic Gamma Rays, Neutrinos and Related Astrophysics", ed. M.M. Shapiro and J.P. Wefel, Publ. by Kluwer, Dordrecht, Holland, p. 491.

Simon M., in these proceedings.

Smith, L.F., and Maeder, A. 1989 Astron. Ap. 211, 71.

Swordy, S.P. 1989 Invited paper, Bull. Am. Phys. Soc. 34, 1200.

Unger, S.W., Pedlar, A., Axon, D.J., Wilkinson, P.N., and Appleton, P.N. 1984 MNRAS, 211, 783.

Vanbeveren, D. 1984 Astron. Ap. 139, 545.

Vanbeveren, D. 1987 Astron. Ap. 182, 207.

Völk, H.J. and Biermann, P.L. 1988 Ap. J. (Letters) 333, L65.

Weaver, T.A., Woosley, S.E. and Fuller, G.M. 1985 in "Numerical Astrophysics", ed. J. Centrella, J. Leblanc and R. Bowers, (Boston: Jones and Bartlett), p. 374.

Webber, W.R. 1975 14th Internat. Cosmic Ray Conf. (Munich) 5, 1597.

Webber, W.R. 1981 17th Internat. Cosmic Ray Conf. (Paris), 2, 80.

Webber, W.R., Kish, J.C. and Schrier, D.A. 1985 19th Internat. Cosmic Ray Conf. (La Jolla), 2, 88.

Webber, W.R., Kish, J.C. and Schrier, D.A. 1990 Phys. Rev. 41, 520, 533, 547 and 566.

Wefel, J.P. in these proceedings.

Weiler, K.W., Sramek, R.A., Panagia, N., van der Hulst, J.M. and Salvati, M. 1986 Ap. J. 301, 790.

Weiler, K.W. and Sramek, R.A. 1988 Ann. Rev. Astronomy and Astrophys. 26, 295.

COSMIC-RAY AGE AND THE INTERSTELLAR MEDIUM

Vladimir S. Ptuskin
Institute of Terrestrial Magnetism, Ionosphere and
Radio Wave Propagation
USSR Academy of Sciences
142092 Troitsk, Moscow Region
USSR

ABSTRACT. Diffusion and nuclear fragmentation of relativistic nuclei are considered in a galactic model with a halo. The inhomogeneous spatial distribution of the galactic gas proves to be very essential for the interpretation of the data on the content of secondary stable and radioactive isotopes in the cosmic rays. Constraints on a galactic wind and on cosmic-ray distributed acceleration in the interstellar medium are discussed.

1. Introduction

The high isotropy and relatively large number of secondary nuclei in cosmic rays indicate an effective intermingling and a long travel time for the high-energy particles in the Galaxy. Here the galactic magnetic field plays a decisive role. Most often the propagation of cosmic rays is considered in the framework of the diffusion model (Ginzburg and Syrovatskii, 1964), and the current state of the problem is discussed by Ginzburg (1990). The diffusion model provides an understanding of numerous observations on the composition, spectra, and anisotropy of the various components in the cosmic rays. Radio-astronomical and gamma-ray data are included as well. Such a semi-empirical model is confirmed by the kinetic theory of the motion of relativistic charged particles in the galactic magnetic field.

The main parameters of the galactic diffusion model include the total power of cosmic-ray sources in the Galaxy, estimated to be 10^{40}-10^{41} erg/s; the size of the halo, H = 1-10 Kpc; and the cosmic-ray diffusion coefficient, D = 10^{27}-10^{29} cm^2/s at kinetic energy per nucleon, E = 2 GeV/nucleon, increasing with energy as D α E^a, a = 0.3±0.3 for E>2 GeV/nucleon. (Note, the value of D likely increases with height above the galactic plane.) It is assumed that the observed cosmic rays up to 10^{17}-3 x 10^{19} eV are produced in the Galaxy, while particles with higher energies are extragalactic in origin.

In the present paper the simplest version of the galactic diffusion model is used to discuss the propagation of stable and radioactive relativistic nuclei in the interstellar medium. Even this simple one-dimensional model with a thin galactic disk and a halo ("flat but fat" in the terminology employed by M.M. Shapiro) seems to be a

119

M. M. Shapiro et al. (eds.), Cosmic Rays, Supernovae and the Interstellar Medium, 119–136.

reasonable approximation to the real situation. A more complicated three-dimensional model was considered by Ginzburg et al. (1980).

Two key points form the physical basis for our consideration. Bradt and Peters (1950) put forward nuclear fragmentation as the explanation for the presence among the cosmic rays of a considerable number of nuclei of elements which are rare in nature. The observed abundance of Li, Be, B and other secondary cosmic-ray nuclei gives, approximately, $x_m = 10$ g/cm^2 for the value of the mean thickness of matter traversed by particles with energy 2 GeV/nucleon in the interstellar medium (Soutoul et al., 1983; Webber, 1990). This value of x is of the order of magnitude of the nuclear destruction pathlength for relativistic nuclei. Such a fortunate coincidence and the large dispersion of the matter thickness traversed by cosmic rays in the Galaxy provide, at the same time, valuable information on the cosmic ray composition at the sources and information on the conditions of cosmic-ray propagation in the interstellar medium (see Shapiro and Silberberg, 1970).

Another important circumstance is the presence of a sufficient number of radioactive isotopes ^{10}Be, ^{26}Al, ^{36}Cl, ^{54}Mn in the cosmic rays. Their mean life-times are comparable to the age of cosmic rays in the Galaxy (see e.g. Simpson and Garcia-Munoz, 1989). Hayakawa et al. (1958) realized that the abundance of a radioactive secondary isotope could be used as a "clock" to determined the cosmic ray age.

2. Stable Secondary Nuclei and the Grammage Distribution Function

The main question in investigating the transport of relativistic nuclei in the Galaxy is how to calculate changes in their chemical composition due to nuclear fragmentation in the interstellar gas. A one-dimensional steady state equation which includes cosmic ray diffusion with a diffusion coefficient $D(z,E)$ and fragmentation with total cross-section σ in a gas with density $n(z)$ has the form:

$$-\partial_z D \, \partial_z N + nv\sigma \, N = q. \tag{1}$$

Here $N(z,E)$ is number density of cosmic-ray nuclei; $v \approx c$ is the velocity of the particles; and $q(z,E)$ is the source term.

A complete solution to the problem requires the use of equations like (1) but taking into account the production of lighter nuclei in the process of fragmentation of heavier nuclei. In fact, it is necessary to analyze a system of coupled equations for successive generations of various kinds of nuclei starting with the heaviest ones. For purely secondary species, the source term is negligible, and the abundances in cosmic rays are completely determined by the splitting of the parent nuclei. Davis (1960) considered the general problem of successive transitions from one kind of nuclei into other kinds of nuclei. He showed that the solution of the total set of transport equations for all kinds of nuclei is reduced to the solution of the singular equation (1). This theorem is valid under some conditions: all primary nuclei have the same spatial distribution in the Galaxy; the diffusion coefficient does not depend on the type of nucleus; and others (see e.g. Ginzburg and Syrovatskii, 1964; Shapiro and Silberberg, 1970; Ginzburg and Ptuskin, 1976; Lezniak, 1979; Margolis, 1986).

Any solution of Eq. (1) may be represented in the form:

$$N(z,E,\sigma) = \int_0^\infty dx \, G(z,E,x) \, e^{-\sigma x},\tag{2}$$

where the function G satisfies the equation (Ginzburg and Ptuskin, 1976):

$$n \, v \, \partial_x \, G - \partial_z \, D \, \partial_z \, G = 0,\tag{3}$$

with the initial condition $G(x=0) = q(z,E)$ and $G=0$ for $x<0$.

The function $G(x)$ is the inverse Laplace transform of the cosmic ray density $N(\sigma)$. It may be interpreted as the pathlength distribution function. The function $G(z,E,x)$ determines the fraction of particles observed at the point z with energy E which after escaping from the sources have passed through a layer of matter of thickness x (without taking into account nuclear fragmentation). The fragmentation is described by the factor $\exp(-\sigma x)$ in Eq. (2). The matter thickness x is measured in cm^{-2}. Multiplied by the mass of the average atom of the interstellar gas, m, yields a matter thickness $x_m = mx$ measured in g/cm^2. Assuming that the interstellar gas consists only of hydrogen, m is the mass of a hydrogen atom. For short, the function G may be called the grammage distribution function. Note that in an inhomogeneous medium the matter thickness x traversed by a particle is not reducible to the length of the trajectory, l, or the travel time t. For an individual particle, $dx=n(r)dl=n(r)vdt$.

In accordance with the Davis theorem, the grammage distribution function G is the main characteristic of the propagation model. G determines the fragmentation of stable relativistic nuclei. Now, suppose that the cosmic-ray sources and the galactic gas are distributed in a thin disk $|z|\leq h$ with densities $q=q_0$ and $n=n_0$, respectively, and $h \ll H$ where H is the height of the galactic cosmic-ray halo. Assume that the diffusion coefficient D(E) is constant over the whole Galaxy, and the boundary condition, $N(|z|=H)=0$, corresponds to free exit out of the Galaxy. Then the solution of Eq. (1) in the galactic disk is approximately (Ptuskin, 1974; Ptuskin and Soutoul, 1990a):

$$N_0 = q_0 \, hHD^{-1} \, (1 + \sigma n_0 \, vhHD^{-1})^{-1}\tag{4}$$

under the condition

$$\sigma n_0 \, vh^2/D \ll 1.\tag{5}$$

Eq. (5) implies that the nuclear fragmentation during one diffusive crossing of the gas disk is small.

The grammage distribution function corresponding to Eq. (4) is an exponential:

$$G \propto \exp(-Dx/(n_0 vhH))\tag{6}$$

(where terms not dependent on x have been omitted). The dependence in Eq. (4) of the density N on the cross section σ and formula (6) both coincide with the corresponding relations for the leaky-box model. The leaky-box model describes nuclear fragmentation by the equation (c.f. Eq. (1)):

$$(T_1^{-1} + \bar{n}v\sigma) \, N = \bar{q} \qquad (7)$$

The corresponding grammage distribution is:

$$G(x) \propto \exp(-x/x_1), \quad x_1 = \bar{n}vT_1. \qquad (8)$$

Here the cosmic ray density N, the source term $\bar{q}$ and the gas density $\bar{n}$ are assumed to be constant over the whole system (the Galaxy). Escape of the cosmic rays from the system is described by the leakage time T_1 and the leakage length x_1.

The leaky-box model is used widely because of its exceptional simplicity. It gives a good fit to the data on the cosmic-ray abundance of various stable, secondary nuclei with a unique value of x_1 (Cowsik et al., 1967; Shapiro and Silberberg, 1970).

The leaky-box model can be obtained as a limiting case of the diffusion model provided that there is little leakage of cosmic rays and strong reflection of the relativistic particles at the boundaries of the Galaxy (see Ginzburg and Syrovatskii, 1964). On the other hand, in the case of strong reflection, when a particle traverses the whole Galaxy many times before it can escape, the approximation needed for obtaining the leaky-box model may be fulfilled automatically. In this case the motion of the particles inside the region of propagation may be not diffusive, but can be of another type, for instance, free motion.

Here we investigate only the case in which the particles can escape freely at the boundaries of the Galaxy. The cosmic-ray spatial distribution is not homogeneous in this case. The density $N(z)$ falls linearly with z in the halo. The leaky-box model may be considered only as a crude approximation. Nevertheless, the expressions for the number density of the stable nuclei, Eq. (4), and the grammage distribution, Eq. (6), in the galactic disk are equivalent to the leaky-box model if we use the following relations between the parameters:

$$x_1 = n_0 \, vhH/D, \quad \bar{n} = n_0 \, h/H, \quad \text{and } \bar{q} = q_0 \, h/H, \qquad (9)$$

and the condition of Eq. (5) is fulfilled, i.e.

$$\sigma x_1 \ll H/h. \qquad (10)$$

According to Soutoul et al. (1985), the observed ratio B/(C+O) up to an energy of 15 GeV/nucleon can be described in a leaky-box model with the mean grammage

$$x_{1,m} = x_{m0}\beta \, R^{-a}, \quad R > R_0,$$
$$x_{1,m} = x_{m0}\beta \, R_0^{-a}, \quad R < R_0, \qquad (11)$$

where R is the particle magnetic rigidity, $x_{m0} = 24.0$ g/cm^2, $\beta = v/c$, $R_0 = 5.5$ GV, and $a = 0.65$. Accepting $x_m = 10$ g/cm^2 at $E = 2$ GeV/nucleon, the condition of Eq. (10) is fulfilled for all nuclei up to iron ($\sigma_{Fe} = 680$ mb) if H/h > 4.

The distribution of interstellar gas near the solar circle has several different components. The neutral HI gas of the galactic disk has $n_0 = 0.37$ cm^{-3} and $h = 135$ pc and the neutral gas with an extended exponential distribution has $n_0 = 0.1$ cm^{-3} and $h = 400$ pc (see Bloemen, 1987). Molecular hydrogen has a narrow distribution with $h = 50$ pc and an average mass density of the order of the HI density (Scoville and Sanders, 1986). The ionized gas with a density at the midplane of $n_0 = 0.025$ cm^{-3} extends to $h = 1.5$ Kpc (Reynolds, 1989). The total mean column density of the gas is approximately $n_0 h = 5 \times 10^{20}$ cm^{-2}, and the effective value of $h = 100$ pc. The distribution of potential cosmic-ray sources (supernovae and pulsars) is concentrated in the same disk. Thus the condition H/h>4 found above is satisfied if the height of the cosmic-ray halo is large, H>0.4 Kpc.

This consideration shows that the leaky-box approximation may be reasonable for treating data on the chemical composition of the stable nuclei even if the real cosmic-ray propagation is diffusive. The relation (9) gives a cosmic-ray diffusion coefficient (at 2 GeV/nucleon):

$$D = n_0 hvH/x_1 = 2 \times 10^{28} \ (H/3Kpc) \ cm^2/s \tag{12}$$

In a number of papers it is claimed that the leaky box model serves only as a first approximation. Observations, while not quite definite, interpreted in the frame of this model indicate an increased Sc-Cr/Fe ratio at a given B/C ratio for energies 0.1-10 GeV/nucleon (Shapiro and Silberberg, 1970; Garcia-Munoz et al., 1987; Soutoul et al., 1990; Ferrando et al., 1990). In the language of the cosmic ray grammage distribution, this means that the real distribution is truncated for small pathlengths (<1-3 g/cm^2) in comparison with the exponential distribution of Eq. (8). This can be explained by assuming that a significant part of the mean grammage is built up in a thick shell of matter screening the cosmic-ray sources (Cowsik and Wilson, 1973).

The theory of the diffusion and nuclear fragmentation of cosmic rays in a cloudy interstellar medium has been developed by Osborne and Ptuskin (1987) and Ptuskin and Soutoul (1990a, 1990b). It is assumed that some fraction of the cosmic-ray sources is located within giant molecular clouds. The finite transparency of giant molecular clouds for diffusing relativistic nuclei makes it possible to explain the deviation of the distribution function G from an exponential. Giant molecular clouds are randomly distributed in the galactic gas disk. The density of the gas and the diffusion coefficient inside the clouds may differ considerably from the corresponding values in the intercloud medium. This theory is based on the transport equation for the cosmic ray density averaged over random spatial variations of the diffusion coefficient, the gas density, and the source distribution. Under the condition of Eq. (5), the cosmic-ray density in the galactic disk is now:

$$N_0 = q_0 hHD^{-1} \{1-(1-T)Q\}/\{1+\sigma x_1 [1-(1-T)M]\}. \tag{13}$$

Here $Q \leq 1$ is the fraction of cosmic ray sources inside the clouds as compared to the total number of sources in the Galaxy, and $M \leq 1$ is the fraction of the gas in the galactic gas disk contained in the giant molecular clouds. The value $T \leq 1$ characterizes the transparency of the clouds. For a statistically uniform distribution of internal sources inside spherical clouds,

$$T=(3/y^2)(1-thy/y)[D_i/D + (1-D_i/D) \, thy/y]^{-1}, \tag{14}$$

where $y^2 = \sigma n_i \, v \, R^2/D_i$; n_i and R are proton number density and the radius of the cloud; D_i is the cosmic-ray diffusion coefficient inside the cloud; and D is the diffusion coefficient in the intercloud medium and in the halo. The cloudy leaky-box model of Eq. (13) reduces to the usual leaky-box model of Eq. (4) for transparent clouds when $T = 1$.

Taking the values $n_i = 200$ cm^{-3}, $R = 20$ pc, and $D = D_i = 2 \times 10^{28}$ cm^2/s, then for relativistic iron nuclei $T = 0.8$ and for carbon nuclei $T = 0.95$. The dependence of the transparency of Eq. (14) on the nuclear cross section gives the difference in the predicted concentrations of secondaries in the cloudy leaky-box model as compared with the usual leaky box. Ptuskin and Soutoul (1990a) found that data on B/C and Sc-Cr/Fe ratios may be explained if not less than 70% of the galactic cosmic-ray sources are located inside the clouds.

The grammage distribution function $G(x)$ for the cloudy leaky box model may be found as the inverse Laplace transform of the function $N(\sigma)$ of Eq. (13). Its complicated form has an exponential tail at large grammage $x \geq x_1$ and truncation for small grammage if Q is larger than some critical value. The position of the truncation is determined by the value of $x_{cm} = m n_i v R^2/D_i = 3.6 \times 10^{28}$ cm^{2}s^{-1}/D$_i$ in g/cm^2 which is the mean matter thickness traversed by the particle in the cloud. The mean grammage in the cloudy galactic model is $\bar{x} = [x_1 + x_c \, (0.2 + D_i/D)Q/3]$.

3. Decaying Nuclei and the Age Distribution Function: The Size of the Cosmic Ray Halo

Stable secondary nuclei give important information on the parameters of the propagation model of cosmic rays in the interstellar medium, but they give only indirect evidence on the time that the particles spend in the Galaxy. The escape time for the one-dimensional system is $H^2/2D$. According to Eq. (12), knowledge of the mean grammage fixes the ratio H/D. Thus, additional data are needed to find the age of cosmic rays. For a reasonable spread of the halo size, $H = 1-10$ Kpc, an estimate of $H^2/2D = 2 \times 10^7 - 2 \times 10^8$ years is obtained at $E = 2$ GeV/nucleon using Eq. (12).

One can, in principle, determine the size of the halo and the age of the cosmic rays from the relative content of radioactive nuclei. Secondary nuclei are particularly convenient, since there is no problem in determining the amount of such nuclei in the sources. Usually the isotope ^{10}Be is considered. It's lifetime at rest is $\tau = 2.2 \times 10^6$ years (^{10}Be $\Rightarrow {}^{10}$B) as determined by Yiou and Raisbeck (1972). The isotopes ^{26}Al, $\tau = 1.2 \times 10^6$ yrs, ^{54}Mn, $\tau \sim 10^6$ yrs, and ^{36}Cl, $\tau = 4 \times 10^5$ yrs may also be used. It should be stressed that in describing the propagation of decaying nuclei the diffusion model and the leaky-box model turn out not to be equivalent (Prishchep and Ptuskin, 1975; Ginzburg and Ptuskin, 1976).

For decaying nuclei the equation of cosmic ray diffusion Eq. (1) has to be modified by the addition of the term N/τ on the left side. It is convenient to use the quantity:

$$f = N(\tau)/N(\tau=\infty) \tag{15}$$

which is the surviving fraction of a radioactive isotope. The formally introduced quantity of the density $N(\tau=\infty)$ is calculated in the model under the assumption that the isotope is stable. In our one-dimensional diffusion model with a halo $H \gg h$, the surviving fraction is given, approximately as follows:

$$f = (1 + \sigma x_1)(1 + \sigma x_1 + T_{eff}/\tau)^{-1} \tag{16}$$

where

$$T_{eff} = \begin{cases} H^2/3D & \text{for } \tau \gg H^2/D, & (17) \\ (H^2\tau/D)^{1/2} & \text{for } h^2/D \ll \tau \ll H^2/D, & (18) \\ hH/D & \text{for } \tau \ll h^2/D. & (19) \end{cases}$$

The condition of Eq. (10) is assumed to be fulfilled. The form of the function T_{eff} in Eq. (17)-(19) depends on the rate of decay of the unstable isotope during the time of diffusion across the galactic disk (h^2/D) and the halo (H^2/D). Diffusion in the cloudy interstellar medium leads to the same equations (16)-(19) but the value of x_1 in Eq. (16) must be multiplied by the factor $[1-(1-T(\sigma))M]$ defined in Eq. (14).

The density of the decaying isotope in the framework of the leaky-box model is given by Eq. (7) with the additional term N/τ on the left side. The surviving fraction of a radioactive isotope is then determined by expression (16), where T_{eff} is the leakage-time, i.e.

$$T_{eff} = T_1. \tag{20}$$

The comparison of expressions (17)-(19) with Eq. (20) shows that there is no simple universal relation between the diffusion time H^2/D and the leakage time T_1. (An exception is the case of slowly decaying isotopes, $t \gg H^2/D$ when the value of T_{eff} in Eq. (17) has the meaning of the cosmic-ray age, since $H^2/3D$ is just the mean age of the particles at $z=0$ in the one-dimensional diffusion model with a large halo $H \gg h$.)

The diffusion model and the leaky-box model are not equivalent for the description of the data on the decaying cosmic-ray isotopes. For the same observed surviving fraction of the decaying isotope, the leaky-box model gives a smaller cosmic ray age and a smaller size of the halo than does the diffusion model (if $\tau < H^2/D$). This is explained by the fact that in the leaky-box model the densities of all types of nuclei, both stable and radioactive, are assumed to be constant over the whole volume of the Galaxy. In the diffusion model the densities depend on the coordinates, and this dependence is primarily determined by the lifetime of the nucleus. Thus, stable nuclei occupy the whole halo, and short-lived nuclei are concentrated in the neighborhood of the disc ($|z| \leq (D\tau)^{1/2}$) where the sources and the gas are concentrated. Therefore, for the same power of the sources of radioactive nuclei (the fragmentation of heavier nuclei may play the role of sources), the measured density of radioactive nuclei is higher than the value averaged over the whole volume of the Galaxy, and the halo size and escape time of the cosmic rays determined by the formulae of the leaky-box model are apparently less than in the diffusion model.

This is also confirmed by analyzing the problem using the age distribution function. The age distribution function G_* (z,E,t) of the particles in the problem of the propagation of decaying nuclei arises precisely in the same way as the grammage distribution function $G(z,E,x)$ resulted from solving the problem of the fragmentation of stable nuclei. The function $G_*(z,E,t)$ determines the fraction of the particles which at the point of observation z with the energy E have an age t (the age of a particle is measured from the moment of escape from the source). The age distribution function can be found from the equation:

$$\partial_t G_* - \partial_z D \partial_z G_* = 0 \tag{21}$$

with the initial condition G_* (t=0) = q(z,E) and $G_* = 0$ for t<0.

The grammage distribution function G determined by Eq.(3) and the age distribution function G_* determined by Eq. (21) coincide in the case of a uniform gas distribution. In this case x=nvt, where the gas density n=constant.

For our diffusion model, the age distribution function for an observer at the galactic plane may be approximated as:

$$
G_* \ (t) =
\begin{cases}
3DH^{-2} \exp(-3Dt/H^2) & \text{for } t \gg H^2/D, & (22) \\
(\pi H^2 t/D)^{-1/2} & \text{for } h^2/D \ll t \ll H^2/D, & (23) \\
D/hH & \text{for } t \ll h^2/D. & (24)
\end{cases}
$$

This function has an exponential tail at large age $t \gg H^2/D$ and increases sharply for small ages.

The age distribution for the leaky-box model is a pure exponential:

$$G(t) = \exp(-t/T_1). \tag{25}$$

Particles with a low age make an important contribution to the flux of decaying nuclei, which have a comparatively short lifetime $t \ll H^2/D$. In the leaky box model there are fewer such particles than in the diffusion model, which leads to an underestimate of the density of the radioactive isotope.

All this means that if the real motion of the particles in the interstellar medium is diffusion with a free exit from the Galaxy, then data on the content of radioactive isotopes can not be treated with the leaky box model. The leakage time T_1 as the parameter of the leaky-box model has no meaning as the real time for the leakage of cosmic rays out of the Galaxy. The exception is the case of very slowly decaying isotopes $\tau \gg H^2/D$ (the surviving fraction is close to f = 1, see Eq. (16)-(17)).

Modern data on the [10]Be abundance (Garcia-Munoz et al., 1977; Webber and Kish, 1979; Wiedenbeck and Greiner, 1980) and the [26]Al abundance (Wiedenbeck, 1983; Webber, 1985) give rather uncertain values for the surviving fractions as shown in Figures 1 and 2 (see Simpson, 1983; Simpson and Garcia-Munoz, 1989 for a discussion). Figures 1 and 2 also show the results of calculations performed as described above (Ptuskin and Soutoul, 1990b). The spread in the various measurements makes it impossible, still, to determine the size of the cosmic-ray halo of the Galaxy. The diffusion model gives the estimate H ~ 3 Kpc and $H^2/2D$ ~ 6 x 10 [7] years. The calculations based on the leaky-box approximation give H = n_0 h/$\bar{n}$ ~ 0.8 Kpc and T_1 ~ 3 x 10[7] years, but the leaky-box model is not applicable in this case.

The Galaxy has a fairly extended cosmic-ray halo. This conclusion requires the diffusion coefficient to be space dependent and the diffusion coefficient in the halo to be larger than in the disc, which is very probable. In this case, the fast decaying radioactive nuclei are even more strongly concentrated around the disk. The radio-astronomical data confirm the existence of an extended radio halo (e.g. Ginzburg, 1990; Phillips et al., 1981; Kanbach, 1983; Beuerman et al., 1985).

4. Constraints On a Galactic Wind

The diffusion model, with a diffusion coefficient determined by comparison with observations, gives a good description of the totality of available data on cosmic rays. But, this still does not exclude the possibility that certain modifications may be necessary as additional information accumulates, both cosmic-ray data and purely astronomical data. In particular, it is possible that in our Galaxy there is large-scale motion of the interstellar gas with a "frozen-in" magnetic field, in which the cosmic rays also take part. We should note that for the transport of cosmic rays, a flux of magnetohydrodynamic waves, not accompanied by a flow of gas, is sufficient. In any case, for the following it is only important that the cosmic rays may not only diffuse, but also can be carried "as a whole" with some convection velocity u.

With convection the equation for the density of nuclei has the following form

$$-\partial_z D\, \partial_z N + \partial_z(u\,N) - 1/3(\partial_z u)\, \partial/\partial E[\frac{2mc^2+E}{mc^2+E} E\,N] + nv\sigma\, N + N/\tau = q. \quad (26)$$

Here E is kinetic energy per nucleon; m is the nucleon mass; and u(z) is the velocity of convective particle transport perpendicular to the galactic plane. The third term in Eq. (26) describes a change in the energy of the particles in the flow with div u ≠ 0, (see Skilling, 1975; Ginzburg, 1990 for details).

The large-scale motion of the medium may have a random character and on average, over scales much larger than the principal scale L of the turbulence, the motion of the particles in some cases (for D « uL/3) is actually diffusion with an effective coefficient of turbulent diffusion of order uL/3. Let us consider the role of regular motion of the interstellar gas out of the Galaxy (the galactic wind). Formally, one usually uses "wind" to mean only a flow pattern in which the gas reaches

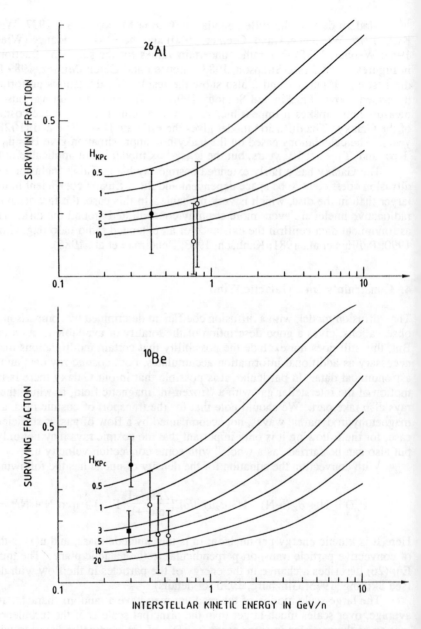

Figure 1. The surviving fraction of the isotopes [10]Be and [26]Al in the cloudy diffusion model as a function of the halo size H (Ptuskin and Soutoul, 1990b). Data points for [10]Be are: Garcia-Munoz et al. (1977), Wiedenbeck and Greiner (1980), Webber and Kish (1979). Data points for [26]Al are: Wiedenbeck (1983) and Webber (1985).

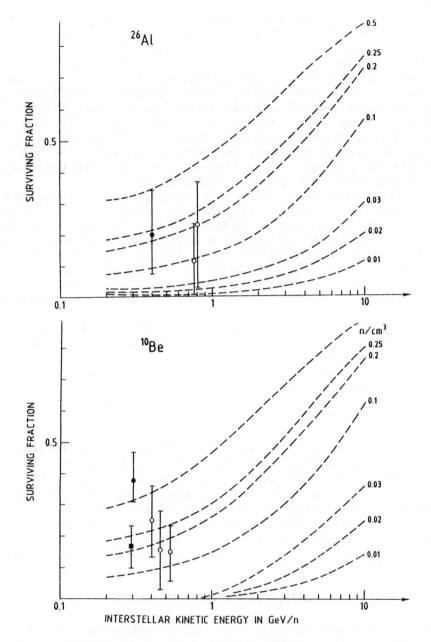

Figure 2. The surviving fraction of the isotopes ^{10}Be and ^{26}Al in the leaky box model calculated as a function of the mean gas density $n = n_0 h/H$ (Ptuskin and Soutoul, 1990b). Data points are the same as Figure 1.

velocities higher than the escape velocity for the given galaxy. Otherwise, the gas cools down in the halo and forms separate clouds at the galactic plane. If there are no additional sources of heat in the halo, then the wind in the Galaxy should originate with the temperature of the gas in the disk, which is several millions of degrees higher, and with a density less than approximately 10^{-2} cm^{-3} (for details see Habe and Ikeuchi, 1980). A stationary flow can be maintained by means of the energy of supernova explosions and stellar winds (McKee and Ostriker, 1977; Bregman, 1980). Also the pressure of cosmic rays plays a definite role (Ipavich, 1975; Breitschwerdt et al., 1987). Actually, in a certain approximation we can also speak of a "wind" in the case in which the gas does not escape from the Galaxy, but the scale of the flow is rather large, for example, if the gas flows out of the greater part of the disc and falls back on its periphery (see Ikeuchi, 1988; Spitzer, 1990).

The transport of relativistic nuclei in a diffusion-convection model with a galactic wind taken into account was investigated by Jokipii (1976), Owens and Jokipii (1977), Jones (1979), Prishchep and Ptuskin (1979), and Freedman et al. (1980). A one-dimensional model was used. In the simplest case the wind has a constant velocity u in the halo and zero velocity in the disk. The diffusion coefficient D is constant over the whole system. The relative role of convection and diffusion in the removal of cosmic rays from the galaxy depends mainly on the value of the parameter uH/D, which determines the ratio of the times of diffusive and convective escape of the particles.

In the diffusion-convection model, it is impossible to determine, uniquely, the diffusion coefficient from the concentration of secondary stable isotopes (as could be done in a pure diffusion model), since the escape of particles from the Galaxy is due both to diffusion and to convective transport. It is useful to introduce a critical value of the convection velocity (the velocity of the wind) as:

$$u_c = 3 \ (\gamma+2)^{-1} \ n_0 \ hv/x_1 \sim 20 \ \text{km/s}, \qquad (27)$$

where $\gamma =2.7$ is the power-law index of the cosmic-ray spectrum. The grammage x_1 is used here as the parameter determining the content of the secondary stable nuclei. If the convection velocity u is less than u_c, then escape from the halo by diffusion dominates. In this case the model reduces to the pure diffusion model considered above. The corresponding diffusion coefficient is given by Eq. (12). If the convection velocity u_c, is much larger than u, then the particles are rapidly swept out of the Galaxy and practically none return from the halo to the disc. The content of secondary nuclei is determined in this case by the diffusion of cosmic rays in the gaseous disk with the diffusion coefficient:

$$D \sim 5 \ n_0 h^2 v/12 x_1 \sim 3 \times 10^{26} \ \text{cm}^2/\text{s}. \qquad (28)$$

An observer at the midplane can collect particles traveling in a halo region which is limited to $|z| \leq D/u$. For particles beyond this region, the convective outflow dominates diffusion. Thus, direct information on cosmic rays in the outer halo is lost. For this reason, a study of the propagation of radioactive nuclei reveals that the halo in the diffusion-convection model is larger than in the pure diffusion model when the abundances of stable secondary nuclei and radioactive nuclei are the same.

On the whole, the conclusion is that a uniform flow which covers the whole halo with a velocity 20 km/s and with a diffusion coefficient which is somewhat less than in the diffusion model is, in principle, enough to ensure the transport of cosmic rays from the Galaxy. Apparently, a flow with a much higher velocity is excluded since it is difficult to reconcile with the fact that the isotope ^{10}Be observed at the Earth has mostly decayed. This critical velocity of convective transport is small compared with typical velocities of 400 km/s usually found in models for the galactic wind, and this may be indirect evidence against the presence of a wind in our Galaxy, at least in the extremely simple version of the flow that has been considered. If the flow actually moves with a velocity u(z) which depends on the distance above the galactic plane (as in the model by Lerche and Schlickeiser, 1982b), then the restriction on the velocity holds only for a height up to approximately one kiloparsec. Higher in the halo the velocity can be much larger.

The relative role of convection and diffusion may depend on the energy of the particles, if $D(E) \neq$ constant, which apparently corresponds to reality. In particular, if the decrease of the grammage x_1 for $E \geq 2$ GeV/nucleon is associated with a decrease of the escape time of cosmic rays from the galaxy and with a corresponding increase of the diffusion coefficient, then the role of convection in the escape of the particles should be small for this energy region. As regards the region of relatively low energies, here the role of convection may, in principle, be significant (Jones, 1979).

Note that the comparatively low limit $u_c = 20$ km/s of the velocity of convective transport is close to the value of the Alfven velocity for the interstellar medium. Therefore, it is not excluded that, if convection is at all important for cosmic rays, it comes about by means of a flow of magnetohydrodynamic waves from the galaxy and is not connected with macroscopic motion of the interstellar gas.

Future progress in understanding the role of a galactic wind in cosmic-ray transport is connected with detailed analysis of the nonthermal galactic radio emission (see Lerche and Schlickeiser, 1982a; Ginzburg, 1990). Radio observations can give indirect information on the cosmic rays in the outer halo region.

5. Distributed Reacceleration of Cosmic Rays in the Interstellar Medium

The acceleration of cosmic rays over the whole Galaxy, accompanied by nuclear fragmentation in the interstellar gas cannot be the main mechanism for accelerating particles with energies E > 2 GeV/nucleon. Indeed, in the case of continuous acceleration, particles of higher energy should spend a longer time in the system, which would result in an increase in the relative content of secondaries as energy increases (Hayakawa, 1969). This qualitative statement is confirmed by detailed calculations performed by Giler et al. (1985; 1987) and Cowsik (1986). However, observations show that for energies E>2 GeV/nucleon the fraction of secondary nuclei in cosmic rays decreases with increasing energy.

Surprising at first glance was the result of the numerical calculations by Simon et al. (1986). They found that weak reacceleration of cosmic rays in the interstellar medium can provide the decrease with energy of the relative abundance of secondaries, even with a weaker increase of the cosmic-ray confinement time with energy as compared to the case with an absence of any reacceleration (see also

Wandel et al., 1987; Ferrando and Soutoul, 1987; Osborne and Ptuskin, 1988; Giler et al., 1987; Cesarsky, 1987; Heinbach and Simon, 1990). Here this problem is considered in the leaky-box approximation using the language of the grammage distribution function.

The equation for the cosmic-ray number density in the framework of the leaky-box model with regular reacceleration is:

$$N(E)/x_1(E) + \sigma \, N(E) + \partial/\partial E(b(E)E \, N(E)) = q(E). \tag{29}$$

Here the rate of acceleration of an individual particle in the interstellar medium is given by the relation $dE/dx = b(E)E$. Thus, $b(E) \geq 0$ is the rate of the acceleration.

It is easy to find the solution to Eq. (29) and using the definition of Eq. (2) to write down the grammage distribution function as:

$$G(E,x) = \frac{b(s(x)) \, s(x) \, q(s(x))}{b(E) \, E} \exp\left[-\int_{s(E)}^{E} dE_1 \, (b(E_1) \, x_1(E_1) \, E_1)^{-1} \right]$$

$$\theta\left[-x + \int_{E_0}^{E} dE_1 \, (b(E_1) \, E_1)^{-1} \right] \tag{30}$$

where the function $s(x)$ is determined from the equation:

$$x = \int_{s(x)}^{E} dE_1 \, (b(E_1) \, E_1)^{-1}, \tag{31}$$

and E_0 is the minimum energy of the particles at which acceleration starts. The step function θ determines the cutoff of the function G for large x. The cutoff is explained by the regular gain of energy for each particle. All particles leaving the source, even those with the minimal energy E_0, would have an energy greater than E after traversing some critical thickness of matter. The function $G(E,x)$ gives the probability (not normalized) that a particle observed at the energy E has traversed the matter thickness x.

Let there be a reacceleration of the particles resulting from their interaction with magnetohydrodynamic waves with a power-law spectrum. Then, ultrarelativistic particles have a power-law energy dependence of the rates of reacceleration and leakage (see e.g. Skilling, 1975; Ginzburg, 1990):

$$b(E) = b_0 \, (E/E_0)^{-a}, \quad x_1(E) = x_0 \, (E/E_0)^{-a}, \quad a = \text{constant}. \tag{32}$$

If the sources generate cosmic rays with a power-law spectrum starting with a minimal energy E_0,

$$q(E) = K \, (E/E_0)^{-\gamma_s} \, \theta(E - E_0), \quad K = \text{constant} \tag{33}$$

then from Eq. (30)-(31) for the cases of weak (bx « 1) and strong (bx » 1) reacceleration, respectively, the grammage distribution function is:

$$G(E,x) \sim q(E) \exp (-x/x_{eff} + 0.5 \, abx^2/x_1) \, \theta(x_1-x) \quad \text{for } abx_1 \ll 1, \qquad (34)$$

$$G(E,x) \sim q(E) \, (1- abx)^{-1-(\gamma_s-1)/a} \, \theta(x_c-x) \quad \text{for } abx_1 \gg 1 \qquad (35)$$

where

$$x_c = (1 - (E_0/E)^a)/ab(E), \qquad \text{and} \qquad (36)$$

$$x_{eff} = x_1 (E) \, [1 + (\gamma_s -1+a) \, b(E) \, x_1(E)]. \qquad (37)$$

Equations (34), (36), and (37) show that the grammage distribution is close to an exponential $G(E,x) = \exp(-x/x_{eff} (E))$ for the case of weak reacceleration. In first approximation the leaky-box model with weak reacceleration ($abx_1 \ll 1$) is equivalent to the leaky-box model without reacceleration, but with a modified effective mean grammage, x_{eff}, determined by Eq. (37). This conclusion is general and also correct for the diffusion model with a weak stochastic reacceleration (in this case we have to change the coefficient of the term bx_1 in the formula analogous to Eq. (37)). The quantity $x_{eff}(E)$, which determines, in particular, the content of secondary nuclei in the cosmic rays, is not a power-law function of energy. This makes it possible to interpret the data on secondary nuclei in a new way. Assuming that cosmic-ray scattering is due to the interaction with Alfven waves and using the standard set of parameters for the interstellar medium, Osborne and Ptuskin (1988) found that the measured percentage of secondary nuclei for $E \geq 2$ GeV/nucleon can be explained by taking into account stochastic reacceleration of the cosmic rays if:

$$x_{1,m} (R) \sim 4.2 \, (R/R_0)^{-0.33} \text{ g/cm}^2, \quad R \geq R_0 = 5.5 \text{ GV}, \qquad (38)$$

where R is the particle magnetic rigidity.

Compared with the standard model without reacceleration of Eq. (11), Eq. (38) requires a weaker energy dependence of $x_1(E)$. In this case, in the ultrarelativistic region the diffusion coefficient of the cosmic rays depends on the energy as $D(E) \propto E^a$ with a = 0.33, which agrees with data on the anisotropy of cosmic rays. Giler et al. (1987) showed that the content of secondary nuclei observed experimentally can in principle be explained in the case of an energy-independent escape time of the cosmic rays from the Galaxy, if the rate of reacceleration drops with energy.

Turning to the case of strong reacceleration ($abx_1 \gg 1$), Equations (35) and (36) give a function $G(E,x)$ rising with x with a cutoff at $x=x_c$. The cutoff grammage x_c increases with energy. The mean grammage also increases with energy in this case:

$$<x> \sim (ab(E))^{-1} \propto E^a \quad \text{for } E \gg E_0, \qquad (39)$$

in contradiction with data on the abundance of secondary nuclei in cosmic rays.

The evolution of the distribution function $G(E,x)$ from an exponential in x in the case of weak reacceleration to almost a delta function for strong reacceleration is especially easy to follow if we assume that b and x do not depend on energy. For the power-law spectrum of Eq. (33) at the source, from Eq. (30) $E > E_0$, the distribution function is:

$$G(E,x) = q(E) \exp(-x/x_1) \exp[(\gamma_s-1)bx] \, \theta(x_c-x), \quad x_c = b^{-1} \ln(E/E_0). \quad (40)$$

The pathlength distribution is determined by the product of the exponential $\exp(-x/x_1)$, which decreases with x, and the increasing exponential $\exp((\gamma_s-1)bx)$ with a cutoff at $x=x_c$ (E). In the case of weak reacceleration, $bx_1 \ll 1$, the first term dominates. For strong reacceleration, $bx_1 \gg 1$ the second term with its sharp peak at $x = x_c$ (E) is decisive. Since the quantity x (E) increases with energy, the latter version does not agree with observations.

Recent attention to the problem of cosmic-ray acceleration in the interstellar medium was stimulated by the popularity of the idea of diffusive shock acceleration in extended supernova remnants. The decisive argument against any substantial cosmic ray acceleration in the course of their propagation and nuclear fragmentation in the interstellar gas is the observed decrease with energy of the relative amount of secondary nuclei in the cosmic-ray composition. Thus, the main scenario of cosmic ray acceleration in the galaxy must be different. If indeed it is shock acceleration in supernova remnants, then high-energy particles are accelerated at the early stages of the evolution of the remnants and gain the main portion of the total traversed grammage after exiting from the "accelerator" (Blandford and Ostriker, 1980). A subsequent weak distributed cosmic-ray reacceleration in the whole interstellar medium is not excluded at $E \geq 2$ GeV/nucleon. The situation for smaller energies where observations of secondaries do not contradict the presence of even strong reacceleration remains unclear (see Silberberg et al., 1983; Meyer, 1985; Cesarsky, 1987; Heinbach and Simon, 1990; Giler and Szabelska, 1990).

6. Acknowledgments

This paper was partly prepared during my stay at the Service d'Astrophysique CEN, Saclay. I thank Catherine Cesarsky and Aime Soutoul for kind hospitality and many helpful discussions. It is a great pleasure to thank Maurice Shapiro and John Wefel for providing me the opportunity to attend the School in Erice.

7. References

Beuerman, K., Kanbach, G., and Berkhuijsen, E.M. (1985) Astron. Astrophys. 153, 17.
Blandford, R.D. and Ostriker, J.P. (1980) Astrophys. J. 237, 793.
Bloemen, J.B.G.M. (1987) Astrophys. J. 322, 694.
Bradt, H.L. and Peters, B. (1950) Phys. Rev. 80, 943.
Bregman, J.N. (1980) Astrophys. J. 236, 577.
Breitschwerdt, D., McKenzie, J.F., and Volk, H.J. (1987) in Interstellar Magnetic Field, ed. Beck R. and Grave R., Springer Verlag, p. 131.
Cesarsky, C.J. (1987) 20th Intern. Cosmic Ray Conf. 8, 87.

Cowsik, R. (1986) Astron. Astrophys. 155, 344.

Cowsik, R., Pal, Y., Tandon, S.N., and Verma, R.P. (1967) Phys. Rev. 158, 1238.

Cowsik, R. and Wilson, L.W. (1973) 13th Intern. Cosmic Ray Conf., 1, 500.

Davies, L. (1960) Proc. Int. Cosmic Ray Conf, Moscow, 3, 220.

Ferrando, P., Lal, N., McDonald, F.B. and Webber, W.R. (1990) 21st Intern. Cosmic Ray Conf., 3, 40.

Ferrando, P. and Soutoul, A. (1987) 20th Intern. Cosmic Ray Conf. 2, 231.

Freedman, I., Giler, M., Kearsey, S., and Osborne, J.L. (1980) Astron. Astrophys., 82, 110.

Garcia-Munoz, M., Mason, G.M., and Simpson, J.A. (1977) Astrophys. J. 217, 859.

Garcia-Munoz, M., Simpson, J.A., Guzik, T.G., Wefel, J.P., and Margolis, S.H. (1987) Astrophys. J. Suppl. 64, 269.

Giler, M., Osborne, J.L., Szabelska, B., Wdowczyk, J., and Wolfendale, A.W. (1987) 20th Intern. Cosmic Ray Conf. 2, 214.

Giler, M. and Szabelska, B. (1990) 21st Intern. Cosmic Ray Conf. 3, 369.

Giler, M., Szabelska, B., Wdowczyk, J., and Wolfendale, A.W. (1985) 19th Intern. Cosmic Ray Conf. 3, 234.

Ginzburg, V.L. (1990) editor, Astrophysics of Cosmic Rays (Berezinsky, V.S., Bulanov, S.V., Dogiel, V.A., Ginzburg V.L., and Ptuskin, V.S.), North-Holland, The Netherlands.

Ginzburg, V.L., Khazan, Ya.M., and Ptuskin, V.S. (1980) Astrophys. Space Sci. 68, 295.

Ginzburg, V.L. and Ptuskin, V.S. (1976) Rev. Mod. Phys. 48, 161.

Ginzburg, V.L. and Syrovatskii, S.I. (1964) Origin of Cosmic Rays, Pergamon Press.

Habe, A., and Ikeuchi, S. (1980) Progr. Theor. Phys. 64, 1995.

Hayakawa, S. Cosmic Ray Physics, Wiley-Interscience, New York.

Hayakawa, S., Ito, K. and Terashima, Y. (1958) Progr. Theor. Phys. Suppl. 6, 1.

Heinbach, M. and Simon, M. (1990) 21st Intern. Cosmic Ray Conf. 3, 361.

Ikeuchi, S. (1988) Fund. Cosmic Phys. 12, 255.

Ipavich, F.M. (1975) Astrophys. J. 196, 107.

Jokipii, J.R. (1976) Astrophys. J. 208, 900.

Jones, F. (1979) Astrophys. J. 229, 747.

Kanbach, G. (1983) Space Sci. Rev. 36, 273.

Lerche, I. and Schlickeiser, R. (1982a) Astron. Astrophys. 107, 142.

Lerche, I. and Schlickeiser, R. (1982b) Astron. Astrophys. 116, 10.

Lezniak, J. A. (1979) Astrophys. Space Sci. 63, 279.

Margolis, S.H. (1986) Astrophys. J. 300, 20.

McKee, C.F, and Ostriker, J.P. (1977) Astrophys. J. 218, 148.

Meyer, J.P. (1985) 19th Intern. Cosmic Ray Conf. 9, 141.

Osborne, J.L. and Ptuskin, V.S. (1987) Sov. Astron. Lett. 13, 413.

Osborne, J.L. and Ptuskin, V.S. (1988) Sov. Astron. Lett. 14, 311.

Owens, A.J. and Jokipii, J.R. (1977) Astrophys. J. 215, 677.

Phillips, S., Kearsey, S., and Osborne, J.L. (1981) Astron. Astrophys. 103, 405.

Ptuskin, V.S. (1974) Astrophys. Space Sci. 28, 17.

Ptuskin, V.S. and Soutoul, A. (1990a) Astron. Astrophys., in press

Ptuskin, V.S. and Soutoul, A. (1990b), to be published.

Prishchep, V.L. and Ptuskin, V.S. (1975) Astrophys. Space Sci. 32, 265.

Prishchep, V.L.. and Ptuskin, V.S. (1979) 16th Intern. Cosmic Ray Conf. 2, 137.

Reynolds, R.J. (1989) Astrophys. J. Letters, 339, L29.

Scoville, N.Z. and Sanders, D.B. (1987) in Interstellar Processes, ed. Hollenbach, D.J. and Thronsen, H.A., D.Reidel, Dordrecht, p.21.

Shapiro, M.M. and Silberberg R. (1970) Ann. Rev. Nuclear Part. Sci. 20, 323.

Silberberg, R., Tsao, C.H., Letaw, J.R., and Shapiro, M.M. (1983) Phys. Rev. Letters. 51, 1217.

Simon, M., Heinrich, W., and Mathis, K.D. (1986) Astrophys. J. 300, 32.

Simpson, J.A. (1983) Ann. Rev. Nuclear Part. Sci. 33, 323.

Simpson, J.A. and Garcia-Munoz, M. (1989) in Problems of Theoretical Physics and Astrophysics, (volume devoted to the 70th anniversary of V.L.Ginzburg), ed. Keldysh, L.V. and Fainberg, V.Ya., Nauka, Moscow, p. 510.

Skilling, J. (1975) Mon. Not. R. A. S. 172, 557.

Soutoul, A., Engelmann, J.J., Ferrando, P., Koch-Miramond, L., Masse, P., and Webber, W.R. (1985) 19th Int. Cosmic Ray Conf. 2, 8.

Soutoul, A., Ferrando, P., and Webber, W.R. (1990) 21st Int. Cosmic Ray Conf. 3, 337.

Spitzer, L. (1989) Ann. Rev. Astron. Astrophys. 27, 1.

Wandel, A., Eichler D.S., Letaw J.R., Shapiro, M.M., Silberberg, R., and Tsao, C.H. (1987) Astrophys. J. 316, 676.

Webber, W.R. (1985) 19th Intern. Cosmic Ray Conf. 2, 88.

Webber, W.R. (1990) 21th Intern. Cosmic Ray Conf. 3, 393.

Webber, W.R. and Kish, J. (1979) 16th Intern. Cosmic Ray Conf. 1, 389.

Wiedenbeck, M.E. (1983) 18th Intern. Cosmic Ray Conf. 9, 147.

Wiedenbeck, M.E. and Greiner, D.E. (1980) Astrophys. J. Letters, 239, L139.

Yiou, F. and Raisbeck, G.M. (1972) Phys. Rev. Lett. 29, 372.

THE PRODUCTION OF ANTIPROTONS IN THE INTERSTELLAR GAS BY PROPAGATING COSMIC RAYS

M. Simon and U. Heinbach
Department of Physics
University of Siegen
P.O. Box 10 12 40
D-5900 Siegen
Federal Republic of Germany

ABSTRACT. The available measurements on the cosmic ray $\bar{p}/p$-ratio show an excess of antiprotons above predictions derived in the framework of the standard picture of cosmic ray origin and propagation. We have present a detailed discussion of the equilibrium antiproton-proton ratio predictions calculated in the Standard Leaky Box Model and in the diffusive reacceleration model, where cosmic ray particles are reaccelerated due to gyroresonant interaction with hydromegnetic waves. It could be shown that the calculated $\bar{p}/p$ ratio is enhanced in the diffusive reacceleration model compared to that derived from the Leaky Box Model, but it remains difficult to bring it into agreement with the data.

1. Introduction

Antiprotons have been found in the cosmic radiation and Fig. 1 shows the current situation on the available data.

Since their discovery the antiprotons have raised scientifically important questions concerning their origin, because it became evident that the measurements showed an excess of antiprotons above predictions which have been derived from the standard picture of cosmic ray origin and propagation developed to account for the heavier cosmic ray nuclei. An excess above predictions by almost a factor of 3 or so was found. One certainly expects a flux of antiprotons in the cosmic ray beam since they are produced as secondaries as a result from high energy collisions of protons with the interstellar gas through the reaction $p + p \rightarrow \bar{p} + x$, where x stands for other hadrons which emerge with the $\bar{p}$ from the interaction. The abundance of the $\bar{p}$ in the cosmic radiation then depends on the conditions of propagation and the characteristics of the pp-interaction. In this paper we want to discuss these things more in detail we will describe the kinematic of the $p + p \rightarrow \bar{p} + x$ reaction, will present the technique how to calculate the inclusive differential cross section for the $\bar{p}$ production as seen in the laboratory system and will apply those to the propagation calculation. We will give solutions for the energy dependent propagation equation which

137

M. M. Shapiro et al. (eds.), Cosmic Rays, Supernovae and the Interstellar Medium, 137–152.

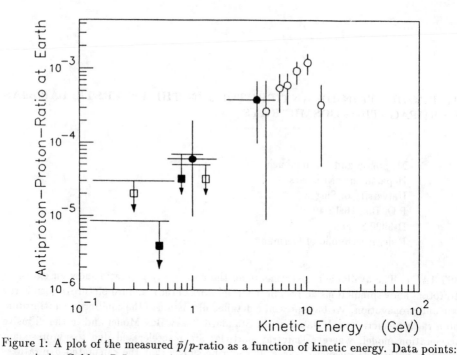

Figure 1: A plot of the measured $\bar{p}/p$-ratio as a function of kinetic energy. Data points:
open circle: Golden, R.L. et al. (1984);
filled circle: Bogomolov, E.A. et al. (1987);
open square: Streitmatter, R.E. et al. (1990), Moats, A. et al. (1990) and Stochaj, S.J. (1990); filled square: Barwick, S.W. et al. (1990)

is a partial differential equation in two variables and will finally calculate the $\bar{p}$-flux under different conditions of propagation including the possibility of reacceleration.

2. The properties of the high energy hadron-hadron collision

2.1. THE KINEMATIC

Antiprotons will be produced as a consequence of high energy interactions between cosmic ray hadrons with the interstellar gas which consists mainly of hydrogen. Since protons dominate in the cosmic ray beam the main interaction which contributes to the $\bar{p}$ production is:

$$p_{cr} + p_{gas} \rightarrow \bar{p} + x$$

and Fig. 2 illustrates the kinematic of this interaction where $\vec{p}_p$, $\vec{p}_{\bar{p}}$ and $\vec{p}_x$ are the momenta of the incoming proton, the outgoing antiproton and the outgoing hadrons named x.

The $\bar{p}$ can emerge from such an interaction with different energies $E_{\bar{p}}(E_p)$ and the energy range of produced $\bar{p}$ depends on the energy of the incoming proton, E_p. This dependence

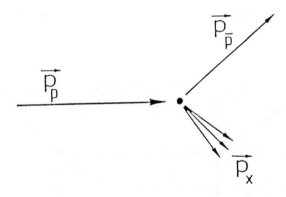

Figure 2: Kinematic of the main antiproton producing interaction. $\vec{p}_p$, $\vec{p}_{\bar{p}}$ and $\vec{p}_x$ are the momenta of the incoming proton, the outgoing antiproton and the outgoing hadrons named x.

can be obtained by considering the kinematic conditions on the momenta and the energies and by making use of the relativistic energy-momentum relations:

$$|\vec{p}_p| \leq |\vec{p}_{\bar{p}}| + |\vec{p}_x|$$

$$\sqrt{E_p^2 - m_p^2} \leq \sqrt{E_{\bar{p}}^2 - m_p^2} + \sqrt{(E_p + m_p - E_{\bar{p}})^2 - m_x^2}$$

The energy of the produced $\bar{p}$ lies then between the two energies $_{1,2}E_{\bar{p}}$ as given by

$$_{1,2}E_{\bar{p}}(E_p) = \frac{b^2(c - 2m^2p)}{2(a^2 - b^2)} \pm \sqrt{\frac{b^2(c - 2m_p)^2}{4(b^2 - a^2)^2} - \frac{c^2 - 4d}{4(b^2 - a^2)}} \tag{1}$$

with

$$a = E_p^2 - m_p^2 \quad, \qquad b = E_p + m_p \quad,$$
$$c = a^2 - b^2 + m_x^2 + m_p^2 \quad, \qquad d = m_x^2 \cdot m_p^2 - b^2 \cdot m_p$$

Fig. 3 illustrates the properties of the kinematic for the case $m_x = 3m_p$. Since the $\bar{p}$ can only be produced in $\bar{p}$-p-pairs in order to conserve the baryon number this reaction requires the lowest threshold energy on the incoming proton E_p to produce an antiproton. At this threshold, $E_p^{th} = 6 \cdot m_p \cdot c^2$, the produced $\bar{p}$-p-pair is at rest in the center of mass system (CMS) leading to an energy of about 1 GeV in the laboratory system (LS). With energies E_p above that threshold the produced $\bar{p}$ can emerge backward or forward from the interaction point leading either to a lower or higher energy than the 1 GeV in the LS. This explains the nonmonotonic shape of the curve in Fig. 3. An incident proton of 10 GeV can thus produce antiprotons with energies ranging from 0.9 GeV to 6.2 GeV. This is illustrated as an example in Fig. 3. As one can see the energies of the produced antiprotons can cover a relatively wide range but the probability to produce a $\bar{p}$ of a certain energy $E_{\bar{p}}$ however depends on the differential cross section, $\frac{d\sigma}{dE_{\bar{p}}}(E_{\bar{p}}, E_p)$, which will be discussed next.

140

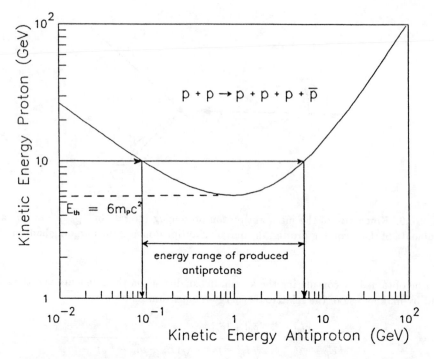

Figure 3: Protons below the threshold of $6 \cdot m_p c^2$ cannot produce any antiproton. Above this threshold they can produce $\bar{p}$ of different energy as indicated for the case of a proton of 10 GeV. The energies refer to those in the laboratory system.

2.2. THE INCLUSIVE $\bar{p}$ PRODUCTION CROSS SECTION FROM A HADRON-HADRON COLLISION

Since the $\bar{p}$ emerge from a hadron-hadron collision with different energies the inclusive differential cross section for the inclusive $\bar{p}$ production reaction $p + p \to \bar{p} + x$ has to be known in order to perform the cosmic ray propagation calculation. It was of great help that in recent years much attention has been paid to these cross sections and Tan and Ng (1983a) have developed a parametrization and for collisions with energies greater than 10 GeV in the CMS ($\sqrt{s} > 10$ GeV) the inclusive differential cross section for the $p + p \to \bar{p} + x$ reaction is parametrised as:

$$\left(E_{\bar{p}}^* \cdot \frac{d^3\sigma}{dp_x^* dp_y^* dp_z^*}\right)_{\sqrt{s} > 10 \text{GeV}} (x_R^*, p_t^*) =$$
$$f(x_R^*) \cdot \exp\{-[A(x_R^*)p_t^* + B(x_R^*) \cdot p_t^{*2}]\}[\text{mbarn GeV}^{-2}c^3] \qquad (2)$$

where p_t^* means the transverse momentum in the CMS and the variable x_R^* means the ratio of the total energy of the $\bar{p}$ in the CMS, $E_{\bar{p}}^*$, to $_{\max}E_{\bar{p}}^*$, the maximum value of $E_{\bar{p}}^*$. The expressions in equation (2) mean:

$$f(x_R^*) = a_1 e^{-a_2 \cdot x_R^*} \cdot F(a_3 - x_R^*) + (W_{00} - a_1)(1 - x_R^*)^{a_4}$$
$$A(x_R^*) = a_5 e^{-a_6 \cdot x_R^*} + a_7 e^{a_8 \cdot x_R^*}$$
$$B(x_R^*) = a_9 e^{-a_{10}(x_R^* + a_{11})} \cdot (x_R^* + a_{11})^{a_{12}}$$
$$F(u) = \begin{cases} 0 & \text{for} \quad u < 0 \\ 1 & \text{for} \quad u \geq 0 \end{cases}$$

and the 13 parameters for the $p + p \to \bar{p} + x$ reaction are:

W_{00}	a_1	a_2	a_3	a_4	a_5	a_6
3.15	$1.05 \cdot 10^{-4}$	10.1	0.5	7.9	0.47	$3.7 \cdot 10^{-2}$

a_7	a_8	a_9	a_{10}	a_{11}	a_{12}
2.31	$1.4 \cdot 10^{-2}$	$3.02 \cdot 10^{-2}$	3.19	0.399	8.39

For energies below 10 GeV in the CMS ($\sqrt{s} \leq 10$ GeV) a further correction factor R is introduced, which has to be multiplied to the expression as given in equation (2):

$$R = 1 - \exp[-[1 - \exp\{-A(x_T^*) \cdot Q^{B(x_T^*)}\}] \times$$
$$\exp\{C(x_T^*) \times Q - D(x_T^*)\}] \tag{3}$$

with

$$A(x_T^*) = b_1 \cdot e^{-b_2 \cdot x_T^*}$$
$$B(x_T^*) = b_3 \cdot e^{b_4 \cdot x_T^*}$$
$$C(x_T^*) = b_5 + b_6 \cdot x_T^* + b_7 \cdot x_T^{*2}$$
$$D(x_T^*) = b_8 \cdot e^{b_9 \cdot x_T^*}$$
$$Q = \sqrt{s} - \sqrt{4 m_p \cdot c^2}$$

with the new variable x_T^*:

$$x_T^* = \frac{x_R^* - x_m^*}{1 - x_m^*} \quad \text{with} \quad x_m^* = \frac{m_p \cdot c^2}{\max E_{\bar{p}}^*}$$

where x_m^* means the minimum value of x_R^* at a fixed $\sqrt{s}$ value and the 9 parameters in equation (3) are:

b_1	b_2	b_3	b_4	b_5	b_6	b_7	b_8	b_9
0.306	0.12	0.0552	2.72	0.758	-0.68	1.54	0.594	2.87

Fig. 4 shows how well the parametrization fits the actual data. This figure was directly taken from Tan and Ng (1983a) publication.

These expressions given above all refer to the situation as seen in the CMS. For cosmic ray propagation, however, one has to describe the interaction in the LS. Since the quantity $E \cdot \frac{d^3\sigma}{dp_x\, dp_y\, dp_z}$ is invariant versus Lorentz transformation one can make use of equation (2)

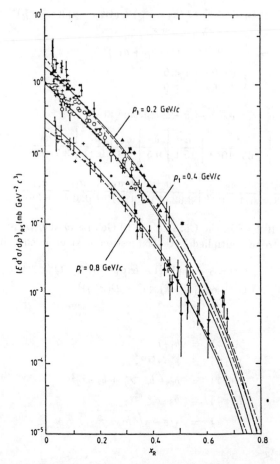

Figure 4: The $\bar{p}$ inclusive differential cross section of pp-interaction for $p_p \geq 100$ GeV/c. The figure was directly taken from the publication of Tan and Ng (1983 a). Full curves from equation 2, broken curves from a preliminary fit of Tan and Ng (1982).

and (3) but one has to go through a number of calculations transforming quantities from the CMS into the LS. These are given below. With those and by also changing the variables from the cartesian coordinates to zylindric coordinates, $p_x\,p_y\,p_z \rightarrow p_{\parallel}\,p_t\,\varphi$, one obtains the differential cross section in the LS and for a given E_p one finds:

$$
\left[\frac{d\sigma}{dE_{\bar{p}}}(E_{\bar{p}}, E_p)\right]_{\mathrm{LS}} =
$$

$$
\int_0^{\max p_t} \frac{2\pi p_t}{c\sqrt{E_{\bar{p}}^2 - c^2 p_t^2 - (m_p \cdot c^2)^2}} \cdot \left[E_{\bar{p}}^* \cdot \frac{d^3\sigma}{dp_x^*\,dp_y^*\,dp_z^*}(x_R^*, p_t^*)\right]_{\mathrm{CMS}} dp_t \qquad (4)
$$

This integral has to be solved numerically and the following relations are further needed.

1) For a fixed E_p and a given p_t in the LS the relation between the energy of the antiproton, $E_{\bar{p}}$, as seen in the LS and $E_{\bar{p}}^*$, as seen in the CMS is given by:

$$E_{\bar{p}}^* = \gamma(E_{\bar{p}} - \beta \cdot \sqrt{E_{\bar{p}}^2 - (m_p \cdot c^2)^2 - c^2 \cdot p_t^2}$$

with

$$\gamma = \frac{\sqrt{s + E_p^2 - (m_p \cdot c^2)^2}}{\sqrt{s}}$$

$$\beta = \frac{\sqrt{\gamma^2 - 1}}{\gamma}$$

$$s = 2E_p m_p c^2 + 2m_p^2 c^4$$

where β means the velocity of the CMS and s is the energy available in the CMS.

2) For a fixed E_p the maximum value of the energy of the antiproton in the CMS $_{\max}E_{\bar{p}}^*$ is given by

$$_{\max}E_{\bar{p}}^* = \frac{s + (m_p \cdot c^2)^2 - (3m_p \cdot c^2)^2}{2\sqrt{s}}$$

The relations 1) and 2) determine the variable x_R^* and it is evident that $p_t^* = p_t$.

3) For a fixed E_p and a given $E_{\bar{p}}$ the p_t varies between zero and $_{\max}p_t$. The maximum transverse momentum is given by

$$_{\max}p_t = \frac{1}{c}\left(E_{\bar{p}}^2 - (m_p \cdot c^2)^2 - \frac{(\gamma E_p - _{\max}E_{\bar{p}}^*)^2}{\gamma^2 \cdot \beta^2}\right)^{1/2}$$

Fig. 5 shows results of calculated inclusive differential cross sections $\frac{d\sigma}{dE_p}(E_p, E_{\bar{p}})$ for different values of E_p using $E_{\bar{p}}$ as a parameter. These cross sections show a steep dependence on the incident energy of the proton, E_p, just above the kinematic threshold and then they level off to almost constant values at energies roughly 10 times the threshold energy of the E_p for a given $E_{\bar{p}}$.

Fig. 6 shows the calculated inclusive differential cross section for different $E_{\bar{p}}$ emerging from an interaction with a proton of a fixed energy of 40 GeV.

From purely kinematic standpoint this proton energy is sufficient to produce antiprotons of very low energies and up to about 36 GeV. But Fig. 6 illustrates that the differential cross section is largest for $\bar{p}$ with energies around 4 GeV and to lower and higher energies it falls off rapidly.

3. The mathematical procedure to calculate the $\bar{p}$-flux in the interstellar medium

The state situation in the Leaky Box model for the production of antiprotons can be described by calculating the $\bar{p}$-flux, $N_{\bar{p}}(x, E_{\bar{p}})$, after different slab thicknesses $x(g/cm^2)$ with

144

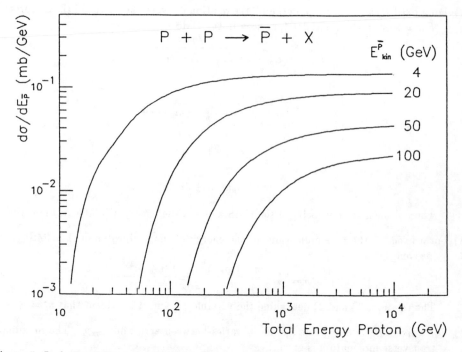

Figure 5: Inclusive differential $\bar{p}$ production cross section of pp-interaction as a function of the incident proton energy; derived from the parametrized cross sections published by Tan and Ng (1983 a) and transformed into the laboratory system.

a subsequent convolution of the distribution of path lengths $P(x, E_{\bar{p}})$ which the particles encounter between their sources and the observer, thus:

$$N_{\bar{p}}(E_{\bar{p}}) = \int_0^\infty N_{\bar{p}}(x, E_{\bar{p}}) \cdot P(x, E_{\bar{p}}) dx \tag{5}$$

where $P(x, E_{\bar{p}})$ is of an exponential form. The solution $N_{\bar{p}}(x, E_{\bar{p}})$ behind a slab $x(g/cm^2)$ by allowing energy changing processes can be obtained after solving the following differential equation:

$$\frac{\partial N_{\bar{p}}}{\partial x}(x, E_{\bar{p}}) = -\frac{N_{\bar{p}}(x, E_{\bar{p}})}{\lambda_{\bar{p}}^{int}(E_{\bar{p}})} - \frac{\partial}{\partial E_{\bar{p}}} \left\{ \left(\frac{\partial E_{\bar{p}}}{\partial x} \right) (E_{\bar{p}}(x)) \cdot N_{\bar{p}}(x, E_{\bar{p}}) \right\} +$$

$$+K \int_{E_{th}^p(E_{\bar{p}}(x))}^\infty \frac{P(E_p, E_{\bar{p}}) \cdot P_{pp}^{\bar{p}}(E_p)}{\lambda_p^{int}(E_p)} \cdot \frac{dN_p}{dE_p}(x, E_p) dE_p \tag{6}$$

with

$$\lambda_{\bar{p}}^{int}(E_{\bar{p}}) = \frac{<m>}{\sigma_{pp}^{tot}(E_{\bar{p}})}(g/cm^2)$$

$$\lambda_p^{int}(E_p) = \frac{<m>}{\sigma_{pp}^{tot}(E_p)}(g/cm^2)$$

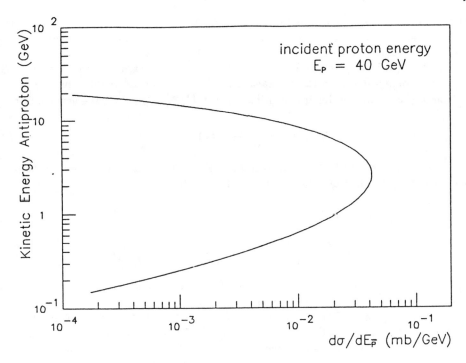

Figure 6: Inclusive differential $\bar{p}$ production cross section of pp-interaction where the incident proton has an energy of 40 MeV; derived from the parametrized cross section published by Tan and Ng (1983 a) and transformed into the laboratory system.

and $< m >$ means the mean mass of the interstellar medium.

$\frac{dN_p}{dE_p}(x, E_p)$ is the differential cosmic ray proton spectrum at position x which produces the $\bar{p}$. Since the cosmic ray density is in first order independent of x one excepts $\frac{dN_p}{dE_p}(x, E_p) = \frac{dN_p}{dE_p}(E_p)$. The integral stretches over all protons which are above the threshold $E_{th}^p(E_{\bar{p}}(x))$ to produce an antiproton of energy $E_{\bar{p}}$, see equation 1 in chapter 2.

$P_{pp}^{\bar{p}}(E_p)$ means the probability that from a pp-collision with a given E_p an antiproton emerge. Thus

$$P_{pp}^{\bar{p}}(E_p) = \frac{\sigma_{pp}^{tot}(p + p \to \bar{p} + x)}{\sigma_{pp}^{tot}(E_p)} \tag{7}$$

and $P(E_{\bar{p}}, E_p)$ means the probability that a proton with an energy E_p produces an antiproton with energy $E_{\bar{p}}$. Thus

$$P(E_{\bar{p}}, E_p) = \frac{d\sigma}{dE_{\bar{p}}}(E_{\bar{p}}, E_p) \cdot \frac{1}{\sigma_{pp}^{tot}(p + p \to \bar{p} + x)} \tag{8}$$

The factor K in front of the integral counts for the fact that not only the protons produce the $\bar{p}$ but also the cosmic ray nuclei with $Z \geq 2$. This contribution can be estimated by weighing the total interaction cross sections of the different particles with their abundance relative to the protons. One finds that about 25% of all $\bar{p}$ stem from interactions with the heavy nuclei. It has also to be considered that not only $\bar{p}$ emerge from an interaction but also $\bar{n}$ at the same rate which finally decay into $\bar{p}$. Thus K becomes 2.5.

Equation (6) is a partial differential equation in the two variables $x(g/cm^2)$ and $E_{\bar{p}}$. This more complicated form can be transformed into a linear differential equation in one variable $x(g/cm^2)$ by multiplying equation (6) with $\left(\frac{\partial E_{\bar{p}}}{\partial x}\right)(E_{\bar{p}})$. With the new quantity

$$\tilde{N}_{\bar{p}}(x, E_{\bar{p}}) = \left(\frac{\partial E_{\bar{p}}}{\partial x}\right)(E_{\bar{p}}) \cdot N_{\bar{p}}(x, E_{\bar{p}}) \tag{9}$$

and with relation (7) and (8) and (9) considering that the differential cosmic ray proton spectrum is independent of x one obtains the linear differential equation:

$$\frac{d\tilde{N}}{dx}(x, E_{\bar{p}}) + \frac{\tilde{N}_p(x, E_{\bar{p}})}{\lambda_{\bar{p}}^{int}(E_{\bar{p}})} =$$

$$\frac{K}{<m>} \int_{E_{th}^p(E_p)}^{\infty} \left(\frac{\partial E_{\bar{p}}}{\partial x}\right)(E_{\bar{p}}) \cdot \frac{d\sigma}{dE_{\bar{p}}}(E_{\bar{p}}, E_p) \cdot \frac{dN_p}{dE_p}(E_p) \cdot dE_p \tag{10}$$

As one can see the integral needs all the knowledge on the kinematic and the differential cross sections as discussed in the previous chapter.

The inhomogeneous differential equation (10) can be solved by first solving the homogeneous differential equation and then adding a special solution of the inhomogeneous differential equation which can be found by means of the "variation of the constant". When one further considers the interaction lengths $\lambda_{\bar{p}}^{int}$ and λ_p^{int} to be independent of energy then one finds the following solution:

$$\tilde{N}_{\bar{p}}(x, E_{\bar{p}}^f) = \tilde{N}_{\bar{p}}(0, E_{\bar{p}}^i) \cdot e^{-\frac{x}{\lambda_{\bar{p}}^{int}}} + e^{-\frac{x}{\lambda_{int p}}} \frac{K}{<m>} \cdot$$

$$\int_0^x \left\{ e^{\frac{x'}{\lambda_{\bar{p}}^{int}}} \cdot \left(\frac{\partial E_{\bar{p}}}{\partial x}\right)(E_{\bar{p}}(x')) \int_{E_{th}^p(E_{\bar{p}}(x'))}^{\infty} \frac{d\sigma}{dE_{\bar{p}}}(E_p, E_{\bar{p}}(x')) \frac{dN_p}{dE_p}(E_p)dE_p \right\} dx' \tag{11}$$

with

$$E_{\bar{p}}^f = E_{\bar{p}}^i + \int_0^x \frac{\partial E_{\bar{p}}}{\partial x}(x, E_{\bar{p}})dx$$

This solution becomes much simpler when one ignores any energy changing term. Under these assumption $E_{\bar{p}}^f$ become $E_{\bar{p}}^i$ and the solution is:

$$N_{\bar{p}}(x, E_{\bar{p}}) = N_{\bar{p}}(0, E_{\bar{p}}) \cdot e^{-\frac{x}{\lambda_{\bar{p}}^{int}}} + \frac{K}{<m>} \cdot \lambda_{\bar{p}}^{int}(1 - e^{-\frac{x}{\lambda_{\bar{p}}^{int}}}).$$

$$\int_{E_{th}^p(E_p(x'))}^{\infty} \frac{d\sigma}{dE_{\bar{p}}}(E_{\bar{p}}, E_p) \cdot \frac{dN}{dE_p}(E_p)dE_p \tag{12}$$

the integral has to be solved numerically. But in a situation in which one allows that the energy may change during propagation which is more the realistic case one cannot separate the coupled double integral in equation 11 since $E_{\bar{p}}(x)$ depends on the path $x(g/cm^2)$. Under these circumstances one has to replace the integral over the path $x(g/cm^2)$ in equation 11 by a sum by changing x only by a little amount Δx and by assuming to have the energy not changed on this little path. For such a little path from x to $x + \Delta x$ one obtains the following solution.

$$\tilde{N}_{\bar{p}}(x, E_{\bar{p}}(x)) \approx \tilde{N}_{\bar{p}}(x - \Delta x, E_{\bar{p}}(x - \Delta x)) \cdot e^{-\frac{\Delta x}{\lambda_{\bar{p}}^{\text{int}}}} +$$

$$e^{-\frac{\Delta x}{\lambda_{\bar{p}}}} \cdot \frac{K}{<m>} \cdot \left[e^{\frac{(x - \frac{\Delta x}{2})}{\lambda_{\bar{p}}^{\text{int}}}} \cdot \left(\frac{\partial E_{\bar{p}}}{\partial x} \right) (E_{\bar{p}}(x - \frac{\Delta x}{2})) \right] \Delta x \cdot$$

$$\int_{E_{th}^p(E_{\bar{p}}(x - \frac{\Delta x}{2}))}^{\infty} \frac{d\sigma}{dE_{\bar{p}}}(E_p, E_{\bar{p}}(x - \frac{\Delta x}{2})) \cdot \frac{dN_p}{dE_p}(E_p) \cdot dE_p \qquad (13)$$

with

$$E_{\bar{p}}(x - \Delta x) = E_{\bar{p}}(x) + \int_x^{x - \Delta x} \frac{\partial E}{\partial x}(E_{\bar{p}}(x'))dx'$$

$$\approx E_{\bar{p}}(x) + \frac{dE_{\bar{p}}}{dx}(E_{\bar{p}}(x - \frac{\Delta x}{2})) \cdot \Delta x$$

The remaining integral over the variable E_p has to be solved numerically. With equation (13) one can obtain $\tilde{N}_{\bar{p}}(x, E_{\bar{p}}^f)$ behind a certain path $x(g/cm^2)$ by starting with $x = 0$ and by increasing the path stepwise by an amount of Δx always using equation (13). After dividing $\tilde{N}_{\bar{p}}(x, E_{\bar{p}}^f)$ by the energy changing term $\frac{\partial E_{\bar{p}}}{\partial x}(E_{\bar{p}}^f(x))$ one obtains $N_{\bar{p}}(x, E_{\bar{p}}^f(x))$ which one finally has to weigh with the appropriate path length distribution according to equation (5).

4. Results

The steady state situation in the Leaky Box Model is described by weighing the slab solutions with the path length distribution $P(x, E)$. This path length distribution and its mean, $\lambda_{\text{esc}}(E)$, is an important astrophysical parameter since it determines the amount of matter traversed by cosmic rays between their sources and the observer. This parameter links to the condition of propagation and confinement. The mean $\lambda_{\text{esc}}(E)$ is usually determined by comparing the observed secondary to primary ratios of cosmic ray nuclei with the calculations. Fig. 7 shows the data on the B/C-ratio and the curve that fits these data is based on a calculation in the Leaky Box Model assuming an energy dependence of $\lambda_{\text{esc}}(E)$ as given by curve A in Fig. 8, Heinbach and Simon (1990a), see also Garcia-Munoz et al. (1987).

This $\lambda_{\text{esc}}(E)$ dependence was applied to the $\bar{p}$ calculation. Curve A in Fig. 9 presents as an example the relative yield of the production of 3 GeV antiprotons by propagating protons as a function of the initial proton energy. The path in this example was fixed to 8 g/cm^2. As one can see the antiprotons produced in the interstellar gas stem from protons whose energy is a factor of about 5 higher than the energy of the $\bar{p}$. The falloff towards high energies is due to the equilibrium proton spectrum, which is a power law in kinetic energy with exponent -2.7. The low energy cutoff is due to the production threshold of 3 GeV antiprotons, which is 7.0 GeV.

Curve A in Fig. 10 presents the $\bar{p}$ abundance normalized to the principle progenitor, namely protons. The falloff in the expected ratio above 20 GeV is due to the decreasing

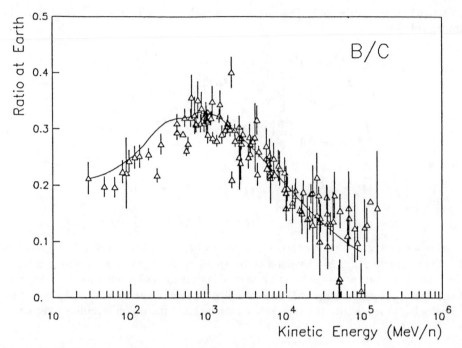

Figure 7: Data on the B/C-ratio of earth. The measurements were taken from a data compilation of Garcia Munoz et al. (1987). The curve was calculated in the framework of the Leaky Box Model with a mean path length given by curve A in figure 8.

galactic residence time at higher energies (see Fig. 8, curve A) and the low energy cutoff is due to the convolution of the steep cosmic ray proton spectrum with the cross section for $\bar{p}$ production, see equation 12. One realizes that the data on the antiprotons are a factor of 4 or so above the predicted abundance.

As a result of this discrepancy a number of ideas have been discussed invoking also alternatives to the Standard Leaky Box situation such as reacceleration, Simon et al. (1986). In this scenario one still accepts that the cosmic ray particles are preaccelerated at their sources and injected into space but allows that the particles gain some energy while they propagate. In a recent paper by Heinbach and Simon (1990 a, 1990 b) the sites of reacceleration were linked to the gyroresonant interactions with the hydromagnetic waves, which leads to an energy dependent moderate Fermi-type acceleration. Under these conditions the efficiency of reacceleration becomes energy dependent and the relative rigidity gain becomes inversely proportional to the diffusion coefficient, $\Delta R/R \sim 1/D(R)$. Since the mean escape length $\lambda_{esc}(R)$ couples in this diffusive model inversely proportional to the diffusion coefficient the relative rigidity change per unit path length can be expressed as

$$\frac{1}{R}\frac{\partial R}{\partial x} = \alpha \cdot R^{-a} \tag{14}$$

where α stands for the strength of reacceleration and a is the exponent of the rigidity

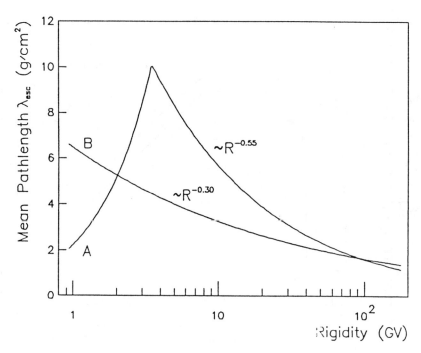

Figure 8: Mean path length of a cosmic ray particle as a function of particle rigidity derived by Heinbach and Simon (1990 b) in order to fit the B/C-ratio under different reacceleration conditions. Curve A gives the mean path length for the case of no reacceleration energy gain, curve B under the assumption of diffusive reacceleration with $\alpha = 0.12$.

dependence of $\lambda_{esc}(R)$. The most interesting consequence of this propagation condition is that the data on the secondary to primary ratios of cosmic ray nuclei can be well fitted with an energy dependence of $\lambda_{esc}(R)$ which stands over the whole energy range as a power law with an index of 0.3, see curve B in Fig. 8, where α was chosen to be 0.12. Such a rigidity dependence is expected from a Kolmogorov type spectrum of hydromagnetic wave turbulences. The reacceleration strength to obtain such a dependence is really moderate. As an example the relative rigidity gain for a 10 GeV proton is only 6% per unit path lenth under these conditions.

If this reacceleration scenario is applied to the production of $\bar{p}$, one expects more antiprotons since protons, which start initially below the production threshold can contribute to the $\bar{p}$ production if their energy is shifted above the threshold due to reacceleration. This is illustrated by curve B in Fig. 9. As one can see protons, which started below the kinematic threshold indeed contribute to the production of 3 GeV antiprotons.

The calculated $\bar{p}/p$-ratio for different energies and under reacceleration conditions is shown by curve B in Fig. 10. This result was obtained with a reacceleration strength of $\alpha = 0.12$ and a mean path length as given by curve B in Fig. 8.

As one can see reacceleration indeed enhances the $\bar{p}$ abundance but it is also not capable to explain the observations. It is also noteworthy to mention that the different slopes of the

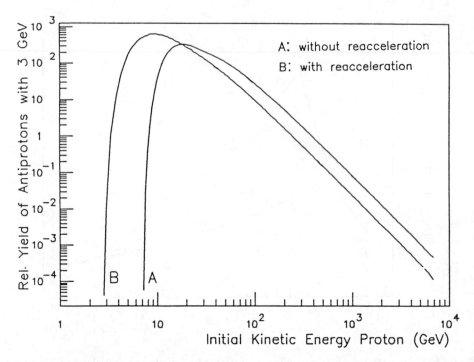

Figure 9: Relative yield of $\bar{p}$ with $E_{\bar{p}} = 3$ GeV produced within $8g/cm^2$ by propagating protons as a function of initial proton energy. Curve A presents the situation under the assumption of no reacceleration, curve B under the assumption of diffusive reacceleration with $\alpha = 0.12$.

$\bar{p}/p$-ratios to higher energies are due to the different exponents of the $\lambda_{esc}(R)$ dependence as given by the two curves in Fig. 8.

5. Conclusion

It could be shown that the Standard Leaky Box calculation which only considers energy losses due to the ionization process cannot explain the abundance of the measured antiprotons. It became also clear that reacceleration does not solve the problem unless one allows the cosmic ray nuclei to encounter different propagation conditions than the most abundant protons. A number of ideas have been further discussed in the literature allowing modifications like postproduction energy-changing processes, Golden et al. (1984), or energy-dependent escape probablities, Stephens (1981), including also models in which $\bar{p}$ are produced in denser regions, Cowsik and Gaiser (1981), Cesarsky and Montemerle (1981), Tan and Ng (1983 b). All these calculations reveal problems by accommodating the results with the observed data. In this discussion interpretations have been tried such as premordial $\bar{p}$ contribution or the existence of Higgsinos or other weakly interacting Majorana particles, predicted by supersymmetry theories, which can contribute to the antiprotons,

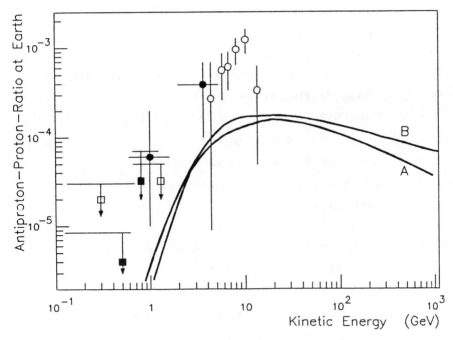

Figure 10: Calculated $\bar{p}/p$-ratio under different propagation conditions. Curve A represents the Standard Leaky Box situation and curve B the diffusive reacceleration situation with $\alpha = 0.12$. Data point references: see Fig. 1.

Rudaz and Stecker (1988). At this time the $\bar{p}$-puzzle cannot be sufficiently explained and remains as one of the most interesting issues on particle astrophysics. It is certainly true that more measurements on the $\bar{p}/p$-ratios would help to approach the problem. It would be very important not only to see the increase of the $\bar{p}/p$-ratio in the low energy region between 1 and 10 GeV with a better statistic but also the decrease to higher energies as one expects from purely propagation conditions.

In future programs it is aimed to improve the situation in the low energy range with balloon borne experiments, whereas the high energy range will be covered by the Wizzard experiment on Astromag, which is planned to fly on the Space Station at the end of the century.

References

Barwick, S.W. et al., (1990), Proc. of the 21st ICRC (Adelaide), 3, 273

Bogomolov, E.A. et al., (1987), Proc. of the 20th ICRC (Moscow), 2, 72

Cesarsky, C. and Montmerle, T., (1981); Proc. of the 17th ICRC (Paris), 9, 207

152

Cowsik, R. and Gaisser, T.K., (1981), Proc. of the 17th ICRC (Paris), 2, 218

Garcia-Munoz, M. et al., (1987), Astrophy. J. Supp., 64, 269

Golden, R.L. et al., (1984), Astrophys. Let., 24, 75

Heinbach, U. and Simon, M., (1990 a), Proc. of the 21st ICRC (Adelaide), 3, 361

Heinbach, U. and Simon, M., (1990 b), in preparation

Moats, A. et al. (1990), Proc. of the 21st ICRC (Adelaide), 3, 284

Rudaz, S. and Stecker, F.W., (1988), Astrophys. J., 325, 16

Simon, M., Heinrich, W. and Mathis, K., (1986), Astrophys. J., 300, 32

Simon, M., Heinbach, U. and Koch, Ch., (1987), Astrophys. J., 320, 699

Stephens, S.A., (1981), Sp. Space, Sci., 76, 87

Stochaj, S.J. (1990), Thesis

Streitmatter, R.E. et al. (1990), Proc. of the 21st ICRC (Adelaide), 3, 277

Tan, L.C. and Ng, L.K. (1982), Phys. Rev. D, 26, 1179

Tan, L.C. and Ng, L.K. (1983 a), Nucl. Phys., 9, 1289

Tan, L.C. and Ng, L.K. (1983 b), J. Phys. G, Nucl. Phys. 9, 227

Acknowledgement

We thank the Deutsche Forschungsgemeinschaft DFG for supporting this work under grant number Si 290/3.

THE SOURCE COMPOSITION OF GALACTIC COSMIC RAYS AND THE CONDENSATION PROCESS OF THE ELEMENTS IN CIRCUMSTELLAR AND INTERSTELLAR GASES

Kunitomo SAKURAI
Institute of Physics, Kanagawa University
Rokkakubashi, Yokohama 221

ABSTRACT. Both refractory and siderophile elements are relatively overabundant in the chemical composition of the cosmic ray source matter as compared to that of the solar atmosphere. Since the condensation temperature for each of these elements is usually higher than 800K, the mechanism for the cosmic ray source matter to be formed seems to be causally connected to the condensation process of those elements in the circumstellar gases or in the matter ejected from supernova explosions. In fact, it has been known that those elements are efficiently condensed into chondritic matter which is found in the circumstellar gases.

1. INTRODUCTION

It is known that the observed data on high energy gamma ray emissions from the galactic space are necessarily useful to search for the places where galactic cosmic rays are possibly generated, since these gamma ray emissions seem to be directly connected with the acceleration mechanism of those cosmic rays (e.g., Shapiro, 1988: Oda, Nishimura and Sakurai, 1988). In order to find these places, it is, however, necessary to have the data on the source composition of galactic cosmic rays. Really speaking, these data may give us some crucial hint to look for the source regions of those cosmic rays.

According to the observed data currently available for the source composition of cosmic rays, the elements whose first ionization potentials are usually lower than 10 ev are relatively overabudant in the chemical composition of the comsic ray source matter as compared to that of the solar atmosphere (e.g., Simpson, 1983: Israel, 1985). However, it is noted that these elements relatively overabundant in the cosmic ray source matter are classified as either refractory or siderophile. This means that the

M. M. Shapiro et al. (eds.), Cosmic Rays, Supernovae and the Interstellar Medium, 153–162.
© 1991 *Kluwer Academic Publishers. Printed in the Netherlands.*

154

most of these overabundant elements are easily condensed
into chondritic dusts which seem to have been produced as a
result of the cooling of these elements down into a state
of temperature as low as 1000K (Sakurai, 1987, 1989).   It
is, therefore, necessary to investigate the mechanism how
those elements, both refractory and siderophile, have been
picked up into the cosmic ray source matter in its forming
process in the galactic space.   This mechanism thus becomes
important to our understanding of the origin of galactic
cosmic rays.

2.   THE COSMIC RAY SOURCE COMPOSITION AND ITS PROPERTIES

It has been known that, as shown in Fig. 1 (Israel, 1985),
the elements with the first ionization potentials lower
than 10 ev are relatively overabundant in the chemical composition of the cosmic ray source matter as compared to
that of the solar atmosphere.   Taking into account this
property of the source composition of galactic cosmic rays,

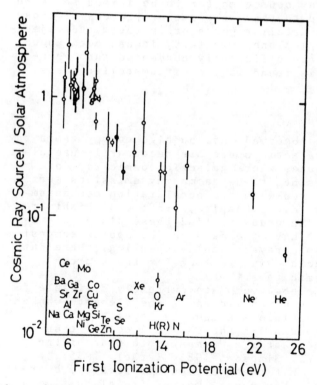

Figure 1. The
chemical composi-
tion of the cosmic
ray source matter
as compared to
that of the solar
atmosphere as a
function of the
first ionization
potentials of the
elements.

the ambient temperature of the cosmic ray source matter has
been inferred as 10^6K or less (Cassé and Goret, 1978).

Since various atoms in this matter are only partially ionized in such a state as in this temperature, those elements
with relatively lower potentials for the first ionization
can be more effectively accelerated than those whose poten-
tails are higher than 10 ev, for instance. In this case,

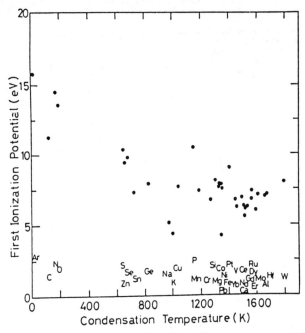

Figure 2. Relation between the first ionization potentials
and the condensation temperatures of the elements.

we have assumed that, with respect to the momentum gain,
galactic cosmic rays are mainly accelerated by means of the
Fermi acceleration mechanism (e.g., Sakurai, 1974).
    It is, however, remarked that, as clearly seen in Fig.
2, the first ionization potentials of the elements are well
correlated with the condensation temperatures of the elements. The condensation temperature for each element really
plays an important role for the elements to be condensed
into chondritic matter in the circumstellar gases surrounding the red giant stars. The temperature ambient in such
gases is usually very low as a few 1000K so that the elements with relatively lower potentials for the first ionization are efficiently condensed into chondritic dusts or
grains in those gases. This thus suggests that the most
elements with the condensation temperature higher than
about 1000K are more efficiently concentrated into the cosmic ray source matter in comparison with those with the
condensation temperature less than 1000K, say. By referring

to the properties of the elements as shown in Fig. 2, it
follows that, as shown in Fig. 3, the chemical composition
of the cosmic ray source matter is overabundant in the
elements with the temperature higher than 1000K for the
condensation as compared to those with the temperature
lower than 1000K (Sakurai, 1989, 1990a).

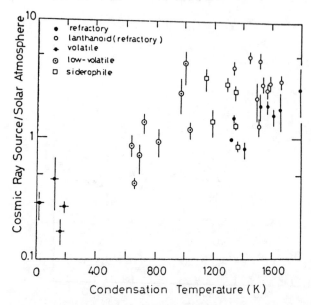

Figure 3.   The chemical composition of the cosmic ray
source matter as compared to that of the solar atmosphere
versus the condensation temperature of the elements.

    Since all the elements overabundant in the comsic ray
source matter are classified as either refractory or siderophile and, of course, defined as non-volatile, it is said
that the overabundances of these elements are well seen
on the chemical composition of the cosmic ray source matter
relative to that of the solar atmosphere.   This means that
non-volatile elements are efficiently concentrated into the
cosmic ray source matter.

3.   POSSIBLE RELATION TO THE CONDENSATION PROCESS OF MATTER IN CIRCUMSTELLAR AND INTERSTELLAR GASES

The relative overabundances of the refractory and siderophile elements in the cosmic ray source matter as compared
to those in the solar atmosphere suggest that the cosmic
ray source matter must have been formed in the regions
where the ambient temperature is low enough for these

elements to condense very effectively into this matter.
In order for such condensation to occur efficiently, the
temperature ambient in these regions must have been at 1000K
or less. If not so, these regions in which the condensation
has taken place in forming the cosmic ray source matter
should have passed, at least once, through such a state of
temperature as low as several 100K. Such regions can be,
therefore, identified as the circumstellar ones around the
red giant stars (Sakurai, 1990a) or dense dark gases in
giant molecular clouds (Wolfendale, 1990). Really speaking,
in such regions, non-volatile elements as refractory and
siderophile ones is efficiently condensed to form chondritic
dusts or grains there. Furthermore, the matter ejected
from supernova explosions may be also considered as candidates for the cosmic ray source matter, since they are
later quickly cooled down into a state of the temperature
as 1000K or less during their expansion in the space surrounding the supernovae.

It is thus concluded that, in the galactic space, the
effective condensation of both refractory and siderophile
elements in the regions, where the ambient temperature is
lower than 1000K or so, plays an important role to the
formation of the cosmic ray source matter. However, it is
noted (Ellison, 1990) that there exist some difficulties to
this idea, because it is necessary that these elements as
condensed into the cosmic ray source matter must be reheated
and then ionized before they are accelerated into cosmic ray
energy.

4. FORMATION OF THE COSMIC RAY SOURCE MATTER AS RELATED TO THE CONDESATION PROCESS IN THE GALACTIC SPACE

It seems that the chemical composition of the cosmic ray
source matter is similar to that of carbonaceous chondrites
as classified as C2 (or, CM), because this matter has
effectively lost volatile elements as carbon, nitrogen and
oxygen in comparison with the chemical composition of the
solar atmosphere. As is well known, carbonaceous chondrites
classified as C1 have the chemical composition almost the
same as that of the solar atmosphere (e.g., Wasson, 1985).
In order that the cosmic ray source matter is formed in the
galactic space, volatile elements should have been efficiently lost from the matter whose chemical composition
is almost equal to that of the solar atmosphere. Even if
so, volatile elements are still being kept quite well as
compared to carbonaceous chondrites classified as C3, the
best sample of which is now available from the debris of
the Allende meteorite. If we compare the chemical composition of the cosmic ray source matter with that of the
Allende meteorite, in particular, CAI component, it becomes

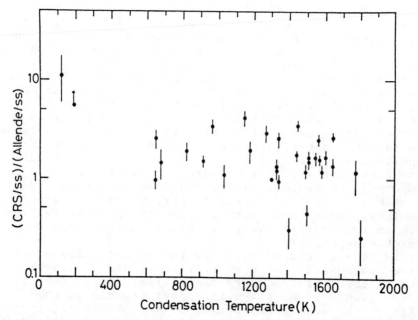

Figure 4. The chemical composition of the cosmic ray source matter as compared to that of the Allende meteorite as a function of the condensation temperature of the elements.

clear, as shown in Fig. 4, that volatile elements are still retained more effectively by a factor five to ten in the former than in the latter.

The observed data on the interstellar depletion of various elements (e.g., Bohlin et al., 1983) also support the results that, as clearly seen in Fig. 5, the cosmic ray source matter has lost effectively volatile elements as compared to both refractory and siderophile elements. In this figure, volatile elements as carbon, nitrogen and oxygen are not much depleted from the circumstellar matter, because the interstellar depletions for various elements mainly occur in the space near the stars under study (Sakurai, 1989). In fact, the most of the circumstellar matter is responsible for these depletions.

At the present moment, the isotopic abundances of medium nuclei in the cosmic ray source matter are also considered in the study on the origin of galactic cosmic rays. It has been suggested that the isotopic abundances of both carbon and nitrogen may give a clue to identify the regions in the galactic space where the cosmic ray source matter is formed. However, there is no usable observed data on the isotopic ratios of the element nitrogen (e.g., Simpson, 1983: Mewaldt, 1989). If we could have the isotopic abundances of both carbon and nitrogen, it becomes possible

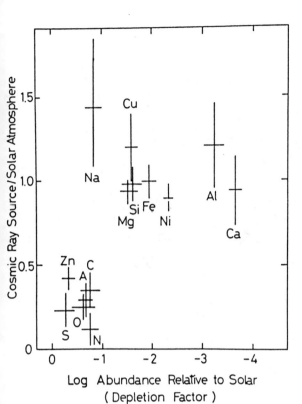

Figure 5. Relation between the interstellar depletions of the elements and the chemical composition of the cosmic ray source matter as compared to that of the solar atmosphere.

to infer what kind of matter is the most important for the formation of the cosmic ray source matter, since these two abundances are highly dependent on the thermonuclear processes which seem to have taken place during the last phases of the stellar evolution. Though the data on the isotopic ratios of nitrogen are lack at present, the isotopic ratios of carbon, $^{12}C/^{13}C$ in number, are shown in Fig. 6 with respect to various samples available now (e.g., Breneman and Stone, 1985: Amari et al., 1990). Though tentative, this figure indicates that the isotopic ratio for the cosmic ray source matter as denoted by GCRS (Mewaldt, 1989) is well coincident with that for the interstellar matter and the circumstellar matter as defined by STAR (ISM) (Hawkins, 1988).

5. CONCLUDING REMARKS

It has been shown that the source composition of galactic cosmic rays cannot be interpreted without referring to the efficient condensation of non-volatile elements, both refractory and siderophile, into chondritic matter being formed in the circumstellar gases or in gases ejected from

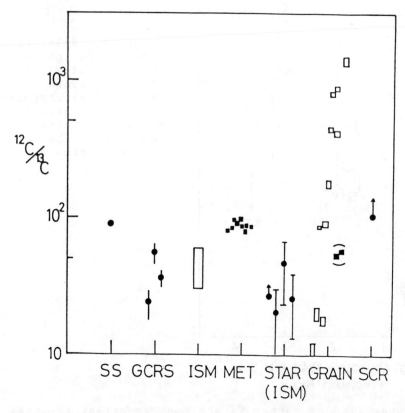

Figure 6. The isotopic ratios of the element carbon for various samples as the solar system (SS), the cosmic ray source matter (GCRS), the interstellar matter (ISM), meteorites (MET), the circumstellar matter (STAR), the interstellar grains (GRAIN) and solar cosmic rays (SCR) (Sakurai, 1990b).

Supernova explosions. In order that this condensation occurs effectively in these regions, they must have passed through such a state as 1000K or less in tempreature in the circumstellar gases or in the gases expanding from the sites of supernova explosions. As shown in this paper, the source composition of galactic cosmic rays cannot be produced by means of such a simple mechanism as the simultaneous origin of both cosmic ray acceleration and supernova explosions.

It is noted that, at the present moment, we need to have the isotopic composition of nitrogen to be able to find what process is the most important in the formation of the cosmic ray source matter among the various processes as the explosive hydrogen burning, the CNO cycles, the helium burning and a mixing process of both the helium burning and the explosive hydrogen burning in the final stage of the stellar evolution, in particular, supernova explosions and associated ejection of the outer envelopes of supernovae.

REFERENCES

Amari, S., Anders, E., Virag, A. and Zinner, E. (1990) Nature 345, 238.

Bohlin, R.C., Hill, J.L., Jenkins, E.B., Savage, B.D., Snow, T.P., Spitzer, L. and York, D.G. (1983) Astrophys. J. Suppl. 51, 277.

Breneman, H.H. and Stone, E.C. (1985) Astrophys. J. 299, L57.

Cassé, M. and Goret, R. (1978) Astrophys. J. 221, 703.

Ellison, D.C. (1990) Proc. 21st Internatl. Cosmic Ray Conf. (Rapporteur Paper), Adelaide 11, 133.

Hawkins, I. (1988) in Origin and Distributions of the Elements (ed., G.J. Mattews), p. 239, World Scientific, Singapore.

Israel, M. (1985) in Proc. 12th Texas Symp. Relativistic Astrophysics, Annals of New York Acad. Sci. 470, 188.

Mewaldt, R.A. (1989) in Cosmic Abundances of Matter, AIP Conf. Proc. 183, p. 124, Amer. Inst. Phys., New York.

Oda, M., Nishimura, J. and Sakurai, K. (eds.) (1988) Cosmic Ray Astrophysics, Terra Scientific Pub., Tokyo.

Sakurai, K. (1974) Astrophys. Space Sci. 28, 375.

Sakurai, K. (1987) Proc. 20th Internatl. Cosmic Ray Conf., Moscow OG-1, 243.

Sakurai, K. (1989) Adv. Space Res. 9, 149.

Sakurai, K. (1990a) Proc. 21st Internatl. Cosmic Ray Conf., Adelaide OG-4, 34.

Sakurai, K. (1990b) Proc. 22nd ISAS Symp. Lunar Planet. Sci., ISAS (in press).

Shapiro, M.M. (ed.) (1988) Genesis and Propagation of Cosmic Rays, Kluwers, Dordrecht.

Simpson, J.A. (1983) Ann. Rev. Particle Nuclear Sci. 33,

323.

Wasson, J.L. (1985)   Meteortites: Their Record of Early Solar System History, W.H. Freeman, New York.

Wolfendale, A.W. (1990)   in These Proceesings.

THE DISTRIBUTION OF SUPERNOVA REMNANTS IN THE GALAXY

D.A.GREEN
Dominion Radio Astrophysical Observatory
Herzberg Institute of Astrophysics
National Research Council
P.O. Box 248, Penticton,
British Columbia, V2A 6K3, Canada

ABSTRACT. Difficulties in deriving the distribution of SNRs in the Galaxy from their observed distribution on the sky are discussed. These include the selection effects that apply to the identification of SNRs, and the uncertainties in the distances of most SNRs. Although it is clear that the distribution of high surface-brightness remnants is concentrated in a nuclear disk, it is not possible to derive the distribution for SNRs within the solar circle in any detail.

1. Introduction

Supernova remnants (SNRs) are an important element in studies of the energetics and dynamics of the interstellar medium, and studies of their distribution are of considerable interest, not least as they are the probable source of many cosmic rays. Such studies are, however, not straightforward. There are significant selection effects that apply to current catalogues of Galactic SNRs, and, as SNRs show a considerable range of intrinsic properties, their "average" properties derived from statistical studies may be inappropriate. In particular this means that there are no reliable distance estimates available for most identified SNRs.

2. The Selection Effects

The identification of SNRs is generally made from radio surveys, and is basically limited by two selection effects. First, the surface-brightness of the remnant must be above the sensitivity limit of the observations and be readily distinguishable from the Galactic background emission. Second, in general, the angular size of the SNR must be at least several times the resolution of the observations for it to be recognised as such.

2.1 SURFACE-BRIGHTNESS (Σ) LIMITS

It is not possible to quote a single surface-brightness completeness limit for current cata-logues of SNRs, not only because the background emission varies in different regions of the Galactic plane, but also because different regions have been surveyed with different instru-ments. However, most SNRs so far recognised at southern declinations ($\delta \lesssim -20°$) have been identified from the Molonglo 408-MHz survey of the Galactic plane ($195° \leq l \leq 55°$) with follow-up Parkes 64-m observations at 5 GHz. Clark and Caswell (1976) in their statis-tical study of SNRs following the Molonglo–Parkes survey conclude that their lists of SNRs

163

M. M. Shapiro et al. (eds.), Cosmic Rays, Supernovae and the Interstellar Medium, 163–166.
© 1991 *Kluwer Academic Publishers. Printed in the Netherlands.*

are complete over most of the survey region to a surface-brightness which corresponds to $\Sigma_{1\,\mathrm{GHz}} \approx 8 \times 10^{-21} \mathrm{W\,m^{-2}Hz^{-1}sr^{-1}}$. This limit is, however, probably optimistic for regions near $l = 0°$. At more northerly declinations ($\delta \gtrsim -20°$) SNRs have been identified from a variety of surveys and observations. Most high declination remnants are included in, or were first identified from the recent survey at 2.7 GHz with the Effelsberg 100-m antenna ($358° \leq l \leq 240°$; Reich et al. 1990; Fürst et al. 1990). Reich & Fürst (1988) discuss the new remnants identified from the Effelsberg survey, and give a detection limit close to $\Sigma_{1\,\mathrm{GHz}} \approx 2 \times 10^{-22} \mathrm{W\,m^{-2}Hz^{-1}sr^{-1}}$, although this applies only to regions where the background emission is weak ($|b| \gtrsim 0°.5$).

2.2 ANGULAR SIZE (θ) LIMITS

Incompleteness with respect to faint remnants has long been recognised, but the incompleteness of catalogues of Galactic SNRs with respect to small angular size remnants has not been so well appreciated (see Green 1988 for further details). A lower limit of ≈ 8 arcmin to the angular size of remnants identified from the Molonglo–Parkes survey is suggested, as the resolution of the Molonglo 408-MHz survey is 3 arcmin. This in turn implies that, from the Molonglo–Parkes survey, any remnants with diameters up to at least 23 pc over 10 kpc away (i.e., at least half the Galaxy) could not have been identified. A somewhat larger limit on diameters is applicable to remnants identifiable directly from the Effelsberg 2.7-GHz survey, which has a resolution of 4.6 arcmin.

3. Distances for SNRs

The fact that there are no high surface-brightness SNRs with large diameters has often been expressed in terms of a "$\Sigma - D$" relation (usually of the form $\Sigma \propto D^{-n}$, relating surface-brightness, Σ, to linear diameter, D). If such a relation can be calibrated with remnants at known distances, then diameters and hence distances can be derived for any SNR from its observed surface-brightness. For some time it appeared that the properties of SNRs at known distances were well correlated in the $\Sigma - D$ plane (e.g., Clark & Caswell 1976; Milne 1979), thus allowing useful diameter estimates to be made for other SNRs. However, other studies (Green 1984; Berkhuijsen 1986) show that the correlation in the $\Sigma - D$ plane is poor (SNRs of similar surface-brightness have approximately an order of magnitude range in diameters), and the full extent of the range of properties of Galactic SNRs in the $\Sigma - D$ plane is not currently known, as the identification of faint and/or small remnants is difficult because of current selection effects. Consequently only an upper limit to the diameter, and hence to the distance, of an SNR can be deduced with any confidence from a given surface-brightness (see Green 1984 and Berkhuijsen 1986 for further discussion).

4. Discussion and Conclusions

A major problem with statistical studies of the distribution of SNRs in the Galaxy is that the Σ-selection effect is not independent of Galactic coordinates, and it is difficult to disentangle this bias from any intrinsic variation in the properties of SNRs with Galactic coordinates. SNRs in the 2nd and 3rd quadrants (i.e., $90° < l < 270°$), which are easier to identify because the Galactic background emission is faint, are all outside the Solar circle, at large Galactocentric radii. Of course the problems caused by the Σ-selection effect on statistical studies can be reduced if such studies are restricted to relatively bright remnants, for which current catalogues are thought to be complete (although small high surface-brightness remnants will still be missed, and more easily so at larger distances). Restricting studies to remnants with $\Sigma_{1\ GHz} \gtrsim 8 \times 10^{-21}\mathrm{W\ m^{-2}Hz^{-1}sr^{-1}}$ (*i.e.*, the nominal Molonglo–Parkes surface-brightness completeness limit) reduces the number of identified SNRs (from an updated version of the catalogue published in Green 1988) from a total of 174 to only 70, so that small number statistics in different regions of the Galactic plane are a relatively more important problem.

van den Bergh (1988a, b) discussed the distribution of observed SNRs and noted that the high surface-brightness remnants ($\Sigma_{1\ GHz} \gtrsim 3 \times 10^{-21}\mathrm{W\ m^{-2}Hz^{-1}sr^{-1}}$) are concentrated toward $b = 0°$ in the region $300° \lesssim l \lesssim 60°$. van den Bergh's main conclusion, that the observed distribution of SNRs outlines a thin nuclear disk, is strengthened by the Σ-selection effect (as noted by Fürst's comments to van den Bergh 1988b), as remnants as faint as $\Sigma_{1\ GHz} \approx 3 \times 10^{-21}\mathrm{W\ m^{-2}Hz^{-1}sr^{-1}}$ are easier to detect away (in both l and b) from the observed concentration of remnants which represent the nuclear disk. Moreover, van den Bergh only considered remnants with $S_{1\ GHz} > 12$ Jy. This flux density limit was an attempt to define a complete sample, although as discussed above the observational selection effects that apply to the identification of SNRs are best considered in terms of surface-brightness and angular-diameter selection-effects. Figure 1 shows the distribution in Galactic coordinates of all identified SNRs, and that for remnants with $\Sigma_{1\ GHz}$ above the nominal Molonglo–Parkes surface-brightness completeness limit. The concentration of brighter remnants in a nuclear disk shown in Figure 1b is more striking than van den Bergh's result for a flux density limited sample. This is because of van den Bergh's somewhat optimistic Σ-limit, and his restriction on the flux density of observed SNRs. This flux density limit selects against small, distant, high surface-brightness remnants (more of which are expected in the 1st and 4th quadrants than in the 2nd and 3rd quadrants), and it includes large, close, low surface-brightness remnants (which are more easily identified in the 2nd and 3rd quadrants than elsewhere). However, another of van den Bergh's conclusions, that the near uniform distribution of remnants in the region $300° \lesssim l \lesssim 60°$ suggests a annular distribution rather than a disk, is weakened when observational selection effects are taken into account. The Σ-selection effect makes it more difficult to detect SNRs near $l = 0°$ than elsewhere, because the background Galactic radio emission is higher, and the Molonglo–Parkes limit may be optimistic near $l = 0°$. So, if the true distribution of SNRs were a disk rather than an annulus, the excess of remnants near $l = 0°$ would not be easy to detect.

Leahy & Wu (1989) also discuss the distribution, of SNRs in the Galaxy. They used two sets of SNRs, including one restricted to brighter remnants (with $\Sigma_{1\ GHz} \gtrsim 7 \times 10^{-21}\mathrm{W\ m^{-2}Hz^{-1}sr^{-1}}$) which reduces problems with the Σ-selection effect (although small diameter remnants are still likely to be missed because of the θ-selection effect). However, Leahy & Wu's derivation of the true distribution of Galactic SNRs from the observed distribution depends on a $\Sigma - D$ relation to derive distances from each remnant. As discussed above, a $\Sigma - D$ relation does not provide reliable distance estimates for SNRs. Also Leahy & Wu attempt to correct for observational selection effects that apply to their samples by calculating incompleteness correction factors for different regions of the Galactic disk. These correction factors are "bootstrapped" from annuli close to the Sun out to large distances, and systematic biases are likely to be introduced by this procedure. Moreover, one of the assumptions in Leahy & Wu's incompleteness correcting procedure, that the correction factor near $l = 0°$ for a given range of distances from the Sun is the same as for regions at the same distance from the Sun but away from $l = 0°$, is incorrect. Even for the higher surface-brightness sample, remnants near $l = 0°$ are more difficult to identify that similar remnants away from $l = 0°$.

The observed concentration of bright SNRs in a nuclear disk implies a higher density of remnants inside the Solar circle than outside, but the uncertainties in the distances to

166

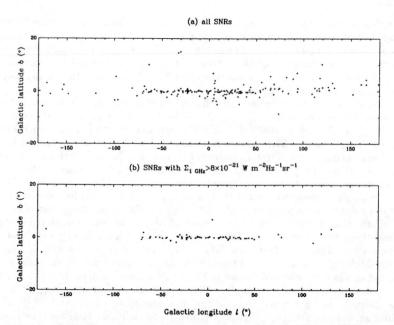

Figure 1. Plot of distribution in Galactic coordinates of: (a) all identified SNRs; (b) SNRs with $\Sigma_1\ _{GHz} > 8 \times 10^{-21}\,\mathrm{W\,m^{-2}\,Hz^{-1}\,sr^{-1}}$. (Note that the latitude scale is exaggerated compared to the longitude scale.)

most remnants makes it impossible to derive the form of the distribution in any detail. Although future improved observations may allow larger samples of SNRs to be studied, with lower Σ-limits and θ-limits, the uncertainty in the distances to SNRs will remain a major problem for deriving the actual distribution of SNRs in our own Galaxy.

Finally, it should be remembered that it is far from clear that the observed SNR distribution actually represents their parent supernovae distribution. This is because the factors that affect the brightness and lifetime of appreciable radio emission from SNRs are not well understood.

References

Berkhuijsen, E.M. (1986). *Astr. Astrophys.*, **166**, 257.
Clark, D.H. & Caswell, J.L. (1976). *Mon. Not. R. astr. Soc.*, **174**, 274.
Fürst, E., Reich, W., Reich, P. & Reif, K. (1990). *Astr. Astrophys. Suppl.*, in press.
Green, D.A. (1984). *Mon. Not. R. astr. Soc.*, **209**, 499.
Green, D.A. (1988). *Astrophys. Space Sci.*, **148**, 3.
Leahy, D.A. & Wu, X. (1989). *Publ. Astr. Soc. Pacific*, **101**, 607.
Milne, D.K. (1979). *Aust. J. Phys.*, **32**, 83.
Reich, W. & Fürst, E. (1988). In: *Supernova Shells and Their Birth Events*, p.48, ed. Kundt, W., (Springer-Verlag, Berlin).
Reich, W., Fürst, E., Reich, P. & Reif, K. (1990). *Astr. Astrophys. Suppl.*, in press.
van den Bergh, S. (1988a). *Publ. Astr. Soc. Pacific*, **100**, 205.
van den Bergh, S. (1988b). In: *Supernova Shells and Their Birth Events*, p.44, ed. Kundt, W., (Springer-Verlag, Berlin).

GAMMA RAYS FROM SUPERNOVA 1987A

R. S. WHITE
Department of Physics and
Institute of Geophysics and Planetary Physics
University of California
Riverside, California 92521
U.S.A.

ABSTRACT. A review is given of the observation of gamma rays from the decay of ^{56}Co in the debris of the supernova SN1987A, from August, 1987 to May, 1989. The properties of the ^{56}Co lines and their variations with time are discussed. Measurements from Ge, NaI(Tl), and double Compton scatter detectors are described and their results given. Theoretical models fitted to the light curve of SN1987A support the standard model for a Type II supernova burst from a blue supergiant of mass 20 $M_\odot$, radius of 3 x 10^7 km and mass of manufactured ^{56}Co of 0.1 $M_\odot$. Since June 1987 the light curve has decayed with the mean lifetime of ^{56}Co of 114 d.

1. Introduction

The supernova, SN1987A, was discovered on February 24, 1981 in the Large Magellonic Cloud from plates exposed at Las Campanas Observatory by Ian Shelton, University of Toronto, a few hours after the explosion. Its progenitor was the 12th magnitude 83I blue giant Sanduleak -69 202 (Kirshner et al., 1987) with luminosity 10^5 L$_\odot$. The time of the explosion was fixed at 7:35:35$\pm$1 min UT, February 23, 1987 by bursts of neutrinos observed by the Kamiokande II underground proton decay detector of Hirata et al. (1987) and at 7:35:41.37$\pm$.05 s UT by the Irvine, Michigan, Brookhaven detector of Bionta et al. (1987). Kamiokande II detected 11 neutrinos from 7-36 MeV in 13 s and IMB, 6 neutrinos from 20-40 MeV in 6 s. As expected no gamma rays were observed at that time.

Soft x-rays of 10 to 30 keV were first observed in June, 1987 by Dotani et al. (1987) with the 4,000 cm^2 proportional detector on the Ginga satellite. The flux rose rapidly then leveled off in September at 5 x 10^{-11} erg cm^{-2}s^{-1}. The March-April time period gave upper limits only. They found an unusually hard energy distribution. Hard x-rays of 20 to 300 keV were first observed on 10 August, 1987 by the high energy x-ray experiment on the Mir-Kvant satellite observatory (Sunyaev et al., 1987) that showed little variation to September 15, 1987. The energy distribution was quite hard with a power law index of -1.4. The luminosity was about 2 x 10^{38} erg from 20-300 MeV.

M. M. Shapiro et al. (eds.), Cosmic Rays, Supernovae and the Interstellar Medium, 167–176.

2. Type II Supernova Model

In the classical model of stellar evolution, gas and matter condense into a star under the force of gravity. The star approaches the main sequence of the Hertzsprung-Russel diagram along the Hayashi line. The higher mass stars enter the main sequence at the higher temperatures. They take less time to reach the main sequence where they stay a shorter time burning faster than the lower mass stars. While burning nuclear hydrogen to make helium the interior becomes hotter and the star eventually leaves the main sequence. It then burns helium to make carbon, the interior rises still higher in temperature and the exterior expands and cools as the star becomes a red giant. The star burns successively higher and higher mass nuclei and the interior becomes hotter and hotter until the nuclear fuel is consumed. During this time the star moves back and forth across the Hertzsprung-Russel diagram. This fusion releases net energy only for atomic nuclei below iron. When fusion stops the internal pressure abruptly decreases. Since the star can no longer withstand the gravitational compression, the star collapses to a neutron star or a black hole where it comes to a stop. At the high MeV temperatures the neutrinos produced in the nuclear reactions send out a shock wave that blasts the outer layers of radioactive material into space. Most of the high atomic number nuclei present in the universe have been produced by successive neutron captures and beta decays during the first few seconds of supernova explosions.

Several authors have modeled supernova explosions including Weaver and Woosley (1980), Woosley et al. (1987), and Pinto and Woosley (1988). Predictions of gamma ray line fluxes may be found in these and the papers of Gehrels et al. (1987) and Chan and Lingenfelter (1987). The 10 $M_\odot$ hydrogen envelope model of Pinto and Woosley starts with a 20 $M_\odot$ star originally on the main sequence. About 4 $M_\odot$ is lost during evolution. The helium core mass inside the hydrogen is 6 $M_\odot$. The star produces 0.075 $M_\odot$ of ^{56}Co. A sketch of the central core and debris is shown in Figure 1 shortly after the explosion. The layer of ^{56}Co is interior to the rest of the ejecta and is traveling at a lower velocity. The ^{56}Co decays with a half-life of 79 d to excited states of ^{56}Fe. As the layers expand, the ejecta eventually becomes thin enough for the decay gamma rays from the excited levels of ^{56}Fe to escape.

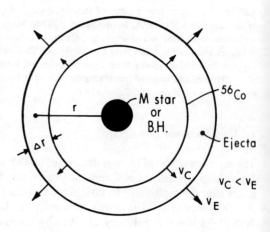

Figure 1. Sketch of ejecta a few months after the explosion of SN 1897A. The ejecta shell is at radius r, with thickness Δr. The velocity of the outer edge, v_E, is greater than that of the inner edge v_C.

The ^{56}Co is formed from the electron capture of ^{56}Ni with a half life of 6.1 d as shown in Figure 2. The decay of ^{56}Co to ^{56}Fe releases 3.27 MeV/reaction in gamma rays. From the energy levels of ^{56}Fe and their decays it can be seen that all but 3 weak lines pass through the 0.847 MeV level. Consequently the line from the 0.847 MeV level to the ground level is the most intense. Some of the stronger lines are listed in Table 1. If the 0.847 MeV line is taken as intensity 1.00, the 1.238, 1.771, 2.035, 2.599 and 3.253 MeV lines follow with intensities of 0.69, 0.16, 0.08, 0.17 and 0.07, respectively. These lines and their widths can be measured with Ge detectors that have energy resolutions as good as 1 keV. However, NaI and Compton scatter detectors with energy resolutions $\Delta E/E$ of 6% to 8% are not able to resolve the single lines, but instead resolve the groups of lines listed in Table 2.

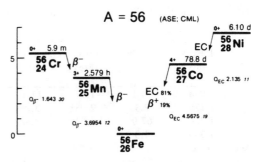

Figure 2. Decay of nuclei of mass number 56. The decay releases 3.57 MeV/reaction in γ-rays [Lederer et al., 1978].

TABLE 1. List of relative intensities of gamma ray lines from decay of ^{56}Co.

Energy (keV)	Relative Intensity	Energy (keV)	Relative Intensity
263.41	0.022	1640.54	0.060
411.38	0.025	**1771.351**	15.700
486.54	0.055	1810.4	0.640
733.72	0.200	1963.99	0.720
787.88	0.310	**2015.181**	3.080
846.772	100.000	2034.755	7.890
896.56	0.070	2113.85	0.385
977.485	1.440	2213.16	0.350
997.33	0.112	2276.36	0.110
1037.840	14.000	2373.71	0.080
1089.03	0.050	2523.86	0.060
1140.28	0.150	**2598.458**	16.900
1160.08	0.100	3009.591	1.000
1175.102	2.280	3201.962	3.040
1198.78	0.050	3253.416	7.410
1238.282	67.600	**3272.990**	1.750
1272.2	0.020	3369.69	0.011
1335.56	0.125	**3451.152**	0.875
1360.25	4.330	3547.925	0.180
1442.75	0.200	3600.69	0.016
1462.34	0.077	3611.69	0.007

Table 2.   Gamma-ray line energies and intensities from ^{56}Co decay relative to the 0.847 line.

	Group [a]1		Group 2		Group 3		Group 4	
	Energy (MeV)	Intensity (%)	Energy (MeV)	Intensity (%)	Energy (MeV)	Intensity (%)	Energy (MeV)	Intensity (%)
	1.038	14.1	1.771	15.5	2.566	16.7	3.010	1.0
	1.175	2.3	2.051	3.0			3.202	3.0
	1.238	67.0	2.035	7.8			3.254	7.4
	1.360	4.3					3.273	1.7
Ave	1.21		1.88		2.57		3.23	
Total		87.5		26.3		16.7		13.1

[a] The lines are grouped for NaI and Compton scatter detectors with resolutions of 6 to 8% FWHM.

The gamma rays cannot be detected until they escape from the ejected material. Initially the ejecta is very dense, many optical depths thick, so the gamma rays are absorbed. After a few months the ejecta thins out, its density is reduced and gamma rays no longer Compton scatter or are absorbed before reaching the detector. The optical depth is defined as $\tau = \Delta r/\delta$ where Δr is the ejecta shell thickness and δ the total gamma ray interaction length that includes Compton scattering, pair production and absorption. The density of the ejecta is

$$\rho = \frac{M}{4\pi r^2 dr}$$

where M is the mass of the ejecta and r the radius of the shell. The explosion kinetic energy is

$$E = \frac{1}{2}Mv^2 = \frac{1}{2}M\left(\frac{r}{t}\right)^2$$

where v is the mean velocity of the ejecta and t is the time since the explosion. From these relations we find

$$\tau = \frac{m^2}{8\pi E t^2 (\rho\delta)}$$

where $(\rho\delta)$ is the interaction length in g/cm^2. Taking the ejecta mass as 15 M$_\odot$, 3.0×10^{34} g, E as 1.31×10^{51} erg and t as 417 d, the optical depth becomes

$$\tau = \frac{21}{(\rho\delta)(g/cm^2)}$$

The $(\rho\delta)$ for a gamma ray of 0.847 MeV in 10 M$_\odot$ of hydrogen and 5 M$_\odot$ of helium and higher Z material is about 10 g/cm^2. The optical depth under these conditions is $\tau = 2.1$ and the fraction of gamma rays remaining after escape is 0.122. The probability of escape as a function of time with the ejecta mass as a parameter is given in Figure 3 (Gehrels et al., 1987). Their value for 15 M$_\odot$ ejecta uses M$_{56}$ = 0.1 M$_\odot$ so their corresponding $\tau = 33/\delta\rho$. From

Figure 3 their equivalent $\rho\delta = 6.4$ g/cm^2 gives $\tau = 5.12$ and $e^{-\tau} = 6 \times 10^{-3}$. Our simple model here overestimates $(\rho\delta)$ by a factor of 1.56 and $e^{-\tau}$ by a factor of 3.

The flux of 0.847 MeV gamma rays at the detector, a distance R from the supernova, is

$$F_{0.847} = \frac{M_{56}}{m_{56}} \frac{1}{4\pi R^2} \frac{\lambda\lambda'}{\lambda-\lambda'} (e^{-\lambda't} - e^{-\lambda t}) e^{-\tau}$$

where M_{56} is the mass of ^{56}Ni in the ejecta, m_{56} is the mass of the nucleus of ^{56}Ni, $M_{56}/m_{56} = 1.73 \times 10^{54}$ nuclei of ^{56}Ni, $\lambda = 1.31 \times 10^{-6}$/s and $\lambda' = 1.02 \times 10^{-7}$/s are the decay constants for ^{56}Ni and ^{56}Co, respectively. The number of 0.847 MeV gamma rays/s emitted by the source is

$$N = \frac{\lambda\lambda'}{\lambda-\lambda'} (e^{-\lambda't} - e^{-\lambda t})$$

Taking $M_{56} = 0.08$ M$_\odot$, R $= 1.50 \times 10^3$ly, and t $= 417$ d we get

$$F_{0.847} = 6.44 \times 10^{-3} gammas/cm^2 - s$$

Using more sophisticated models, Gehrels et al. (1987) and Chan and Lingenfelter (1987), Figure 4, obtain fluxes of about 10^{-4} gamma/cm^2-s compared to experimental values of about 10^{-3} gammas/cm^2-s. Similar calculations for the other lines gave a comparable flux for the 1.238 MeV line and lesser fluxes for the 2.599, 1.771 and 1.038 MeV lines.

3. Gamma Ray Observations

The gamma ray spectrometer, GRS, on the SMM satellite pointed continuously toward the sun but was able to see SN1987A at large angles to the axis of the aperture through the CsI shield. On each orbit around the earth, source or background was measured when the GRS was unoccluted or occulted by the earth. Gamma rays from SN1987A were first observed by GRS from August 1 to October 31, 1987 (Matz et al., 1988). The 0.847 MeV line from the first excited state of ^{56}Fe was seen along with some evidence for the second excited state of 1.238 MeV. Later the 2.599 and 3.250 MeV lines were also

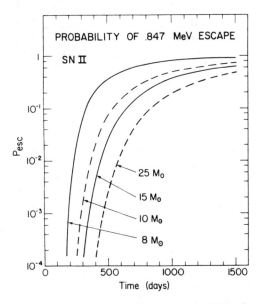

Figure 3. The calculated escape probabilities for 0.847 MeV γ-rays generated in the ^{56}Co shell by four different SN II models. The 15 M$_\odot$ model parameters are approximations to those given by Weaver and Woosley (1980). The parameters for the 10 and 25 M$_\odot$ cases were scaled from those of the 15 M$_\odot$ model. The 8 M$_\odot$ model parameters are for a typical "plateau" SN II discussed by Litvinova and Nadyozhin (1983) [Gehrels et al., 1987].

172

measured. These 4 lines were monitored continuously until disappearing into the background late in 1988 (Leising and Share, 1990). See Figure 5.

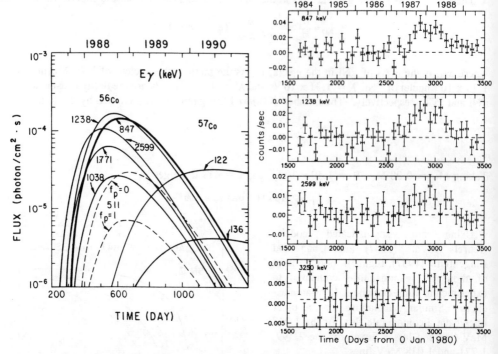

Figure 4. Time dependent intensities of the principal gamma-ray lines from the decay of ^{56}Co and ^{57}Co calculated for the 15 M$_\odot$ supernova model of Weaver and Woosley (1980). The flux of the positron annihilation line at 511 keV is shown for the two limiting cases of the fraction of positron annihilaton via positronium f_p, equal to 0 and 1 [Chan and Lingenfelter, 1987].

Figure 5. The measured count rates of four ^{56}Co lines. The dashed lines are the weighted means of the points before day 2611 (1987 February 23, the time of the core collapse and explosion). The mean counts in each line before SN 1987A are consistent with zero. The error bars shown are 1σ statistical uncertainties [Leising and Share, 1990].

Shortly after the SN1987A explosion of February 24, 1987, NASA initiated expeditions to Alice Springs, Australia for the Fall of 1987 and the Springs of 1988 and 1989 and to Antartica in 1988 for balloon flights of detectors to observe the gamma rays from the supernova. One was the CIT coded aperture detector sensitive to low evergy gamma rays of 0.040 to 1.30 MeV (Cook, et al., 1988). The position sensitive NaI scintillator 5 cm thick by 41 cm dia. detected gamma rays through a rotating hexagonal-celled uniformly redundant array of equal numbers of lead and open cells. The separation between the scintillator and the array was 2.5 m. With this detector it was possible to image the sky in the vicinity of SN1987A and obtain the low energy gamma ray spectrum. The 14° field of view around SN1987A in Figure 6 shows the center of the maximum of the gamma ray signal within 1° of the optical direction of the supernova. No other source of significance is in the field of view.

Sandie et al. (1987), using Ge detectors carried on a balloon launched from Alice Springs, Australia with observations October 29-31, 1987, reported the 0.847 MeV line flux of 5 x 10^{-4} photons/cm²-s. A 3σ upper limit of 4 x 10^{-4} gammas/cm²-s was obtained for the 1.238 MeV line. Continuum values of 6.4 ± 0.5 and 2.9 ± 0.2 x 10^{-5} gamma/cm²-s-keV (statistical errors only) were measured at energies of 50-100 and 100-200 keV. The energy distribution of the gamma rays (Cook et al., 1988), given by the diamonds in Figure 7, shows a continuum with the two gamma ray lines at 0.85 and 1.24 MeV. The solid line is a comparison with the Monte Carlo computer calculations for day 250 (Pinto and Woosley, 1988). This data combined with the Mir satellite results in late 1987 and early 1988 give a continuum index of -1.2 as shown in Figure 8.

The best measurements of the positions and widths of the gamma ray lines were made by the GRIS germanium detector of GSFC-Bell Labs-Sandia (Tueller et al., 1990). The GRIS detector is a pointed array of 7 large high-purity n-type cryogenically cooled coaxial germanium detectors. The active volume of Ge is > 1500 cm³. It is surrounded by a 396 kg active anticoincidence NaI scintillator that collimated the field of view to 19° FWHM at 847 keV. Balloon flights were carried out from Alice Springs, Australia on days 433 and 613 after the SN1987A explosion. On the first flight, the 847 and 1238 keV lines were observed at 2.3 and 4.3 σ significances and on the second, the 847, 1238 and 2599 keV lines with 4.6, 3.4 and

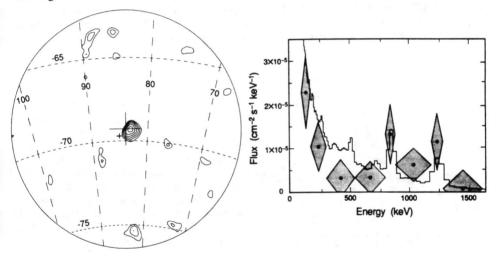

Figure 6. Image of the SN 1987A region from 40 to 1300 keV covering a 14° field of view. Right ascension (vertical lines) and declination (horizontal lines) are indicated. The contours indicate the number of excess counts in a given direction calibrated in units of the statistical significance of the excess, with contours beginning at the 2σ level and spaced by 0.5σ intervals. The large cross indicates the expected position of SN 1987A. The small cross indicates the expected position of LMC X-1 [Cook et al., 1988].

Figure 7. Flux measurements compared with the results of Monte Carlo calculations of the expected fluxes on day 250 after the supernova explosion (Pinto and Woosley, 1988). The measurements are indicated by diamonds with the widths indicating the energy intervals of the measurements. The Monte Carlo histogram has been convolved with a Gaussian representation of the instrumental energy resolution [Cook et al., 1988].

1.9 σ significances. The 847 keV line profile is shown in Figure 9. The solid line is the best fit to the data. The dashed line is the predicted line profile for the 10HMM model. The peak energies of all lines are lower in energy and the widths greater than predicted. The displacement suggests emission from Doppler shifted gamma rays and the width indicates mixing. The red shift of the lines indicates that the gamma rays must be coming from receding matter. Perhaps the matter is in dense knots or filaments optically thick with spaces between, through which the back side of the receding ^{56}Ni mass can be seen. Or the matter might be in a flattened disk over which the detector sees the receding material. Because the ^{56}Co reaches low optical depths at times earlier than expected, there must be mixing, jets or fragmentation of ^{56}Co in the ejecta.

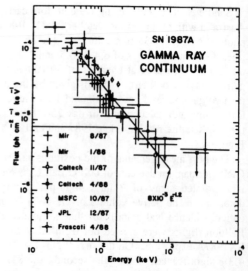

Figure 8. All continuum measurements. A representative spectral shape is given by the line [Gehrels et al., 1988].

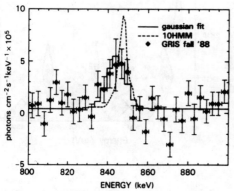

Figure 9. GRIS data for the 847 keV line from the decay of ^{56}Co in SN 1987A debris is shown for day 613. The top of atmosphere photon spectrum is shown in 3 keV bins which are larger than the FWHM resolution of the instrument. The solid line is a best fit to a Gaussian line profile. The dashed line is the predicted line profile for the 10 HMM model. Although this model and similar spherically symmetric mixed models predict the line flux correctly, there is a clear discrepancy with the measured line profile [Tueller et al., 1990].

The time dependences of the fluxes of 847 keV and 1238 keV gamma rays from SN1987A are shown in Figure 10. The solid and dotted lines are the 10HMM and 5L models of Pinto and Woosley (1988). The 10HMM model starts with a star of 20 $M_\odot$ on the main sequence that loses 4 $M_\odot$ during evolution. The He core mass of 6 $M_\odot$ is inside a hydrogen core mass of 10 $M_\odot$. The ^{56}Ni mass ejected is 0.075 $M_\odot$. There must be mixing. The straight dot-dash line is the exponential decay of ^{56}Co with a half-life of 79 d. It can be seen that the 10HMM model is a reasonable fit to the data and that the experimental points are approaching the decay curve at long times. Furthermore, most if not all of the luminosity of SN1987A by day 900 can be explained by the decay of ^{56}Co.

The prediction of the properties of a supernova explosion and its verification with gamma ray observations is one of the greatest achievements in the history of astrophysics. We are fortunate to live in 1990 and experience the major astrophysical triumph of the Century.

4. SN1987A Pulsar Search

On January 18, 1989, The Astronomical Telegram, IAU Circular 4735 announced the discovery, at the Cerro Tololo Telescope, of the SN1987A Pulsar with a frequency of 1968.6299 Hz (period of 0.507967 ms), and a time rate of change of the period, $dP/dt < 3 \times 10^{-14}$ s/s. The results were published 2 months later, Kristian et al., 1989, "Submillisecond optical pulsar in SN1987A", Nature, _338_, 234. Attempts to verify on January 21, February 15 and 16 were all negative. During the initial observation the brightness increased as the apparent magnitude, m, decreased from 19 to 18 during the 7 hr of observation. The frequency changed sinusoidally with amplitude 1.5×10^{-3} Hz and period of 8 h. If interpeted as a binary, the companion would be a jupiter size companion orbiting at 10^6 km. Significant second, 2f, and third, 3f, harmonics were seen. An even better fit to a sine curve was obtained after Doppler correction for the velocity of the earth around the sun. Twelve minutes after the run, the telescope was pointed toward the globular cluster NGC3201 for 0.5 h observation. No significant signal was seen.

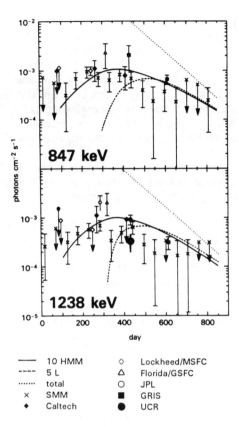

Figure 10. The GRIS line flux measurements are shown with theoretical predictions and the measurements of other instruments. All of the measurements are in reasonably good agreement with the 10HMM model. _Solid line_, 10HMM model; _dashed line_, 5L model without mixing; _dotted line_, unattenuated line flux; all models from Pinto and Woosley (1988). Measured values from SMM, Leising and Share (1990); Caltech, Cook et al. (1988); Lockheed/MSFC, Sandie et al. (1988); Florida/GSFC, Rester et al. (1988); JPL, Mahoney et al. (1988) [Tueller et al., 1990].

The pulsar was 7 m dimmer than the 11 m of the total supernova signal on January 18, nearly the same difference as for the Crab pulsar and its nebula. Even the ratio of the amplitudes of the first 3 harmonics were similar: SN1987A 1:1.8:1.6, PSR0531+21 1:1.8:1.1.

There were some problems. (1) For a neutron star of 10 km radius and period 0.5 ms, the surface velocity would be 0.4 c. The neutron star would have difficulty holding together. (2) The dipole power radiated by both the Crab pulsar and SN1987A are about 10^{38} erg/s, the Crab pulsar frequency and magnetic field 33 ms, and 10^{12} G. Scaling by $B^2\omega^4$, the SN1987A magnetic field is found to be 10^9 G, a very low value. (3) The companion at a distance of 10^6 km would have been well within the radius of Sanduleak 69-202 so could not have been there before the explosion. (4) Attempts by the authors and many others over the next year produced no verification. The pulsar was well hidden.

Finally in January, 1990 at Las Campanas Observatory, the authors saw a clear signal at 7874 Hz, the 4th harmonic of the orginal signal. A T.V. camera, the same type used at Cerro Tololo, was responsible. The authors returned to Cerro Tololo. On the night of February 5-6 observing, they again saw the original 1968.6299 SN1987A frequency--while viewing the Crab pulsar.

Why did the signal go away on January 18, 1989 when observing the Globular Cluster? The observation was made at dawn and the T.V cameras, extremely sensitive to light, were turned off to protect them from damage.

5. References

Ait-Ouamer, F., et al. (1991), "Compton Telescope Observations of Gamma Rays from SN1987A," submitted to Ap. J., January.

Bionta, R.M., et al. (1987), Phys. Rev. Letters 58, 1494.

Chan, K.W., and Lingenfelter, R.E. (1987) Ap. J. 318, L51.

Cook, W.R., et al. (1988) Ap. J. 334, L87.

Dotani, T., et al. (1987) Nature 330, 230.

Gehrels, N., et al. (1987) Ap. J. 320, L19.

Gehrels, N., et al. (1988) in Nuclear Spectroscopy of Astrophysical Sources (AIP Conf. Proc. 170) ed: N. Gehrels and G.H. Share (N.Y.: AIP), p. 87.

Hirata, K., et al. (1987) Phys. Rev. Letters 58, 1490.

Kirshner, R.P., et al. (1987) Ap. J. 320, 602.

Kristian, J., et al. (1989) Nature 338, 234.

Lederer, C.M., et al. (1978) Table of Isotopes, 7th edition, Wiley-Interscience.

Leising, M.D., and Share, G.H. (1990) Ap. J. 357, 638.

Litvinova, I.Yu. and Nadyozhin, D.K. (1983), Ap. Space, Sci. 89, 89.

Mahoney, W.A., et al. (1988) Ap. J. 334, L81.

Matz, S.M., et al. (1988) Nature 331, 416.

Pinto, P.A. and Woosley, S.E. (1988) Ap. J. 329, 820.

Reppin, C., et al. (1988) in Nuclear Spectroscopy of Astrophysical Sources (AIP Conf. Proc. 170) ed: N. Gehrels and G.H. Share (N.Y.: AIP), p. 37.

Rester, A.C., et al. (1988) Ap. J. 342, L71.

Sagdeev, R.Z. (1988) Physics Today, May, p. 30.

Sandie, W.G., et al. (1988) Ap. J. 334, L91.

Sunyaev, R., et al. (1987) Nature 330, 227.

Tueller, J., et al. (1990) Ap. J. 351, L41.

Ubertini, P., et al. (1988) IAU Circular 4590.

Weaver, T.A., and Woosley, S.E. (1980) Annals N.Y. Academy of Sciences 336, 335 (9th Texas Symp. on Relativistic Astrophysics).

Wilson, R.B., et al. (1988) in Nuclear Spectroscopy of Astrophysical Sources (AIP Conf. Proc. 170) ed: N. Gehrels and G.H. Share (N.Y.: AIP), p. 73.

Woosley, S.E., et al. (1987) Ap. J. 318, 664.

ACCELERATION OF COSMIC RAYS AT YOUNG SUPERNOVA REMNANTS

Todor Stanev
Bartol Research Institute
University of Delaware
Newark, DE 19716, U.S.A.

ABSTRACT. The majority of cosmic rays are believed to be accelerated at the blast shocks of supernova remnants. This process is theoretically well studied and can account for all galactic cosmic rays with energies below $\sim$100 TeV. In this talk the acceleration during the first years after the supernova explosion is discussed which may achieve higher maximum energy and maintain for a short period of time high cosmic ray luminosities. Accelerated cosmic rays will interact on the material of the supernova shell and give rise to high energy neutrino and γ-ray signals.

1. INTRODUCTION

Models which accelerate cosmic rays at the late stage of supernova expansion have been very successful in matching the fluxes and composition of the bulk of cosmic rays observed at Earth. The energy source in such models is the kinetic energy of the expanding supernova shell and the mechanism is first order Fermi acceleration. The main shorcomming of this class of models is their inability to achieve energies higher than $\sim$100 TeV (10^{14} eV), where there are still no experimental indications for any change in the acceleration and propagation mode of the cosmic rays.

The maximum energy E^{max} achievable by a proton beeing accelerated at a shock is obviously a function of the fractional energy gain per one crossing of the shock ϵ and the total number of crossings during the acceleration. In first order Fermi mechanisms $\epsilon \simeq 4/3\beta$ where β is the relative velocity of the plasma flow at the shock. The number of crossings reflects the residence time of the proton at the shock before it diffuses away. Diffusion time is $t_d = R_s^2/D$. Lagage&Cesarsky[1] use average supernova shell parameters and a minimum diffusion coefficient $D_{min} = cR_L/3$ to derive the maximum acceleration energy at blast shocks as $E_{max} \leq Z \times 3 \times 10^4$ GeV. The magnetic field value used for calculating the Larmour radius R_L in this estimates is 3μGauss and the acceleration time is $\sim$ 1000 years. To achieve higher energies one should find conditions where either the

177

M. M. Shapiro et al. (eds.), Cosmic Rays, Supernovae and the Interstellar Medium, 177–186.

shock radius R_s is much bigger, or D_{min} is much smaller, i.e. the magnetic field is much stronger. We shall concentrate here on the second possibility by examining the conditions at young supernova remnants (YSNR).

The basic acceleration mechanism is still shock acceleration[2] proceeding at various shocks developed by interactions of the expanding shell with the interstellar medium and/or energetic processes inside the remnant. The main advantage is the wealth of the YSNR energy balance. Assuming that all galactic cosmic rays in the range 10^{15}-10^{17} eV are accelerated at YSNR requires that the average remnant contributes a cosmic ray luminosity of 10^{40} erg/s for only three years. Such luminosity is 0.3% of the total L_{CR} per remnant estimated by Ginzburg&Syrovatskii[3].

2. ACCELERATION SCENARIOS.

2.1 SNR Shocks in Stellar wind Cavities.

In the standard picture cosmic rays are accelerated at the blast shock created at the boundary of the expanding envelope and the interstellar medium (ISM). The magnetic field at the shock is thus the one typical for the interstellar medium, $O(3\mu G)$. Völk and Biermann[4] argue that the typical Type II supernova remnant actually expands inside the winds of the pre-supernova star (Fig. 1), rather than in the average ISM. The magnetic field B_s at the shock will then depend on the surface magnetic field of the progenitor star B_*.

$$B_s = \frac{B_* r_* \Omega_*}{R_s V},\qquad(1)$$

where r_* and Ω_* are the progenitor star radius and angular velocity, and V is the wind velocity. The maximum proton energy is

$$E^{max} \simeq ZeB_s R_s \dot{R}_s,\qquad(2)$$

where Z is the charge of the accelerated particle. Using the progenitor parameters for

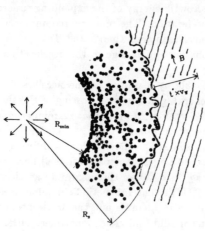

Fig. 1. In the model of Völk and Biermann the supernova shell is expanding in a cavity filled with the progenitor star wind. The shock is at the position of the outer edge of the shell.

SN1987A $(r_* = 2 \times 10^{12}$ cm and $V = 10^8$ cm s$^{-1})$ one obtains the asymptotic E^{max} of $1.5 \times 10^{14} Z$ eV only 1 year after the explosion. A higher maximum energy of $3 \times 10^{15} Z$ eV is achieved for a more typical supernova progenitor, a red giant, where the stellar radius r_* is larger and the wind velocity V smaller. Some other highly evolved stars with high surface magnetic fields could reach maximum acceleration energies up to $10^{17} Z$ eV.

2.2. Two Shock Model.

Berezinsky&Ptuskin[5] consider in some more detail the shock propagation inside the supernova shell. Exact hydrodynamical solutions of the supernova shell expansion show that the compression of the gas at the blast shock creates a reverse shock that in the shell system propagates back toward the center of the remnant. In the Lab system, however, the reverse shock is dragged by the expanding envelope and propagates outwards with a slower speed. The shell is then (Fig. 2) bracketed by these two fronts.

A simplified version of the model uses simple analytic expressions to describe the gas flow in the system. The shell density is

$$\rho_{sh} = \rho_0 r_{16}^{-k} t_7^{k-3},$$ (3)

where r_{16} is the distance in units of 10^{16} cm and t_7 is in 10^7 s. The wind density is

$$\rho_w = \frac{\varrho \dot{M}}{4\pi r_{16} V},$$ (4)

where $\dot{M}$ is the progenitor mass los. An effective shell position R_{sh} is calculated by equationg these two densities and the shell velocity is calculated as $\dot{R}_{sh}$. The kinetic energy of the gas injected into the shell through the outer shock can be then estimated $\dot{W}_k \simeq \dot{M} \dot{R}_{sh}^3 / 2V$. $\dot{W}_k$ determines the energy density of the accelerated cosmic rays.

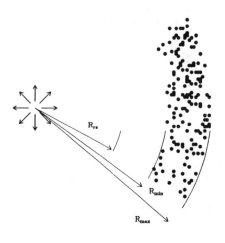

Fig. 2. The supernova shell is contained between the blast shock at R_{max} and the reverse shock at R_{rs}, which is inside the contact discontinuity (R_{min}).

The magnetic field strength at the shell B_{sh} is determined through equipartition and is of order of 10^{-3}G. The maximum acceleration energy is

$$E^{max} \simeq 100 B_{sh} R_{sh} \dot{R}_{sh}/c \sim 10^{14}\text{eV} \times t_7^{\frac{4}{10}}. \tag{5}$$

Both the power is accelerated cosmic rays and E^{max} depend mostly on the mass loss of the progenitor star and the wind velocity. Once again the blue giant progenitor of SN1987A does not have enough $\dot{M}$ to accelerate an observable amount of cosmic rays. A typical red giant explosion in LMC, however, should be observable.

2.3. Pulsar Wind Model.

The principle difference of the pulsar wind model with the ones described above is its power source. While until now we discussed acceleration powered by the kinetic energy of the shell, the pulsar wind model[6] taps the energy of the pulsar created in the supernova explosion. The pulsar luminosity is

$$L_p = 4 \times 10^{39}\text{ergs/s} B_{12}^2 P_{10}^{-4}, \tag{6}$$

where B_{12} is the pulsar surface magnetic field in units of 10^{12} G and P_{10} is its period in units of 10 ms. L_p drives a relativistic MHD wind which creates a standing shock inside the contact discontinuity of the ejecta (Fig. 3).

The pulsar wind model has been created to explain how the energy of the Crab pulsar is

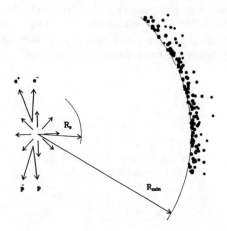

Fig. 3. In the pulsar wind model the cosmic rays are accelerated at R_s inside the contact discontinuity. The pulsar powers the acceleration through the relativistic MHD wind.

transferred to the nebula[7,8]. The detailed application to the Crab[9] puts the Lorentz factor of the wind electrons and positrons to $\simeq 10^6$.

The location of the shock can be calculated by balancing the ram perssure in the wind with the accumulated energy density of the shocked wind. This gives

$$R_s = \sqrt{v_{min}/3c} \times R_{min} \simeq 3.5 \times 10^{13}\text{cm} t_{yr} v_{500}^{3/2}, \tag{7}$$

where the subscript *min* refers to the inner radius of the ejecta. The magnetic field at the shock B_s can be obtained either from equipartition arguments or from the observation that the pulsar dipole magnetic field will fall off as r^{-3} to the light cylinder and as r^{-1} after that. Both arguments give

$$B_s = 10\mathrm{G} \times B_{12} P_{10}^{-2} t_{yr}^{-1} v_{500}^{-3/2}. \tag{8}$$

It is interesting to note that although B_s is determined by the pulsar magnitosphere, it reflects the total pulsar luminosity ($B_s \sim \sqrt{L_p}$ rather then the pulsar surface magnetic field strength. Using the arguments of Lagage&Cesarsky[1] one can now obtain the maximum acceleration energy

$$E^{max} = eZB_s R_s \simeq 10^{17}\mathrm{eV} B_{12} P_{10}^{-2} Z \tag{9}$$

The total power of accelerated cosmic rays depends on the acceleration efficiency and is related to the mixing of the wind with the ejecta in the vicinity of the shock and the composition of the wind.

2. PRODUCTION OF SIGNALS.

The fact that acceleration happens in young, relatively dense, SNR makes it observable because in the vicinity of the shock there is enough column density for the accelerated cosmic rays to interact and produce secondary particles. In the low density medium of the shell all produced mesons decay giving rise of γ-ray and neutrino fluxes. While the neutrinos leave the shell without any loss, γ-rays initially lose all of their energy on interactions with the gas of the shell. The γ-ray flux becomes visible after time t_1 at which the total thickness of the shell is less that one radiation length λ_R. Woosley[10] estimates the line of sight thickness of the SN1987A shell as $\sim 7 \times 10^4 \mathrm{g/cm}^2 \times (t/10^6 \mathrm{s})^{-2}$, giving $t_1 \simeq 1$ yr.

The production of neutrino and γ-ray signals continues until time t_2, when the loss to adiabatic expansion starts dominating the collision loss[11]. Assuming an uniform mixing of the accelerated cosmic rays with the ejecta we can calculate

$$t_2 = \frac{\lambda_N}{c} \frac{(4/3)\pi (vt)^3}{M}, \tag{10}$$

where M is the mass of the ejecta and λ_N is the nucleon interaction length. $(t_2/t_1) \simeq (\lambda_R/\lambda_N)^{1/2} \times (c/v)^{1/2} \simeq 10$. For a smaller degree of mixing the adiabatic losses will start dominating at an earlier epoch.

The duration of the γ-ray flux depends also on the diffusion of the accelerated cosmic rays through the supernova shell. Gaisser *et al.*[6], as well as Berezinsky&Ptuskin[5], predict that the accelerated particles will be confined by the magnetic fields in the vicinity of the shock and will only slowly diffuse away. In this scenario cosmic rays propagate through many interaction lengths of matter and the accelerated nuclei lose essentially all their energy in hadronic cascades developing inside the ejecta. This picture contains, as we shall see later, some intriguing potential for storage of the accelerated particle beam if the acceleration proceeds in the contact discontinuity region with a minimal amount of mixing with the shell. An alternative point of view, in which the accelerated nuclei are of sufficiently high energy and propagate through the shell in straight line, has been considered by Sato[12]. In the latter case the duration of the γ-ray signals will be much shorter as the column density of the ejecta decreases with the square of the time. Fig. 4 shows the light curves predicted for SN1987A in the two scenarios. In the unconfined case a significant γ-ray flux is prediced with a duration of ~ 1 year, while with confinement the duration of the emisiion is 3 to 10 yrs, depending on the amount of mixing between the accelerated beams and the supernova shell.

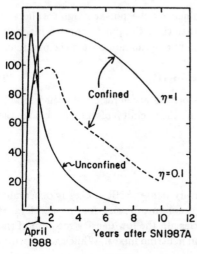

Fig. 4. Comparison of the light curves in high energy γ-rays for models with confinement and free propagation. η is the degree of mixing of the accelerated nuclei with the ejecta.

3. THE CASE OF SN1987A.

There is an overall luminosity factor in all acceleration scenarios discussed above. In the mechanisms using the kinetic energy of the expanding shell it is determined by the parameters of the pre-supernova winds. In the pulsar wind model it is the total pulsar luminosity. The light curve of SN1987A has been carefully watched in a broad frequency band[13] and no deviation from a nuclear power source has been observed. The decline of the supernova luminosity has been perfectly consitent with the halflife of the isotopes ^{56}Co and ^{57}Co, which are results of nucleosynthesis[14] during the propagation of the blast shock through the inner layers of the shell. This allows us to set an upper limit on the pulsar luminosity in the SN1987A remnant. The exact value depends on the energy spectrum of the pulsar emission and the absorption of the shell and is certainly less than 10^{38} ergs/s. Only a fraction of this luminosity will emerge in the form of accelerated cosmic rays, which already makes SN1987A unsobservable by VHE ($>10^{12}$ eV) and UHE ($>10^{14}$ eV) γ-rays. This is in perfect agreement with the experimental results, a compilation of which is shown on Fig. 5. All data points obtained by six different detectors are upper limits, with one single exception - the observation of a VHE burst by the JANZOS air-cherenkov telescope[15].

3.1. The TeV γ-ray Burst of SN1987A.

Cherenkov telescopes observe the light that relativistic particles emit in their propagation through the atmosphere. The energy threshold for this particular telescope is 3×10^{12} eV. The telescope, which is located in New Zealand, had observed SN1987A for 14 nights in December 1987 and January 1988. The time average result is consistent with no signal, however on two consecutive nights (January 14 and 15, 1988, see Fig. 6) a flux of 2×10^{-11} cm^{-2}s^{-1} is observed. It is roughly coincident with a big X-ray outburst in the remnant. Taken on its face value this results requires a TeV γ-ray luminosity equal or higher than

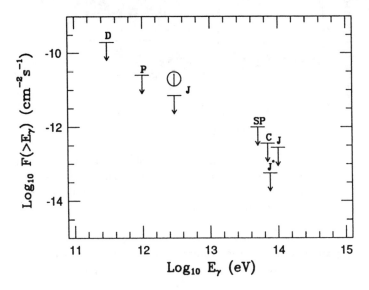

Fig. 5. Results of the observations of SN1987A in VHE and UHE γ-rays. The only positive result is the JANZOS point at $E_\gamma=3$ TeV.

the upper limit on the total pulsar luminosity from SN1987A. Is this observation a proof for the particle acceleration at SN1987A, indication for a different process, or simply a statistical fluctuation?

Berezinsky&Stanev[16] consider the first point of view. They develop lengthy arguments about the difficulties with an electromagnetic origin of the burst and come forward with the following scenario, shown on Fig. 7. A shock was formed by the pulsar wind and proton acceleration started at a level below the observational threshold well before the burst. Significant cosmic ray beams were accumulated, in the storage rings fashion, inside the contact discontinuity. When a nonlinear Rayleigh-Taylor instability developed, the stored beams, which have already diffused throughout the contact discontinuity, streamed out into the nebular gas. The traversed column density is close to the total thickness of the shell, about 50 g/cm^2 at the time of the burst. The total energy output in the burst is $(3\text{-}6)\times10^{44}$ ergs. If all protons accelerated at SN1987A were consumed in the burst the continuous cosmic ray luminosity would be 10^{37} ergs/s for the first year after the explosion. Cosmic rays streaming out of the ejecta enhance its mixing, and may thus contribute to the increase of the X-ray flux.

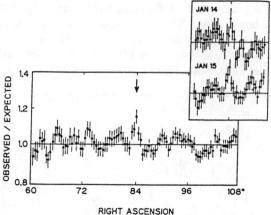

Fig. 6. The ratio of the observed and expected counts in a declination bin including the supernova as a function of the right assension (from Ref. 15). The position of the SN1987A is indicated with an arrow. The inset shows the data for the two nights of the outburst separately.

The pulsar wind model is essential for this picture only through its ability to store the accelerated particle beams in the contact discontinuity and generate a superluminous burst. Different versions are possible, where the acceleration goes through magnetic

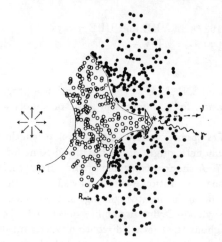

Fig. 7. The TeV γ-ray burst in the scenario of Berezinsky and Stanev.

reconnection caused by the Rayleigh-Taylor instability itself[17]. Honda *et al*[18] suggested a different picture, where cosmic rays are accelerated outside the ejecta on a clump of circumstellar matter in the Völk&Biermann fashion, and produce both the X-ray outburst and the TeV γ-ray flux in traversing back through the nebula. In their picture the acceleration happens on the back side of SN1987A. The only problem with this picture is the increased energy requirement, some 2×10^{46} ergs for the burst.

4. CONCLUSIONS.

The acceleration of cosmic rays at young supernova remnants appears to be not only possible, but to a certain extent inevitable. The shocks developing at the interfaces of the expanding supernova shell with the circumstellar matter, the strong magnetic fields related to the central engine, and the MHD turbulence, create a framework, which is very suitable for acceleration of particles to very high energy. The models discussed need to utilize a relatively small fraction of the total energy of the remnant to supply a large fraction of all energetic galactic cosmic rays.

The best part of all is that the acceleration of cosmic rays at the early stage of supernova remnants may be a directly observable process. The cosmic rays accelerated at large scale shocks diffuse away to become a part of the galactic cosmic ray pool. In contrast, the significant column density of the ejecta provides enough material for particle interactions, which generate significant fluxes of high energy neutrinos and γ-rays. It is unfortunate that SN1987A, the only young SNR close enough to become observable in a wide energy band, seems to be a dissapointing example. The low mass loss of the progenitor star, coupled with a weak pulsar, makes the level of cosmic ray acceleration too low for steady observations. The average (as we believe) supernova, with a red giant progenitor, or/and with a powerful pulsar, would have generated an observable amount of VHE/UHE gamma-rays. In the case of a supernova explosion in our Galaxy, with energy requirements for observation 25 times lower, it might be even possible to distinguish between different possible models of cosmic rays acceleration.

ACKNOWLEDGEMENTS. This lecture is to a big extent result of my collaboration with T.K. Gaisser, A.K. Harding and V.S. Berezinsky. My research is supported in part by the National Science Foundation and NASA. I also wish to thank the organizers of this course, Drs. M.M. Shapiro and J. Wefel, and the Center for Scientific culture 'E. Majorana', for their hospitality and for the creative atmosphere in Erice.

REFERENCES.

1. P.O. Lagage and C.J. Cesarsky, *Astr. Ap.* **125**, 249 (1983).
2. R. Blandford and D. Eichler, *Phys. Rept.* **154**, 1 (1987); L. O'C. Drury, *Rept. Progr. Phys.* **46** 973 (1983).
3. V.L. Ginzburg and S.I. Syrovatskii, *The Origin of Cosmic rays*, (Pergamon Press, 1964).
4. H.J. Völk and P.L. Biermann, *Ap. J.* **333**, L65 (1988).
5. V.S. Berezinsky and V.S. Ptuskin, *Astr. Ap.* **215**, 39 (1989).

6. T.K. Gaisser, A.K. Harding and T. Stanev, *Nature* **332**, 314 (1988); *Ap. J.* **345**, 423 (1989).

7. F. Pacini and M. Salvati, *Ap. J.* **186**, 249 (1973).

8. M.J. Rees and G.E. Gunn, *N.N.R.A.S* **167**, 1 (1974).

9. C.F. Kennel and F.V. Coroniti, *Ap. J.* **283**, 649 (1984); **283**, 710 (1984)

10. S.E. Woosley, in *Supernova 1987A in the Large Magelanic Clouds*, ed. M. Kafatos and A. Michalitsianos (Cambridge University Press, 1988) p. 289.

11. V.S. Berezinsky and O.F. Prilutski, *Astr. Ap.* **66**, 325 (1978).

12. H. Sato, *Progr. Theor. Phys*, **58**, 549 (1977); T. Nakamura, Y. Yamada and H. Sato, *Progr. Theor. Phys.* **79**, 1065 (1987).

13. R.M. Catchpole and P.A. Whitelock, a series of papers by the SAAO in *N.M.R.A.S.*, (1987-1989).

14. P.A. Pinto and S.E. Woosley, *Nature* **333**, 534 (1988).

15. I.A. Bond *et al.*, *Phys. Rev. Let.* **61**, 2292 (1988).

16. V.S. Berezinsky and T. Stanev, *Phys. Rev. Letters* **63**, 1037 (1989).

17. V.S. Berezinsky and V.L. Ginzburg, *Nature* **329** 807 (1987).

18. M. Honda, H. Sato and T. Terasawa, *Progr. Theor. Phys.* **82**, 315 (1989).

THE EFFECT OF RELATIVISTIC PARTICLE BEAMS ON THE EVOLUTION OF SUPERNOVA ENVELOPES: SELF-CONSISTENT SOLUTIONS

J.H. Beall
E.O. Hulburt Center for Space Research
Naval Research Laboratory, Washington, D.C.
St. John's College, Annapolis, MD., and
Sachs-Freeman Associates, Landover, MD.

ABSTRACT. We consider the effect of a relativistic particle beam produced as part of the collapse process of a supernova core into a neutron star or black hole on the evolution of the expanding envelope. Relativistic bremsstrahlung is the dominant energy loss mechanism until the material through which the beam propagates becomes ionized. After an ionized channel is formed, plasma processes and inverse Compton losses become the dominant loss mechanisms. The energy loss processes associated with the beam impart significant momentum to the irradiated segments of the shell. This suggests a natural explanation for the asymmetric expansion of some supernovae, including SN1987a, and may account for the early mixing seen in that object. It also implies that some fraction of the X-ray light from very early in a supernova explosion originates in an inverse Compton emission process wherein relativistic electrons from the beam collide with optical photons from the expanding envelope. In this paper we present self-consistent solutions to the rate equations for the energy loss due to collective processes and calculate the momentum transferred to the envelope by the beam. We then comment on the expected X-ray emission from SN1987a using such a model (Beall 1979), and make estimates of the associated γ-ray flux.

1. Introduction

The detection of X-rays from supernova explosions is of considerable astrophysical interest. In combination with the radio fluxes detected from supernovae, X-ray emission suggests the presence of relativistic particles.

The acceleration mechanisms which produce relativistic particles in supernovae appear to operate on a number of time scales. For example, radio and X-ray emission from supernova remnants arises on time scales of decades after maximum light. The detection of such emission clearly represents the presence of relativistic particles accelerated by the Fermi mechanism, and seems to occur after the expanding shell of material begins to slow appreciably due to its interaction with the interstellar

187

M. M. Shapiro et al. (eds.), Cosmic Rays, Supernovae and the Interstellar Medium, 187–205.

medium.   Prompt radio and X-ray emission (within a few days or weeks of maximum light) is also of interest, since it illuminates the nature of the interaction between the ejecta thrown out from the explosion and the ambient medium near the precursor star.

Between these two extremes (on time scales of months to years), as the overburden of expanding material becomes optically thin, it is generally assumed to be possible to detect the presence of the collapsed object left as the remnant of the star's core.   Such emission would at first be highly absorbed at X-ray frequencies.

The occurence of a comfortably nearby supernova during the current era has provided a wealth of data on the early evolution of such objects. The detection of X-ray emission from SN1987a (see e.g. Sunyaev et al. 1987,   Dotani et al. 1987) provides an interesting addition to the generally expected picture of X-ray emission from supernovae.   A number of models have been developed to explain the observed X-ray spectrum, which seems to have arisen earlier than expected.   Itoh et al. (1987) have modeled the optical light curve as being powered with ^{56}Co mixed uniformly up to the outer edge of the helium layer.   They note that such mixing is essential to fit the observed optical light.   Sunyaev et al (1987) have modeled the X-rays from the source by a pulsar embedded in the expanding, optically thick ejecta.   Their calculations show that the emission detected in August 1987 was brighter than that expected by roughly a factor of five. Sutherland et al. (1987) have also calculated a plausible model in which the X-ray radiation is produced by degradation of γ-rays via Compton scattering to produce the observed X-ray spectrum.   In their calculation, they also assume that extensive mixing has occurred between the processed material in the remnant's core and the overburden.

The high-energy X-ray spectrum of the source has been measured by a number of experiments (see, e.g. Dotani et al., Sunyaev et al., and Ubertini et al. 1989), which show a relatively constant flux at 50 keV from August 1987 through April 1988 (Fishman et al. 1989) after the initial upper limits early in 1987 (Sood et al. 1988 and Ubertini et al. 1989).   Important corroborations of the presence of processed material come from various reports of nuclear line fluxes at 847 and 1238 keV by Matz et al. (1987), Leising (1988), Leising and Share (1989), Teegarden et al. (1989), and Tueller et al. (1990).

The common theme of these calculations is a requirement for extensive mixing between the core material and the hydrogen envelope (see Bussard, Burrows, and The 1989, Pinto and Woosley 1988, and Grebenev and Sunyaev 1989 for discussions).   Arnett, Fryxell, and Muller (1989) calculate the growth of Rayleigh-Taylor instabilities during shock propagation through a realistic presupernova structure, and show that significant Rayleigh-Taylor mixing (see e.g., Chevalier and Klein 1978) can occur on time scales of order 10^4 seconds.

Added to these arguments is the controversial nature of the low-energy spectrum for the prompt X-ray flux, which was detected by Ginga (see, e.g. Makino 1988), but was not detected by KVANT-MIR instrument (see, e.g. Staubert 1988, Aschenbach et al. 1987).   Bandiera, Pacini, and Salvati

(1988) have suggested that these differences were due to variability of the low-energy portion of the X-ray spectrum produced by early fragmentation of the supernova photosphere.

In a recent paper by Chevalier and Soker (1989), those authors reported analytic calculations of the spherically symmetric expansion of a supernova envelope such as that thought to be present in SN1987a (see e.g. Woosley and Phillips 1988). The asymmetry in the line emitting region suggested by the data (Cropper et al. 1988, Phillips et al. 1988, and Karovska et al. 1988) is roughly 10-30%, and Chevalier and Soker argue that angular momentum or tidal interactions with an unseen companion may be responsible for the initial asymmetry, which is then preserved during expansion of the envelope. Gilmozzi (1990) has reported the asymmetric expansion velocities for SN1987a to be of order 10 kms^{-1}. In addition to the asymmetry in the optical data, there is recently reported evidence for asymmetric γ-ray line profiles from SN1987a at 847 and 1238 keV from the GRIS spectrometer (Tueller et al. 1990). These data also require a relaxation of the assumption of spherically symmetric mixing of the processed material with the hydrogen envelope. There is also evidence for asymmetries in the evolution of ejecta from other supernova explosions (see, e.g. Geldzahler and Shaffer 1982).

In this paper we propose a mechanism for the early mixing or fragmentation of the shell of ejecta and of the asymmetric expansion of supernova envelopes. Specifically, we suggest that the mixing or fragmentation was produced by the propagation of a relativistic particle beam through the overburden of material in the ejecta. The beam can be produced either by a pulsar or via an accretion disk which formed (perhaps temporarily) during the collapse process. The beam both heats the material through which it passes and transfers significant momentum to it.

We proceed by calculating the various energy loss mechanisms for the beam, which include collisional, non-relativistic bremsstrahlung, relativistic bremsstrahlung, synchrotron, inverse Compton, and collective (plasma) effects. Initially, the dominant energy loss mechanism for parameters appropriate to the envelope is relativistic bremsstrahlung, but plasma processes and inverse Compton losses dominate once the relativistic particle beam ionizes a channel through the overburden of material. It is this scenario whose loss mechanisms we calculate.

2. Relativistic Particle Beams and Their Effect on the Envelope

It is clear that processes associated with collapsed objects have the capacity to accelerate particles to relativistic energies. The early work by Goldreich and Julian (1969) showed that the potential, $V = \int E dl = \omega r_o^2 B/c = 2\pi \times 10^{16} P^{-1}$, where ω is the angular frequency, r_o is the radius of the neutron star, B is the strength of the magnetic field, c is the velocity of light, and P is the period of the pulsar. Thus, the highest energy particles can be very relativistic. In a series of papers, Harding (1990), and Gaisser, Harding, and Stanev (1987, 1989) have proposed and refined a model in which an electron-positron wind from a pulsar interacts with matter within the expanding ejecta. Their model assumes spherical symmetry for the relativistic particles, a consequence of the electrons and positrons being trapped within the field lines of the pulsar until the particles reach the light cylinder.

A number of models have also been proposed for acceleration processes in accretion disks which do not require large magnetic fields from the neutron star and which can readily accelerate particles to relativistic energies.

The recent papers on the detection and subsequent retraction of data showing optical pulsations from the remnant (Middleditch et al. 1989, 1990) underscore the difficulty of reliable detection of a newly born millisecond pulsar, even though on a number of other grounds such an object is likely to be present.

The model herein proposed does not require the beam generated as a by-product of the collapse process to have a high degree of collimation in order to transfer significant momentum to the expanding shell. Thus, while an accretion process is likely to be required to generate the beam, a pulsar with a strong magnetic field is not. In any event, the exact relationship between magnetic field strength and beam collimation in supernova explosions needs to be further explored. We note in this regard that Begelman (1988) has pointed out in the context of active galactic nuclei that cascade processes of pairs essentially decouple a significant fraction of the beam particles from the field lines within the core region. He suggests that this would allow coherence of linear structures (beams) to be maintained even in the presence of strong ambient magnetic fields. Similar arguments may hold for the propagation of beams of relativistic particles in the environment of a supernova explosion. Thus, the coherence of a beam of relativistic particles is plausible even in an environment where strong magnetic fields are present.

There are a number of energy loss mechanisms present as the beam propagates through the envelope of the star. Loss mechanisms associated with plasma processes and inverse Compton scattering have been discussed in detail in papers by Rose et al. (1984, 1987) and by Beall (1986, 1990). We discuss in outline the energy loss mechanisms relevant to relativistic particle beams propagating through the overburden of material in a supernova explosion.

2.1 PARTICLE ENERGY LOSS MECHANISMS

There are a number of well-known mechanisms which extract energy from moving particles. In this section we will discuss collisional losses, non-relativistic bremsstrahlung, relativistic bremsstrahlung, synchrotron, inverse Compton, and hadronic collisions as energy loss mechanisms.

Derivations of collisional loss rates can be found in numerous sources (see e.g. Jackson 1960). For a particle of charge z traversing a gas of density N with Z electrons/atom, the energy loss is given by

$$dE_{Coll}/dx = - 4\pi NZ(z^2e^4/mv^2)\ln B, \quad ergs/cm$$

$$where \quad B = \gamma^2 mv^3/ze^2\omega,$$

(1)

and γ is the ratio of the particle energy over the rest mass energy, e is the charge of the electron, v is the electron velocity ($<< c$), ω is a characteristic atomic frequency of motion, M is the mass of the incident particle, and m is the mass of the electron.

It is interesting to compare this loss rate with that associated with non-relativistic bremsstrahlung. This can be expressed as

$$dE(non-rel)_{rad}/dx = (16/3)NZ^2(e^2/\hbar c)z^4(e^2/Mc^2)^2Mc^2,$$

(2)

where $(e^2/\hbar c)$ is the fine structure constant. For non-relativistic velocities, collisional energy losses are the dominant energy loss mechanism. When particle velocities become relativistic, however, bremsstrahlung energy losses dominate over collisional. We may express the energy losses associated with relativistic bremsstrahlung as

$$dE(rel)_{rad}/dx = -(16/3)NZ^2(e^2/\hbar c)(e^2/Mc^2)^2\gamma Mc^2 \ln\beta,$$
$$where \quad \beta = (\lambda 192M/mz^{1/3}),$$

(3)

and λ is a quantum-mechanical fudge factor of order unity.

It is interesting to note (see, e.g. Bethe and Heitler 1934) that the equation above has the form

$$dE/dx = - E/X_o$$

(4)

where X_o is appropriately defined. The solution to this equation has the form $E = E_o \exp(-x/X_o)$, where X_o is the characteristic radiation length. The form of the equation is identical to that of radiation propagating through an absorbing medium. Thus, the propagation length of a beam of particles can be considerably extended beyond some small multiple of the mean free path.

There are two more energy loss mechanisms which are relevant to our discussion: synchrotron and inverse Compton losses. Schott (1912) expressed the energy loss of a particle due to synchrotron radiation as

$$dE_{sync}/dx = - (2e^4/3m^2c^4)\gamma^2H^2$$

(5)

where H is the magnetic field intensity. This equation can be rewritten as

$$dE_{sync}/dx = - (8\pi/3)\sigma_T\gamma^2u_H$$

(6)

with u_H expressing the energy density of the magnetic field. Written in this form, the expression for the energy loss associated with synchrotron emission is similar to the energy loss formula for inverse Compton scattering, which is (Felten and Morrison 1963,66)

$$dE_{IC}/dx = - \sigma_T \gamma^2 u_{ph}, \tag{7}$$

where u_{ph} is the photon energy density.

To compare the energy loss rates associated with these mechanisms with those of plasma processes, we must investigate in some detail the collective (plasma) effects of the interaction of a relativistic particle beam with an ambient medium.

2.2 ENERGY LOSS MECHANISMS ASSOCIATED WITH PLASMA EFFECTS

2.2.1 The Interaction of a Beam of Relativistic Particles with an Ambient Medium

A more complete discussion of the time-dependent energy loss of a relativistic particle beam can be found in Rose et al. (1984, 1987) and Beall (1986, 1990). We herein present a synopsis of that discussion and extend it to include resonant trapping of the beam particles and a self-consistent calculation of the beam energy loss. The first we accomplish by placing a resonant-trapping factor into the equations, while the second, self-consistent element is developed by incorporating cooling mechanisms for the ambient plasma in order to determine the actual plasma temperature.

A relativistic charged particle beam heats and ionizes a background gas. The beam may be composed of electrons, electrons and ions, or electrons and positrons. The interaction between the beam and the background gas may be primarily the result of collective (plasma) effects if the background gas is sufficiently ionized. In this section we will discuss collective effects on the propagation length of the beam.

A low-density relativistic electron beam entering a plasma produces perturbations that are localized to the region of the beam and induces currents that tend to cancel out its magnetic field. In this case steady state injection into the plasma occurs (Rukhadze and Rukhlin 1972).

A high-density electron beam produces hydrodynamic motion as it enters a plasma. We here assume that the beam has entered the background plasma and that the diameter of the beam is sufficiently large that the time scales for subsequent hydrodynamic motions are much longer than the time scales for the growth of plasma instabilities, an assumption which is borne out by the results of the calculations.

If magnetic fields produced by the beam-background plasma interaction can be neglected, then as the beam heats the background plasma, it will expand and thereby produce a plasma of lower density and higher temperature (channel plasma), which will continue to expand until there is an approximate pressure equilibrium between the channel plasma and the background plasma still unaffected by the beam. The electric self-field of the beam will be neutralized by the background plasma on a time scale that is approximately $1/\omega_p$, where ω_p is the plasma frequency of the background plasma. The interaction of the beam with the background plasma occurs through a number of instabilities. We shall discuss these instabilities briefly in what follows, and then calculate their development in the next section for densities relevant to the environment of a supernova explosion. Rose et al. (1984, 1987) and Beall (1986, 1989) have discussed beam energy loss via these mechanisms in low density material appropriate to the environment in active galaxies and quasars, and Beall (1990) has considered these equations without the self-consistent determination of temperature.

2.2.2 Relevant Beam-Plasma Instabilities

The initial interaction of a charge neutralized beam traversing a collisionless plasma is through the two-stream instability. This instability transfers energy from the beam in the form of nearly longitudinal (electrostatic) waves and simultaneously acts through the wave-beam interaction to broaden the beam in momentum space. The propagation distance of a relativistic beam traversing an ambient medium depends on the time scales for beam broadening in momentum parallel to the beam and for scattering transverse to the direction of beam propagation.

If the electron beam and background plasma are cold (i.e., the momentum spread is small) then the electrostatic dispersion relation for the case of a uniform medium and negligible field is (Godfrey, Shanahan, and Thode 1976)

$$1 - (\omega_p^2/\omega^2) - [\omega_{pb}^2/(\omega - k \cdot v_b)^2] \cdot [\sin\theta + \gamma^{-2}\cos\theta] = 0, \tag{8a}$$

where the wave vector k is at an angle θ with respect to the beam direction, $\gamma = (1 - v_b^2/c^2)^{-1/2}$, $\omega_p^2 = 4\pi n_p e^2/m$ is the background plasma frequency, and $\omega_{pb}^2 = 4\pi n_b e^2/\gamma m$ is the relativistic beam plasma frequency. If the plasma is sufficiently magnetized, additional and shifted resonances appear due to gyromotion.

The non-relativistic dispersion relation that applies even when there is significant momentum spread in the beam and plasma is

$$k^2 = \sum_j (4\pi n_j e^2/m_j) \int [k \cdot (\partial f_j/\partial v)/(k \cdot v - \omega)] d^3 v \tag{9}$$

where the summation is over particle streams (beam and plasma) and f_j is the velocity distribution function for the jth stream. The corresponding relativistic dispersion relation is more complicated. In this paper we shall assume that initially the beam has some specified value of γ. If the beam has a power-law energy spectrum with a low-energy cutoff, then the value of γ used in our calculations corresponds to an energy close to the low-energy cutoff where the power-law energy distribution is $N(E) \propto E^{-\alpha}$, $\alpha \gtrsim$ 2-3. When the plasma is collisionless and unmagnetized, the above dispersion relation can be solved for the growth rates of perturbations which vary as $\exp[-i\omega t + ikr]$ (with ω complex). Since the frequency, ω, is complex, some of the solutions to the dispersive wave equation have real solutions which, therefore, grow exponentially. These exponential terms are the Γ's calculated below.

When maximized over unconstrained k, the initial growth rate is (Godfrey, Shanahan, and Thode 1976, Bludman, Watson, and Rosenbluth 1960),

$$\Gamma_1 = Im\omega \simeq (\sqrt{3}/2\gamma)(n_b/2n_p)^{-1/3}\omega_p \tag{10}$$

for a cold beam (hydrodynamic regime of instability). If the relativistic electron beam is warm or scattered (kinetic regime of instability), the growth is (Breizman and Ryutov 1971),

$$\Gamma_1 = Im\omega \simeq \gamma^{-1}(n_b/n_p)(1/\Delta\theta)^2\omega_p, \tag{11}$$

where $\Delta\theta$ is the angular width of the beam momenta. The growth rates for the two-stream instability are approximately the same for electron, electron-proton, and electron-positron beams with similar n_b and γ, and consequently our calculations can be applied to all three cases.

After a sufficient number of e-folding times, localized electric field fluctuations caused by the two-stream instability can become large enough to trap beam electrons if no other nonlinear process intervenes first. Thode and Sudan (1973) found that when electron trapping determines the saturation, resonant waves saturate at an average energy density,

$$\epsilon_w = 2n_b\alpha mc^2 \ (S/2)(1 + S)^{-5/2}; \quad \alpha \sim 1, \ S<1/2 \ \text{(cold beam)} \tag{12}$$

where

$$S = \beta^2\gamma(n_b/2n_p)^{1/2}.$$

However, the growth of resonant waves can be halted or even reversed by nonlinear effects other than trapping of beam electrons. On the time scale of ion motion across a few Debye lengths, high electric field regions (spikes) are formed which tend to exclude plasma ions and electrons by ponderomotive pressure. As these spikes sharpen and collapse (Zakharov 1972), their Fourier spectrum is broadened. This leads to the production of localized density reductions (cavitons). These nonlinear effects imply that either before or after the saturation of resonant waves by beam electron trapping, the wave spectrum can change nonlinearly from waves with nearly a single wave vector to a spectrum that includes oscillation of zero phase velocity and waves in resonance with the tails of the plasma electron distribution. The oscillating two-stream (OTS) instability, which is formally the same as a modulational instability or AC instability (Papadopoulos 1975, Schamel, Lee, and Morales 1975 and Freund et al. 1980), develops as the ponderomotive force of high-frequency resonance waves produces cavitons. It causes the transfer of wave energy from waves resonant with the beam to waves of shorter wavelength.

There is a threshold energy for the onset of the OTS instability

(Papadopoulos 1975). This threshold is reached when ϵ_1, the wave energy density in the resonant waves generated by the two-stream instability, becomes sufficiently large that the condition $\epsilon_1/n\kappa T > (k_1\lambda_D)^2$ is satisfied, where $\lambda_D = (\kappa T/4\pi ne^2)^{1/2}$ is the Debye length and k_1 is the most unstable wave vector associated with the two-stream instability. For the case of a cold beam, Freund et al. (1980) find the growth rate to be

$$\Gamma^{OTS} = \omega_p\epsilon_1/(4n\kappa T) \tag{13}$$

when $3(k_1\lambda_D)^2 < \epsilon_1/n\kappa T < m/m_i$, where m_i is the ion mass,

$$\Gamma^{OTS} = \omega_p[(m/3m_i)(\epsilon_1/n\kappa T)]^{1/2} \tag{14}$$

when $\epsilon_1/n\kappa T > m/m_i$ and $3(k_1\lambda_D)^2$.
  The conditions

$$k_1 = k_2 + k_s \tag{15}$$

$$\omega_1 = \omega_2 + \omega_s, \tag{16}$$

are approximately satisfied when a resonant plasma wave (k_1) is transformed to a nonresonant plasma wave (k_2) and a low-frequency ion acoustic wave (k_s) by means of the OTS instability. As the energy density in the form of low-frequency fluctuations (i.e., ion acoustic waves) increases, they interact nonlinearly with the resonant waves and increase the energy density $(\epsilon_2$ of nonresonant wave). The growth rate for this interaction is (Dawson and Oberman 1962).

$$\Gamma^{D-0} = (k_s\lambda_D)^{-2}W_s\omega_p, \tag{17}$$

where k_s is the wave number of the ion density fluctuations and $W_s = \epsilon_s/n\kappa T$.
  The ion acoustic (sound) waves are damped by the Dupree-Weinstock instability at a rate (Smith, Goldstein, and Papadopoulos 1976)

$$\Gamma^{D-W} = (m/m_i)^{1/2}(k_s\lambda_D)^{1/2}W_s^{1/4}\omega_p , \tag{18}$$

where $W_s = \epsilon_s/n\kappa T$ with ϵ_s the energy density of ion acoustic waves. Ion acoustic waves are also produced when the threshold for a secondary OTS is reached. Following Scott et al.(1980), we take this threshold to be

$$W_2 = (\epsilon_2/n\kappa T) > 4\Gamma_L/\omega_p, \tag{19}$$

where ϵ_2 is the energy density in high frequency nonresonant waves (i.e., k_2). We assume that initially the background plasma has a Maxwell-

Boltzmann distribution and therefore the Landau damping rate is (Boyd and Sanderson 1969)

$$\Gamma_L = (1/32\pi) \; w_p (2\pi/\lambda_D k_2)^3 \; \exp\{-[2\pi^2/(\lambda_D k_2)^2] \; -3/2\},$$
$$(\lambda_D k_2)^2 \ll 1. \quad (20)$$

Jackson (1960) has shown that as $k_2\lambda_D \to 1$, $\Gamma_L \to w_p$ and thus λ_D is the minimum wavelength for longitudinal oscillations that propagate through the plasma.

The rate equations that describe the growth of the wave energies are

$$\partial W_1/\partial t = 2[\Gamma_1\theta(W_{\epsilon w}-W_1) - \Gamma^{D-O}(W_s)]W_1$$
$$- 2\Gamma^{OTS}(W_1)W_2\theta(W_1-k_1{}^2\lambda_D{}^2), \quad (21)$$

$$\partial W_2/\partial t = 2\Gamma^{D-O}(W_s)W_1 + 2\Gamma^{OTS}(W_1)W_2\theta(W_1-k_1{}^2\lambda_D{}^2)$$
$$- 2\Gamma_L W_2 - 2\Gamma^{OTS}(W_2)\theta(W_2-4\Gamma_L/w_p)W_s - W_s/\tau_2, \quad (22)$$

$$\partial W_s/\partial t = [2\Gamma^{OTS}(W_1)\theta(W_1-k_1{}^2\lambda_D{}^2) + 2\Gamma^{OTS}(W_2)\theta(W_2-4\Gamma/w_p)$$
$$- 2\Gamma^{D-W}]W_s - W_s/\tau_s, \quad (23)$$

where $W_1 = \epsilon_1/n\kappa T$, $W_2 = \epsilon_2/n\kappa T$, $W_s = \epsilon_s/n\kappa T$, and the θ's are step functions. The terms $- W_2/\tau_2$ and $- W_s/\tau_s$ take into account the circumstance that waves tend to move outside the path of the beam. We estimate that $\tau_2 \simeq (r_0/\sin 45°)/V_g$ and $\tau_s = (r_0/\sin 45°)(2\kappa T/m_i)^{-1/2}$, where r_0 is the beam radius, V_g is the approximate group velocity of the high-frequency non-resonant waves, and $(\kappa T/m_i)^{1/2}$ is the ion sound velocity. The group velocity $= V_g = dw/dk$ for electron plasma waves is obtained from the dispersion formula $w^2 = w_p{}^2 + (\kappa T/m)k^2$, which yields $V_g = (\kappa T/m)/(w/k)$. For the ion acoustic wave we have $V_g \sim [\kappa T_e/m_i + \kappa T_i/m_i]^{1/2}$.

Scott et al.(1980) have discussed steady state solutions for rate equations similar to the above equations. A more extended discussion of the time dependent solutions to these rate equations for parameter ranges appropriate to active galaxies and quasars is included in Rose et al. (1984, 1987), and Beall (1986), and as mentioned earlier, Beall (1990) has considered the non self-consistent solutions to these equations for density and temperature ranges appropriate to supernova envelopes.

2.2.3 Solutions to the Rate Equations

Some general comments are clearly in order. The equations are formally a set of coupled differential equations which have highly non-linear terms. Although it requires a rather subtle algorithm to solve the equations, they are in other ways formally identical to the equations of predator-prey systems in biology. All of one's intuitions about the general nature of the behavior of biological populations apply directly to the system of equations listed above. Thus, boom-bust cycles are possible solutions, as are steady state . Chaotic solutions are <u>possible</u> for these systems, although (somewhat surprisingly, given the intensity of some of the driving terms) no chaotic solutions have been observed for the parameters present in active galaxies or supernovae <u>so far</u>.

In this section we will discuss solutions to equations (21)-(23) subject to the boundary conditions that W_1, W_2 and W_s are small at t = 0. In obtaining these solutions we have replaced the θ functions with analytical functions of the form $\theta(x - y) = 0.5\tanh(q(1-R))$, where q = 100, and R = y/x. This analytical form has the advantage of being closer to the actual behavior of the plasma instabilities at threshold. We also assume that $k_2\lambda_D = 0.2$ (i.e., we let the phase velocity $v_{k2} = 5\omega_p\lambda_D = 5v_e$). Since $k_1 \cdot v_b \simeq k_1 c \simeq \omega_p$, we have $|k_1| << |k_2|$; $|k_s|$ and $|k_2| \simeq |k_s|$ from equation (15).

As a beam excites waves in traversing a background plasma, it loses energy and γ decreases. For an electron-proton beam the principal collisionless interaction is between the beam electrons and background plasma, and consequently the beam electrons will tend to slow down with respect to the beam protons. If the beam-plasma interaction is not very strong, the beam protons will drag the electrons along with them. For an ultrarelativistic beam $v_b = c(1-(1/\gamma^2))^{-1/2}$ and the energy loss through a distance Δl can be found from the equation:

$$v_b n_b m'c^2(d\gamma/dx)\Delta l \simeq -(d(a\epsilon_1)/dt)\Delta l \text{ ergs cm}^{-2}\text{s}^{-1} \qquad (24)$$

where m' = m for an electron beam, m' = m for an electron-positron beam, m' = m_p + m for an electron-proton beam, ϵ_1 is the energy density of the resonant waves, and a is a factor (≥ 1) that corrects for the simultaneous transfer of resonant wave energy into nonresonant wave energy ϵ_2 and ion-acoustic wave energy ϵ_s. From equation (24) we find

$$dE/dx = - (1/n_b v_b)(da\epsilon_1/dt), \text{ and} \qquad (25a)$$
$$\int d\gamma = - \int [d(a\epsilon_1)/dt]/(v_b n_b mc^2). \qquad (25b)$$

Equation 25a can be compared directly with the Equations 1-7 for the individual particle energy loss mechanisms. We note that $a\epsilon_1 = aW_1 nkT$, and that the dt is the cycle time between periods in the oscillatory solutions to the equations, or, for the steady state solutions, roughly $1./\Gamma_1$. The two time intervals are approximately equal.

The propagation length L_p [i.e., the distance over which $\gamma = (1 - v_b^2/c^2)^{-1/2}$ decreases by a factor of ~ 2] becomes

$$L_p \simeq (\gamma/2)v_b n_b mc^2/<da\epsilon_1/dt> \qquad (26)$$

where $<da\epsilon_1/dt>$, the time average rate of excitation of wave energy density, can be obtained from the solutions described below.

Before discussing the specific solutions for supernova, it is illustrative to discuss the general nature of the solutions and to present three-dimensional surfaces which show how the growth of the wave energy in time changes as a function of a second parameter, say the γ of the beam.

Figure 1 shows some solutions to equations (21)-(23) for a relativistic charged particle beam with large beam radius (i.e., the terms $- W_2/\tau_2$ in eq. (21) and $- W_s/\tau_s$ in eq. (23) are neglected). These solutions are parameterized in terms of the growth rate for the two-stream instability Γ_1, the plasma frequency ω_p, and the background plasma temperature T. The solutions demonstrate that, as the wave levels W_2 and W_s grow, the wave energy W_1 is stabilized. The wave energy levels W_1, W_2, and W_s undergo periodic relaxation oscillations for a wide choice of parameters. However, if either the temperature T is increased sufficiently or Γ_1 decreased sufficiently, steady state solutions are obtained.

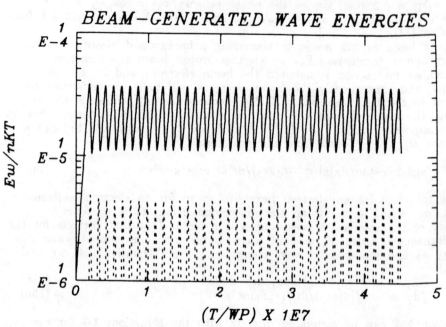

Figure 1. Solutions for the wave energy levels $W_1 = \epsilon_1/n\kappa T$, $W_2 = \epsilon_2/n\kappa T$, and $W_s = \epsilon_s/n\kappa T$ obtained by solving eqs. (21)-(23) a plasma temperature of 10^4K, $n_p = 10^4$, $n_b = 1$, and $\gamma = 10^3$. T/WP is time divided by plasma frequency. These solutions are typical of parameter ranges common in active galactic nuclei.

For the solution shown in Figure 1, the amplitude of the resonant two-stream wave grows to $W_{1(max)} = \epsilon_1/n\kappa T \simeq 0.42 \times 10^{-4}$ and then decreases, because after the threshold for the OTS instability is reached, wave energy is rapidly fed into nonresonant waves (W_2) and to a lesser extent into ion acoustic waves (W_s) more rapidly than it can be gained as a result of the two-stream instability. An observer in the reference frame of the background plasma observes quasi-periodic changes in the amplitudes of the waves (relaxation oscillations). As wave energy is transferred from resonant to nonresonant waves, electron tails are produced as a consequence of Landau damping. The energy that is transferred into ion-acoustic waves is dissipated as heat. For the particular choice of parameters $T = 10^4$, $\gamma = 10^3$, $n_p = 10^4$ cm^{-3} and $n_b/n_p = 10^{-4}$, the cycle is repeated in approximately 0.03 seconds and $<a(d\epsilon_1/dt) \simeq 0.17 \times 10^{-12}$ ergs cm^{-3} s^{-1}. It follows that

$$L_p \simeq (\gamma/2)<cn_bmc^2>/<d(a\epsilon_1)/dt> \simeq 7.2 \times 10^{18} \text{ cm}$$

and
                                                                                              (27)

$$n_pL_p \simeq 7.2 \times 10^{22}\text{cm}^{-2}.$$

Figure 2 shows the nature of the solutions to the equations as we vary for lower γ.

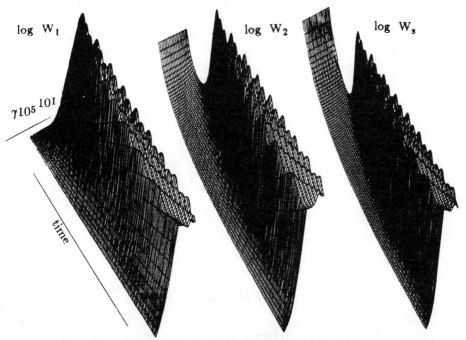

Figure 2. The plot shows the nature of the solutions to the equations as we vary the beam γ ($=E/mc^2$) from $\gamma=10^5$ to $\gamma=10^1$. The γ-axis points north-east in the plot, and the time axis points south-east. Note that the growth of the two-stream instability's resonant wave (W_1) occurs more rapidly for lower γ. The vertical axes represent the log of W_1, W_2, and W_s, respectively.

the beam γ (=E/mc^2) from $\gamma=10^5$ to $\gamma=10^1$. The γ-axis points north-east in the plot, and the time axis points south-east. Note that the growth of the two-stream instability's resonant wave (W_I) occurs more rapidly

We now consider a self-consistent solution to the system of equations to the extent that we allow the beam to heat the plasma. Since the plasma is present as an ionized channel surrounded by the ambient medium (which may also be ionized), we allow the plasma to expand adiabatically until it reaches a pressure balance with the ambient medium. The expansion is done iteratively, so that the rate of energy deposition is affected by the temperature and density in situ. In this calculation the cooling for the plasma is assumed to be by thermal bremsstrahlung, while the method of heating the plasma can be, variously, Joule heating via a return current, anomalous resistivity, or other mechanisms. The mechanisms for heating will be discussed in more detail in a paper currently in preparation. Our discussion at the present is intended to be illustrative.

Figure 3 presents a solution to the rate equations in which the

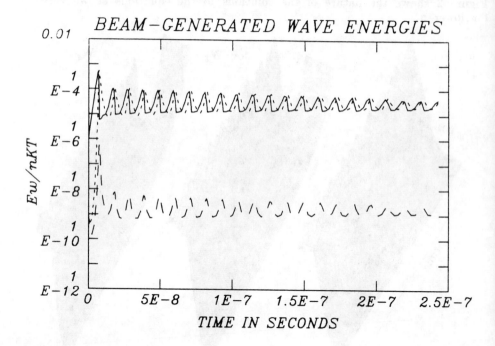

Figure 3. A self consistent solution where the plasma is cooled by thermal bremsstrahlung, the initial T = 10^4, n_p=1x10^{17}, n_b=1x10^{13}, and γ=1x10^3, and the final temperature is of order 1x10^5, and n_p=9x10^{15}. The solution begins as an oscillatory one, but the oscillations are damped as the temperature of the plasma rises.

temperature of the plasma is allowed to change as it is heated by the energy deposition of the beam. The plasma is cooled by thermal bremsstrahlung and heated by a return current and its consequent Joule heating. The presence of a return current implies that the beam has a net charge, an assumption we will discuss in more detail shortly.

Initially, the beam has a $\gamma = 1\times10^3$ and a density of 1×10^{13}, and the ambient plasma has a temperature of 1×10^4K, and a density of 1×10^{17}. As the beam transfers energy to the ambient medium, the temperature rises to a limiting value of order $> 1\times10^5$K. The density at that temperature drops to roughly $< 9\times10^{15}\#cm^{-3}$. The solution begins as an oscillatory one, since the initial temperature is not sufficiently high to damp out the relaxation oscillations. As the temperature rises, however, the beam solutions become stable at a level of $W_1 = 3\times10^{-5}$. This represents an energy deposition rate of 1.6×10^9 ergs cm^{-3} s^{-1}, where for the moment we have allowed $a=1$. The propagation length for such a beam is of order $L_p = 7\times10^{10}$ cm, where plasma effects are the dominant energy loss mechanism. If the beam has a diameter of order 10^8cm, corresponding to the inner region of a solar-mass sized accretion disk, then the volume of material into which the energy is deposited is $L_p\pi r^2 = 2\times10^{27}$. The total luminosity of the cylinder will thus be 3.8×10^{36} ergs s^{-1}, which is of the same order as the typical luminosity of solar-mass size accreting X-ray sources.

It is an obvious corollary to the foregoing discussion that collective processes can transfer significant amounts of momentum to the ambient medium through which the beam propagates. Geldzahler and Shaffer (1987) have pointed out that certain supernova remnants have a bipolar character which seems suggestive of a significant disruption of the expanding envelope. We suggest that the presence of relativistic particle beams produced as part of the collapse process is the cause of this phenomenon.

It is appropriate to comment briefly on the magnitude of the acceleration of the ambient medium which is produced by the interaction with the relativistic particle beam. For an electron or electron-positron beam, the velocity u of the resonant waves with respect to the background plasma is

$$u = [(1-\gamma)/(1+m/m_p)][(m/m_p)(n_b/n_p)]v_b, \tag{28}$$

where we have assumed for the purposes of illustration that the beam consists only of electrons, that current and momentum are conserved, and that the resonant waves have a small velocity relative to the center of mass frame, and that as a consequence, the resonant wave velocity equals the velocity of the plasma with respect to the center of mass. With this calculation of u, it is possible to estimate the acceleration produced by the beam on the plasma channel as (Rose et al. 1984)

$$dv/dt = (u/m_p n_p c^2)(aE^2/8\pi)/\tau, \tag{29}$$

with $E^2/8\pi$ being the energy density of the beam-generated waves, and τ is the inverse of the growth rate Γ_1. For the self-consistent solution presented in Figure 3, and given the assumptions listed above, $u=1.8\times10^7$cm s^{-1}, and $dv/dt = .9\times10^4$cm s^{-2}. If the collapse process continues for on the order of 10^2 s, during which time the beam is generated and interacts with the the overburden of material, then the plasma within the channel will be accelerated to a velocity of order 1×10^6 cm s^{-1} ~ 10 km s^{-1}. For an initial plasma density, $n_p=1\times10^{16}$, $n_b=5\times10^{12}$, $T=10^4$, and $\gamma=5\times10^2$, the average wave energy is of order 1.8×10^{-4}, the energy deposition rate into the plasma is 1×10^9 ergs cm^{-3} s^{-1}, and the propagation length is 2.7×10^{10} cm. The total energy dissipation rate is therefore 9×10^{35} ergs s^{-1}, and the acceleration of the column is of order 2×10^4 cm s^{-1}. In 10^2 s, the column will be accelerated to 20 km s^{-1}. The second set of parameters produce an oscillatory solution. The asymmetric expansion velocities produced by a beam with these sets of parameters is of the same order as the reported asymmetry of the expansion of SN 1987a (Gilmozzi 1990).

For the parameter ranges described herein and for an energy loss mechanism for the plasma of thermal bremsstrahlung (that is, the plasma is not optically thick), plasma (collective) processes are the dominant energy loss mechanism. The inverse Compton X-ray emission represents a rate of energy loss that is < 10 % of the rate at which the beam deposits energy into the ambient medium.

Typical cross sections for p-p reactions to produce pions are of the order of $1 - 2 \times 10^{-26}$ cm^2. Therefore, the mean-free-path (MFP) for pion production is of the same order as the propagation length due to inverse Compton emission. Beall (1989) has shown that the two processes produce X-ray and γ-ray photons at roughly the same rate and this rate is < 10 % of the rate at which the beam looses energy because of collisionless effects.

If the cloud of material is optically thick, inverse Compton losses can be the dominant energy loss mechanism for the beam (Rose et al. 1987).

The X-ray and γ-ray spectra produced by this model have been calculated by Beall et al. (1987) and Bednarek et al. (1990).

Beall (1979) first suggested that inverse Compton radiation might be responsible for the production of a prompt X-ray flux from supernovae. This mechanism for X-ray emission was corroborated for the supernova, SN1980k (Canizares, Kriss, and Feigelson 1982). The detection of radio emission from SN1987a (Turtle et al. 1987), also suggests the possible presence of relativistic particles early on during the explosion, and can be used to determine parameters of the emitting region, if one presumes that the radio emitting relativistic electrons would scatter light from the photosphere to produce an X-ray flux. This scenario has been discussed in the literature (Beall 1986, 1987). Calculations presented therein show that the upper limits from Ginga (Makino 1987)are above the expected flux from the inverse Compton model, given the observed radio flux.

3. Conclusions

We have suggested that a relativistic particle beam is present in some supernovae as a consequence of the collapse process of the stellar core.

We have calculated the relative rates at which individual particle and collective (plasma) energy loss mechanisms extract energy from a beam of relativistic particles propagating through an ambient medium. We have calculated the effect of such a deposition of energy and momentum of the beam upon the overburden of material in the expanding envelope, and show that for reasonable parameters, the beam has the capacity to affect the expansion of the stellar envelope at least to the extent that it can disrupt the spherical symmetry of the expansion. We have pointed out that such a beam provides a natural mechanism for both the asymmetric expansion and the early mixing which seems to be necessary to interpret the observations of SN1987a.

The presence of relativistic particles within or near the supernova photosphere suggests that inverse Compton scattering can provide some of the X-ray flux which has been seen. A calculation of the prompt X-ray flux (as the beam surfaces from beneath the overburden of the ejecta) by Beall (1990) suggests that the inverse Compton X-rays were below the early upper limits established by Ginga.

Flares in the X-ray emission via this mechanism are possible if the compact object accretes clumps of matter.

The model we propose also provides a natural explanation of the "mystery spot" detected shortly after the explosion of SN1987a.

This work is supported by the Office of Naval Research.

4. References

Arnett, D., Fryxell, B., and Muller, E. 1989, Ap.J., 341, L63.
Aschenbach, B. et al. 1987, Nature, 330, 232.
Bandiera, R., Pacini, F., and Salvati, M. 1988, Nature, 332, 418.
Beall, J.H. 1990 Proc. of Vulcano Workshop: Frontier Objects in Particle Physics and Astrophysics, IAS/CNR (in press).
Beall, J.H. 1989, Proc. of the Vulcano Workshop: Frontier Objects in Astrophysics and Particle Physics (Italian Physical Society: Bologna).
Beall, J.H., Bednarek, W., Karakula, S., and Tkaczyk, W. 1987, Proc. of the 20th Intnl. Cosmic Ray Conference, Vol. 1 (NAUKA: Moscow)
Beall, J.H. 1986 Proc. of IAS/Frascati Symposium on High Energy and Ultra-high Energy Behavior of Accreting X-ray Sources (Editrice Compositori:Bologna)
Beall, J.H. 1979, Ap. J., 230, 713.
Begelman, M. 1988, Proc. of IAU Symp. No. 134 on AGN's, Santa Cruz, CA., (Kluwer Publishers: Dordrecht).
Bednarek, W., Karakula, S., Tkaczyk, W., and Giovannelli, F. 1990, Astronomy and Astrophysics, in press.
Bludman, S.A., Watson, K.M., and Rosenbluth, M.N. 1960, Phys. Fluids, 3, 747.

204

Boyd, T.J.M., and Sanderson, J.J. 1969, Plasma Dynamics (New York: Barnes & Noble).

Breizman, B., and Ryutov, D. 1971, Soviet Phys.: JETP. 33, 220.

Brown, R.L., Johnston, K.J., and Lo, K.Y. 1981, Ap. J., 250, 155.

Brecher, K. 1982, Bull. Am. Astr. Soc., 19, 735.

Bussard, R.W., Burrows, A., and The, L.S. 1989, Ap.J., 341, 401.

Canizares, C.R. Kriss, G.A. and Feigelson, E.D. 1982, Ap. J. Letters, 253, L17.

Chevalier, R.A. 1982, Ap. J., 259, 302.

Chevalier, R.A. and Klein, R.I. 1978, Ap.J., 219, 994.

Chevalier, R.A., and Soker, N. 1989, Ap.J., 341, 867.

Chevalier, R.A. 1984, Ann. N.Y. Acad. Sci. 422, 215.

Chevalier, R.A. and Fransson C. 1987, Nature, 328, 44.

Cropper, M. et al. 1988, M.N.R.A.S., 231, 695.

Dawson,J., and Oberman, C. 1962, Phys. Fluids, 5, 517.
        1963, Phys. Fluids, 6, 394.

Dotani, T. et al. 1987, Nature, 330, 230.

Feigelson, E.D. et al. 1981, Ap.J., 251, 31.

Felten, J.E. and Morrison, P. 1963, Phys. Rev. Letters, 10, No.10, 454.

Felten, J.E. and Morrison, P. 1966, Phys. Rev. Letters, 146, No.3, 686.

Fishman et al. 1989, Adv. Space Res., in press.

Freund, H.P., Haber I., Palmadesso, P., and Papadopoulos, K. 1980, Phys. Fluids, 23, 518.

Gaisser, T.K., Harding, A.K., and Stanev, T. 1987, Nature, 329,314.

Gaisser, T.K., Harding, A.K., and Stanev, T. 1989, Ap. J., 345, 423.

Geldzahler, B.J., and Shaffer, D.B. 1982, Ap. J. Lett. 260, L69.

Gilmozzi, R. 1990, Proc. of Vulcano Workshop on Particle Physics and High Energy Astrophysics (IAS/CNR), in press.

Godfrey, B.B., Shanahan, W.R., and Thode, L.E., 1976, Phys. Fluids, 18, 46.

Goldreich, P. and Julian, W.H. 1969, Ap.J. 157, 869.

Grebenev, S.A. and Sunyaev, R.A. 1988, Soviet Astr. Letters, 14, No.8, 765.

Harding, A.K. 1990, Proc. of Vulcano Workshop on Particle Physics and High Energy Astrophysics (IAS/CNR), in press.

Itoh, M., et al. 1987, Nature 330, 233.

Jackson, J.D. 1960, Classical Electrodynamics (New York: Wiley).

Karovska, M., et al. 1988, IAU Circ., No. 4604.

Kato, T. 1976, Ap. J. Suppl., 30, 397.

Kazanas, D. and Ellison, D.C. 1986, Nature 319, 380.

Klein, R.I. and Chevalier, R.A. 1978, Ap.J., 223, L109.

Kristian, J., et al. 1989, Nature, 338, 234.

Leising, M.D., 1988, Nature, 332, 516.

Leising, M.D. and Share, G.H. 1990, Ap.J., 357, 195.

Lovelace, R.V.E., MacAuslan, J., and Burns, M. 1979, AIP Conf. Proc.,56, 399.

Makino, F. 1987, IAU Circ. 4336.

Matz, S.M. et al. 1988, Nature, 331, 416.

Middleditch, J., et al. 1989, IAU Circ., No. 4735.

Ostriker, J.P. 1987, Nature, 327, 208.

Papadopoulos, K. 1975, Phys. Fluids, 18, 1769.

Phillips, M.M, et al. 1988, A.J., 95, 1087.

Pinto, P.A. and Woosley, S.E. 1988, Nature, 333, 534.

Reynolds, S.P. 1982, Ap. J., 256, 38.

Rose, W.K., Guillory, J., Beall, J.H., and Kainer, S. 1984, Ap. J. 280, 550.

Rose, W.K., Beall, J.H., Guillory, J., and Kainer, S. 1987, Ap. J., 314, 95.

Rowland, H.L. 1977, Ph.D. thesis, University of Maryland.

Rukhadze, A.A., and Rukhlin, V.G. 1972, Soviet Phys. - JETP, 34, 93.

Schamel, H., Lee, Y.C., and Morales, G.J. 1975, Phys. Fluids, 19, 849.

Schott, G.A. 1912, Electromagnetic Radiation (Cambridge University Press: Cambridge).

Scott, J.S., Holman, G.D., Ionson, J.A., and Papadopoulos, K. 1980, Ap. J., 239, 769.

Shapiro, S.L., Lightman, R.P., and Eardley, D.M. 1976, Ap. J. 204, 187.

Smith, B., Goldstein, M., and Papadopoulos, K. 1976, Solar Phys., 46, 515.

Sood, R.K. et al. 1988, M.N.R.A.S., 234, 73.

Spitzer, L. 1956, Physics of Fully Ionized Gases (New York: Wiley).

Stocke, J.T. 1978, A.J., 83, 348.

Sunyaev, R. et al. 1987, Nature, 330,227.

Sutherland, P. et al. 1987 Proc. of IAU Symp 108, Tokyo.

Teegarden, B.J., et al. 1989, Nature, 339, 122.

Thode, L.E., and Sudan, R.N. 1973, Phys. Rev. Letters, 30, 732.

Tucker, W.H. 1975, Rad. Proc. in Astrophysics (MIT Press: Cambridge).

Tueller, J., et al. 1990, Ap.J., 351, L41.

Turtle, A.J. et al. 1987, Nature 327, 38.

Ubertini, P. et al. 1989, Ap.J., 337, L19.

Ulvestad, J.S., Wilson, A.S., and Sramek, R.A. 1981, Ap. J., 247, 419.

Vestrand, T.W. 1983, Ap. J. 271, 304.

Walker, R.C. 1984, Physics of Energy Transport in Extragalactic Radio Sources: Proc. of NRAO Workshop No. 9, A.H. Bridle and J. A. Eilek, eds.

Weiler, K.W., Sramek, R.A., and Panagia, N. 1986, Science, 231, 1251.

Woosley, S.E., and Phillips, M.M. 1988, Science, 240, 750.

Wilson, A.S., and Willis, A.G. 1980, Ap.J.,240, 429.

Zakharov, V.E. 1972, Soviet Phys. - JETP, 35, 908.

RADIO SPECTRAL VARIATIONS IN THE CYGNUS LOOP

D.A.GREEN
Dominion Radio Astrophysical Observatory
Herzberg Institute of Astrophysics
National Research Council
P.O. Box 248, Penticton,
British Columbia, V2A 6K3, Canada

ABSTRACT. Radio spectral index studies of the Cygnus Loop between 408 MHz and 2.695-GHz are presented. The strongly limb-brightened, north-eastern arc of the remnant has a radio spectral index, α, of ≈ 0.35, with similar spectral indices for the emission from other portions of the northern part of the remnant. Emission from the southern extension of the remnant generally has a steeper radio spectrum than the north, with α up to ≈ 0.55. These results are discussed in relation to available theories for the radio emission from supernova remnants, and to the radio structure of the remnant.

1. Introduction

Supernova remnants (SNRs) are thought to be source of many cosmic rays, and radio observations of them are of interest in relation to the acceleration of cosmic rays as the spectrum of the radio emission allows us to investigate the spectrum of relativistic electrons present in them. (For a electron energy power spectrum of the form $N(E) \propto E^{-\mu}$, radio synchrotron emission is produced from these electrons in the presence of magnetic fields, with the radio flux density, S, related to observing frequency, ν, as $S \propto \nu^{-\alpha}$, where $\mu = 2\alpha + 1$.) Indeed, the "average" radio spectrum of "shell" SNRs is ≈ 0.5, which agrees well with what is expected from the Fermi shock acceleration mechanism (*e.g.*, Drury, this volume). An interesting and surprising result (*e.g.*, Scheuer 1984; Green 1988) is that, although "shell" SNRs show a considerable range (0.3 to 0.8) of radio spectral index, α, there is little evidence for spectral variations from point-to-point within individual objects. However, this lack of evidence is largely due to observational difficulties in making accurate images of SNRs at widely spaced radio frequencies. Here I briefly describe radio spectral index studies of the Cygnus Loop SNR which reveal significant variations, and provide some clues as to whether or not the shock acceleration mechanism is currently at work (for electrons) within this remnant.

2. Background

The Cygnus Loop is a large ($\approx 3.5 \times 2.5$ degree^2) distorted "shell" SNR that has been studied extensively at a variety of wavelengths. At a distance of ≈ 0.5 kpc (Braun & Strom 1986) the Cygnus Loop is $\approx 30 \times 20$ pc^2, which implies that it is many thousands of years old and it is often considered to be a "typical" middle-aged SNR. In both X-rays (Ku *et al.* 1984) and the infrared (Braun & Strom 1986) the northern part of the Cygnus Loop is a nearly circular limb-brightened "shell" $\approx 1°4$ in radius that is incomplete to the south,

M. M. Shapiro et al. (eds.), Cosmic Rays, Supernovae and the Interstellar Medium, 207–212.
© *1991 Kluwer Academic Publishers. Printed in the Netherlands.*

below a declination of $\approx 29°30'$. These observations are generally taken to imply that the non-circular shape of the Cygnus Loop is due to a "break-out" of the SNR shock front into a region of lower than average density in the south. The obvious asymmetry of the remnant means that it is a good object to observe in search for radio spectral variations, as shock conditions presumably vary considerably between the north and the south. Indeed, the Cygnus Loop is one of only a few Galactic SNRs (e.g., Fürst & Reich 1988) for which there is evidence for spectral variations (Sastry et al. 1981).

Two processes have been put forward to explain the radio emission from "shell" SNRs: Fermi acceleration of electrons by the remnant's shocks (e.g., Drury, this volume); and the enhancement, in the case of older remnants such as the Cygnus Loop, of radio emission from existing interstellar relativistic electrons and magnetic field compressed by the SNR shock (e.g., van der Laan 1962). For the shock acceleration mechanism a radio spectral index, α, of ≈ 0.5 is expected. The radio spectrum of the Cygnus Loop is reported to have a break near 1 GHz, which might be expected if van der Laan's compression mechanism is at work. The spectrum of the Galactic background emission has a break at a few hundred MHz (with α varying from ≈ 0.3 to 0.8; Webster 1974); which would be shifted to higher frequencies.

3.   Observations

The Cygnus Loop was observed at 408 MHz with the DRAO Synthesis Telescope with a resolution of $\approx 6.7 \times 3.3$ arcmin^2 (NS×EW) in 1987 and 1988. Two advantages of the small antenna size of the DRAO Synthesis Telescope are that is has a relatively large field-of-view, and that small interferometer baselines (down to ≈ 13 m) can be observed, so that the synthesized images are sensitive to extended emission on large scales. However, even with the Synthesis Telescope, there is considerable extended emission from the Cygnus Loop and its surroundings that is not properly represented in the synthesized image. But, since the missing large-scale structure corresponds to only small interferometer baselines, they can be deduced from the single-antenna observations of Haslam et al. (1982) to provide an image that is complete in structure on all angular scales down to the resolution of the Synthesis Telescope image. Figure 1 shows the final image of the Cygnus Loop at 408 MHz. This is a CLEANed image, corrected for the primary response of the Synthesis Telescope, and with missing large-scale structure added.

4. Results

4.1   RADIO STRUCTURE OF THE CYGNUS LOOP

Simplistically, the radio structure of the northern "shell" of the Cygnus Loop can be thought of (e.g., Green 1984) as the double limb-brightened arcs expected if the radio emission is from compression of existing relativistic electrons in a large-scale magnetic field, although there are complications to this picture (e.g., the limb brightening is not symmetric, and there is more extended emission from the inside of the "shell" in the west than the east). Alternatively, if the radio emission is due to shock acceleration, the strong limb-brightening of the north-eastern rim and the lack of emission from near 20^h54^m, $29°50'$ and 20^h53^m, $32°0'$ may by due to varying efficiencies in shock acceleration depending on the orientation of the magnetic field with respect to the shock front. In either case, a dominant large-scale magnetic field near to the plane of the sky is required to explain the strong contrast seen in the radio between the bright limb-brightened arc and the regions around it.

408 MHz (smoothed)

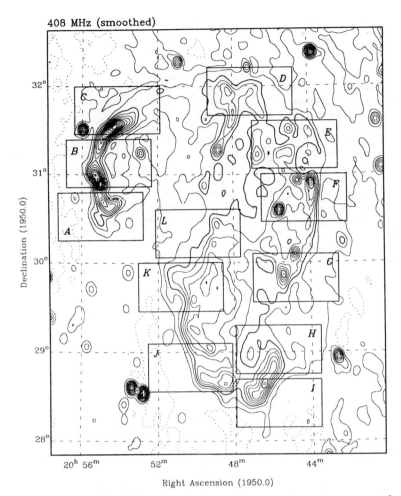

Figure 1. The Cygnus Loop at 408 MHz smoothed to a resolution of of 6.7 × 4.8 arcmin^2 at a position angle of 4°.8. The contours are at 22, 31, 40, ... 166 K in brightness temperature. The lowest two contours are dashed, and the contours at 58, 103 and 148 K are thicker than the others. The the positions of the regions for which T–T plots are shown in Figure 2 are also shown.

4.2 DERIVATION OF SPECTRAL INDICES

For spectral index studies the present observations have been compared with the 2.695-GHz observations of Keen *et al.* (1973). The 408-MHz and 2.695-GHz images were re-gridded to the same projection and smoothed to a common resolution of 6.7 × 4.8 arcmin^2 at a position angle of 4°.8. These smoothed images cannot be compared directly to produce a spectral index image, as the large-scale baselevels of each image have been determined differently. Spectral comparison can, however, be made between these images using plots of brightness temperature at one frequency against that at the other frequency ("T–T plots") for a number of positions in a given region. Provided that regions of limited extent are used the variations in the different large-scale baselevels are small in each region in comparison to the range of the emission from the remnant. Appropriate local baselevels can be chosen for each region, and spectral indices deduced from the slope of a line fitted to the points corresponding to brighter emission. T–T plots have been made for many regions covering the Cygnus Loop, as indicated in Figure 1, each $\approx 0.5 \times 1$ degree^2 (NS×EW) in extent (*i.e.*, the structure within these individual regions at 408 MHz is almost solely dependent on the Synthesis Telescope observations, rather than from the large-scale emission added from the survey of Haslam *et al.*). The T–T plots for these regions are shown in Figure 2. As there are several bright, compact sources within the remnant or nearby, some portions of the 408-MHz image corresponding to these sources were excluded from the data shown in Figure 2. The approximate noise on the images used for these T–T plots, estimated from areas away from the Cygnus Loop, are ≈ 0.02 K for the 2.695-GHz data, and from ≈ 1 K in the south to ≈ 3 K in the north for the 408-MHz data.

For each region, a brightness temperature spectral index, β (where $T \propto \nu^{-\beta}$), was derived by fitting a straight line to the data points above gate values at both 408 MHz and 2.695 GHz which are shown on Figure 2. The uncertainties in the derived spectral indices were obtained from the formal statistical error in the gradient best-fit straight line, and the uncertainty due to varying the chosen gate values slightly (by ± 2 K at 408 MHz, and by ± 0.025 K at 2.695 GHz). The flux density spectral indices, α (where $S \propto \nu^{-\alpha}$, and $\alpha = \beta - 2$), derived for each of the areas are given in Figure 2, together with their uncertainties rounded up to the nearest 0.01. A change of 10 per cent, in one or other of the brightness temperature scales, which is about the expected absolute accuracy of the observations, would result in a systematic change of 0.05 in all of the spectral indices derived here.

5. Discussion and Conclusions

It is clear from Figure 2 that there are significant variations in the average spectral index between 408 MHz and 2.695 GHz of different regions of the Cygnus Loop. The main result of the spectral index studies is that, between 408 MHz and 2.695 GHz, the northern "shell" of the Cygnus Loop generally has a flatter spectrum than that of the southern extension.

This result, can be interpreted in several ways, depending on the mechanism(s) at work. If the integrated spectrum of the Cygnus Loop does indeed have a spectral break, then the compression mechanism is appealing, as it is expected to produce a spectrum with a break. Indeed, Moffat (1971) argued that the whole of the radio emission from the Cygnus Loop can be explained by the compression mechanism. However, the derivation of the expected flux density for a remnant with this model is difficult. First, our knowledge of relativistic electrons and magnetic field in the ISM is limited to observations of the non-thermal Galactic radio emission, which involve integrations along a line-of-sight, and are only available accurately with poor angular resolution. Second, deciding on the correct compression factor is not straightforward. The complexity of the emission seen from the Cygnus Loop at radio and other wavelengths implies that there are regions with a range of compression factors with different filling factors. The effective compression factor for some portions of the Cygnus Loop may in fact be large, as cooling behind the SNR shock may produce highly compressed cylindrical filaments (*e.g.*, Smith & Dickel 1983). Dickel & Willis (1982) discuss the consequences of enhanced compression due to cooling, and show that the radio emission from the remnant can be explained by filaments compressed by a factor of 100 with a filling factor of 1/100. They also argue that, under certain conditions, the enhanced magnetic field in the highly compressed filaments will produce spectral ageing which could produce a break frequency near ≈ 1 GHz (see also DeNoyer 1974).

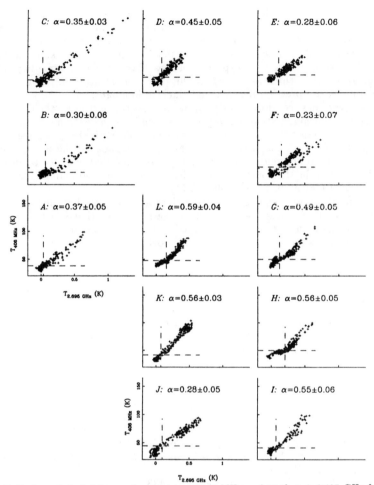

Figure 2. T–T plots of the brightness temperature at 408 MHz against that at 2.695 GHz for the regions shown in Figure 1. The spectral index of the brighter emission in each region, and the estimated uncertainty in this value (see text) are shown on each plot.

If the emission from the whole remnant is from the van der Laan compression mechanism, possibly enhanced by cooling, then either the average compression factor or the ambient magnetic field and underlying spectrum of existing relativistic electrons in the regions around the north and south of the remnant are different. The fact that the northern "shell" is generally more limb-brightened and has more optical filaments than the south implies that the average compression factor, possibly enhanced by cooling, may be larger in the north. So, for an underlying population of relativistic electrons that would produce a radio spectrum with a break, a flatter radio spectrum would be produced in the north compared with the south, because of the larger compression factor. On the other hand, the fact that the southern part of the remnant shows less limb-brightening and fewer optical filaments than the north suggests that the compression mechanism is less efficient here, and the shock acceleration mechanism may instead be dominant. Also, the shock speeds are expected to be larger in the southern extension, a factor which may be important in determining the efficiency of the shock acceleration mechanism (which is thought to be at work in young SNRs which have high shock speeds). Moreover, the radio spectral index in much of the south is near the canonical 0.5 expected from the shock acceleration mechanism, and is comparable to the spectral indices of young shell remnants (*e.g.*, Green 1988). Observations at a third frequency would allow confirmation, or otherwise, of the spectral break if the compression mechanism is indeed dominant.

There is, however, an exception to the main result that the northern "shell" has a flatter spectrum than the southern extension: region J, which is in the extreme southeast of the remnant, has an anomalously low spectral index compared with the other regions in the south. The spectrum of region J, with $\alpha = 0.28 \pm 0.05$, argues against the shock acceleration being at work as it is so different from the canonical $\alpha = 0.5$ that is expected in this case. This anomalous region in the southeast does show some limb-brightening (see the higher resolution images of Green 1984 and Moffat 1971).

The present results provide some interesting clues as to the mechanisms at work accelerating electrons in the Cygnus Loop, including the possibility that shock acceleration is *not* currently dominant in this particular remnant. Further observations of this type will allow better constraints on where and when the shock acceleration mechanism is at work with respect to electrons in SNRs.

Acknowledgements

The DRAO Synthesis Telescope is operated by the National Research Council of Canada as a National Facility. The 408-MHz channel on the Synthesis Telescope is known as the "Reber Facility" in gratitude to Grote Reber, who partially funded its development.

References

Braun, R. & Strom, R.G. (1986). *Astr. Astrophys.*, **164**, 208.

DeNoyer, L.K. (1974). *Astr. J.*, **79**, 1253.

Dickel, J.R. & Willis, A.G. (1980). *Astr. Astrophys.*, **85**, 55.

Fürst, E. & Reich, W. (1988). In: *Supernova Shells and their Birth Events*, p33, ed. Kundt, W., (Springer-Verlag, Berlin).

Green, D.A. (1984). *Mon. Not. R. astr. Soc.*, **211**, 433.

Green, D.A. (1988). In: *Genesis and Propagation of Cosmic Rays*, p205, eds Shapiro, M.M. & Wefel, J.P., (Reidel, Dordrecht).

Haslam, C.G.T., Salter, C.J., Stoffel, H. & Wilson, W.E. (1982). *Astr. Astrophys. Suppl.*, **47**, 1.

Keen, N.J., Wilson, W.E., Haslam, C.G.T., Graham, D.A. & Thomasson, P. (1973). *Astr. Astrophys.*, **28**, 197.

Ku, W.H.-M., Kahn, S.M., Pisarski, R. & Long, K.S. (1984). *Astrophys. J.*, **278**, 615.

Moffat, P.H. (1971). *Mon. Not. R. astr. Soc.*, **153**, 401.

Sastry, Ch.V., Dwarakanath, K.S. & Shevgaonkar, R.K. (1981). *J. Astrophys. Astr.*, **2**, 339.

Scheuer, P.A.G. (1984). *Adv. Space Res.*, **4**, 337.

Smith, M.D. & Dickel, J.R. (1983). *Astrophys. J.*, **265**, 272.

van der Laan, H. (1962). *Mon. Not. R. astr. Soc.*, **124**, 179.

Webster, A.S. (1974). *Mon. Not. R. astr. Soc.*, **166**, 355.

GAMMA RAY ASTROPHYSICS AT ENERGIES UP TO 10 GeV

R.S. WHITE
Institute of Geophysics and Planetary Physics and
Department of Physics
University of California, Riverside
Riverside, CA 92521-0412

R. SILBERBERG
E.O. Hulburt Center for Space Research
Naval Research Laboratory
Washington, D.C. 20375-5000

ABSTRACT. During the last two decades, gamma-ray astronomy has developed into a quantitative science, with accurate flux measurements from several sources. The Crab pulsar emits $6.17 \times 10^{-4} \ E^{-2.2}$ photons $cm^{-2} \ s^{-1} \ MeV^{-1}$ from 50 KeV to 5 GeV. This corresponds to about 2×10^{35} erg s^{-1} in each of two decades of energy. The Vela pulsar emits $3.6 \times 10^{-4} \ E^{-1.6}$ photons $cm^{-2} \ s^{-1} \ MeV^{-1}$ at energies 1 to 30 MeV. The luminosity of gamma rays between 10 MeV and 1 GeV is about 2×10^{34} erg/s. For the Crab nebula, the gamma ray flux is $3 \times 10^{-3} \ E^{-2.3}$ photons $cm^{-2} \ s^{-1}$ MeV^{-1} from 1 KeV to 3 GeV. The flux of the ^{26}Al line of 1.81 MeV (if assumed to be an extended source) is $(4 \pm 0.4) \times 10^{-4}$ photons $cm^{-2} \ s^{-1}$ rad^{-1}. The e^+ annihilation line in the Galactic plane is $(1.6 \pm 0.3) \times 10^{-3}$ photons $cm^{-1} \ s^{-1} \ rad^{-1}$ on which a variable flux of $\leq 1 \times 10^{-3} \ cm^{-1} \ s^{-1}$ from the Galactic center is superimposed at certain times. Theoretical models of the sources and observations relate gamma-ray astrophysics to pulsars, neutron stars, black holes, and interstellar clouds, super-novae and supernova remnants. The processes of nucleosynthesis in supernovae and novae, and pair production near black holes yield gamma-ray lines. Gamma-ray observations are also related to particle acceleration processes at pulsars, neutron stars, supernova remnants, and near black holes.

213

M. M. Shapiro et al. (eds.), Cosmic Rays, Supernovae and the Interstellar Medium, 213–247.
© 1991 Kluwer Academic Publishers. Printed in the Netherlands.

Outline of Topics and Sections

1. INTRODUCTION
2. EARLY HISTORY OF MEDIUM ENERGY GAMMA RAY OBSERVATIONS
3. GAMMA RAY DETECTORS AND TELESCOPES
4. GALACTIC SOURCES
5. GALACTIC LINES
6. NUCLEOSYNTHESIS OF GAMMA RAY EMITTING NUCLEI
* 7. GAMMA RAY BURSTS
8. GEMINGA
* 9. CYG X-1, PROBABLE ACCRETING BLACK HOLE
10. GAMMA RAYS FROM THE INTERSTELLAR MEDIUM
*11. GAMMA-RAY LINES FROM NUCLEAR EXCITATION AND SPALLATION,
AND FROM THE SUN
12. ACTIVE GALACTIC NUCLEI
13. THE GAMMA RAY OBSERVATORY (GRO)

* Brief Highlights, for details refer to 1988 Erice lectures in NATO
ASI book, see references to Hurley, Epstein, Liang and Silberberg et al.
(1989) in this paper.

1. INTRODUCTION

Gamma-ray observations permit the study of many important problems in
high-energy astrophysics, e.g. sites of acceleration of particles,
explosive nucleosynthesis, pulsars, accreting neutron stars and black
holes, active galactic nuclei, and nuclear and electromagnetic
interactions of cosmic rays. Gamma rays can also serve as tracers of
antimatter and the decay of massive particles postulated in some recent
cosmological theories. Observational gamma-ray astrophysics is a
rapidly developing new field--less than a quarter century old. The
year (1991) will see the launch of the Gamma Ray Observatory (GRO) and
some of the lecturers during the next course of the International
School of Cosmic-Ray Astrophysics will be able to discuss the new
observations based on GRO.

In the allotted time, we cannot present an in-depth review of the
field, but present briefly the history, experimental techniques and
problems and highlights of numerous topics. The latter include gamma
rays from (a) pulsars and supernova remnants, (b) time-variable
electron-positron pair production at the Galactic center, and diffuse
emission of e^+ annihilation - probably generated from radioactive
nuclei produced in nucleosynthesis, (c) the observation of the ^{26}Al
line, and possible sites of its nucleosynthesis, (d) nucleosynthesis of
gamma-ray emitting nuclei in supernovae and novae, which are prime
candidates for observation by the GRO OSSE experiment, (e) the gamma-
ray burst objects - still poorly understood, giving rise to numerous
speculative theories, (f) the gamma-ray source, Geminga, whose

identification with weak radio, X-ray and optical sources is still unestablished, (g) accreting black holes in binary systems - Cyg X-1 is an example, (h) gamma rays from solar flare particle interactions in the chromosphere, and (i) gamma rays from active galactic nuclei, which are probably powered by ultra-massive black holes. Also a brief discussion of the GRO detectors and experimental objectives will be presented.

2. EARLY HISTORY OF MEDIUM ENERGY GAMMA RAY OBSERVATIONS

Celestial gamma ray astronomy dates back to the discovery in 1967 of gamma rays from the galactic center direction by George Clark, George Garmire and William Kraushaar (Clark et al., 1968) of the Massachusetts Institute of Technology. They used a wide angle scintillator telescope that detected gamma rays with energies > 100 MeV by electron-positron pair production on the satellite OSO 3. During 16 months of observation they detected 621 cosmic gamma rays with energies above 50 MeV. The gamma rays came primarily from the galactic plane with a major concentration in the direction of the galactic center and a minor one from the anticenter direction. No point sources were identified and cosmic ray interactions with the hydrogen gas in the galactic plane provided a satisfactory explanation of the gamma rays. The detector for this pioneer work was necessarily small with an efficiency of only 2.5 cm²-ster and angular resolution of about 15° half width at half maximum, HWHM. Balloon flights followed with large spark chambers but with short flights of a day that confirmed the galactic gamma rays with energies E > 50 MeV.

The next major contribution to gamma ray astronomy came from the larger higher sensitivity spark chamber flown on the second small astronomy satellite SAS 2, from November 15, 1972 to June 1973 by Carl Fichtel, Don Kniffen, David Thompson, Robert Hartman and others from NASA Goddard Space Flight Center (Fichtel et al., 1975) and Hakki Ogelman, Mehmet Ozel and Tumay Tumer at METU, Ankara, Turkey. This detector, sensitive to gamma rays from about 35 to 200 MeV, had the advantages of large area (640 cm²); better angular resolution (2° for individual photons and 0.5° for local sources); and lower background. Detailed observations of the celestial sphere, concentrated in the region of the galactic plane found that most of the gamma ray sources, excluding point sources, were confined to the galactic plane a few deg thick with a broad maximum in the direction of the galactic center. Four strong gamma ray sources--the Vela pulsar PSR 0833-45; the Crab pulsar PSR 0531+21 and the Crab Nebula; γ195+5 later called Geminga, and Cyg X-3, an x-ray source in the Cygnus region--were discovered along with some weaker sources. Unfortunately, this productive satellite was terminated prematurely when a power system failed.

Much of the gamma ray astronomy information to date for E > 50 MeV came from the 7 years of observations with a spark chamber on the European satellite COS B launched by NASA on August 9, 1975 (Hermsen et al., 1977). The collaboration included scientists from the Max-Planck-Institut für Extraterrestrische Physik, Garching, West Germany; Cosmic

Ray Working Group, Leiden, Netherlands, Istituto di Scienze Fisiche, Universita di Milano with the Instituto Fisica, Cosmica del CNR, Palermo, Italy; Service d'Electronique Physique Centre d'Etudes Nucleaires de Saclay, Gif-sur-Yvette, France and the Space Science Department, ESTEC, Noordwijk, Netherlands. Their spark chamber was similar to that of SAS 2, but with the addition of a calorimeter for recording the energy of the electron-positron pair to estimate the energy of the incident photon. The spark chamber had a maximum area-efficiency product of 50 cm^2 that peaked at 500 MeV and was sensitive from 70 MeV to 5 GeV. The angular resolution varied from 7° FWHM at 70 MeV to 2° FWHM at 5 GeV. The fractional energy uncertainty varied from 0.5 at 70 MeV to 1.0 at 5 GeV with a minimum of 0.4 at 150 MeV. The strongest sources gave count rates of 1 photon/hr and the weakest about 1 photon/d.

In addition to the broad galactic features associated with the galactic arms and molecular clouds are the sharp peaks of the point sources. The most intense gamma ray source observed for E > 50 MeV by SAS 2 and COS B is the Vela Pulsar PSR 0833-45. Two strong sources, the Crab Pulsar PSR 0531+21 and Geminga, 2CG 195+04, are located near the galactic anticenter direction. There is also a prominent wide peak in the Cygnus region.

3. GAMMA RAY DETECTORS AND TELESCOPES

Gamma rays, unlike visible light or other parts of the electromagnetic spectrum, cannot be focused. They are not reflected by mirrors and are not converged by lenses. The gamma rays travel in straight lines from the source and diverge according to the inverse square law. Only those gamma rays that penetrate into and interact in the detector are counted. For this reason and because the interaction mean free paths are long (from a few to a few tens of g cm^{-2}) backgrounds from the atmosphere and material surrounding the detector are high and the fluxes from the celestial sources are low. Thus progress in gamma ray astronomy has been slow compared with astronomies at other energies.

3.1. Sodium Iodide (Thalium) Scintillation Detector

Favorite detectors from about 30 keV to a few MeV are scintillation detectors such as NaI(Tℓ). Gamma rays are absorbed by the photoelectric effect giving up all their energies to the scintillator, part of which is converted to light that is collected and amplified by a photomultiplier; or the gamma rays are Compton scattered by electrons in atoms in the detector giving up part of their energies to the scintillator. The NaI(Tℓ) detector (Johnson and Haymes, 1973), shown in Figure 1 was used by the Rice Group in 1972 to discover the electron-positron annihilation radiation in the direction of the galactic center. The detector was surrounded with an active NaI(Tℓ) collimator with an aperture of 24 deg full width half maximum, FWHM. This detector was flown in a gondola suspended from a balloon flying above all but 3 g cm^{-2} of the atmosphere. The detector could be oriented toward any particular right ascension and declination with the gondola system shown in Figure 2 (Johnson and Haymes, 1973). This type of detector has made many useful measurements but is limited in angular resolution to about 10 deg, energy resolution to about 6% and is bothered by backgrounds produced by interactions of cosmic ray protons and their secondaries in the material of the collimator.

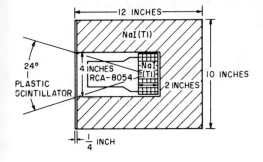

Figure 1. Schematic diagram of the Rice University NaI(Tℓ) scintillation detector system. The well-shaped guard crystal rejects charged particles and suppresses Compton scatters by active anti-coincidences. The plastic scintillator rejects charged particles from the forward direction but is transparent to γ-rays.

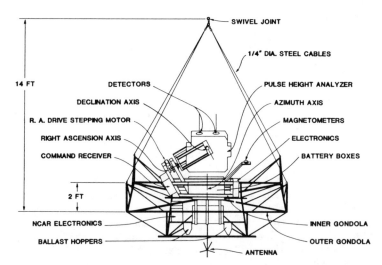

Figure 2. Rice University balloon-borne telescope orientation system showing two detectors mounted parallel in an equatorial mount. The swivel joint, connected to the balloon via the recovery parachute, reduces the coupling of the telescope to balloon rotation.

3.2. Germanium Detectors

It is possible to obtain considerably better energy resolutions of about 1 keV at 550 keV with germanium detectors. These are usually cooled to liquid nitrogen temperatures to reduce noise. An example of a 130 cm³ high purity Ge detector (Leventhal and MacCallum, 1980) is

shown in Figure 3.
This detector was
flown on a balloon by
the Bell Labs-Sandia
Group to measure
accurately the energy
of the positron-
electron annihilation
radiation from the
galactic center
direction. A NaI
active collimator was
used. A cold finger
extended from a
liquid nitrogen tank
to the Ge crystal.
To date, Ge detectors
have been rather
expensive, limited to
several hundred cm³.
They have measured
very accurate
positions and widths
of strong narrow
lines, but because of

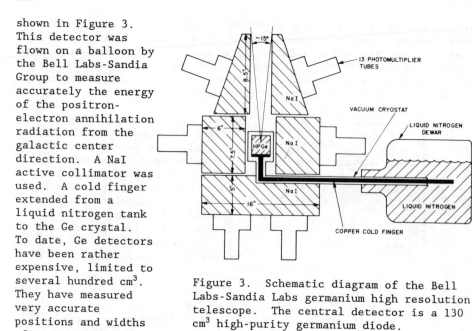

Figure 3. Schematic diagram of the Bell
Labs-Sandia Labs germanium high resolution
telescope. The central detector is a 130
cm³ high-purity germanium diode.

small volumes their sensitivities are low for wide lines and continuous
spectra. Backgrounds of gamma ray lines produced by cosmic ray proton
interactions in the NaI and Ge can also be a problem.

3.3.   Double Compton Scatter Telescopes

To increase the sensitivity for identifying weak sources from 0.3 to 30
MeV, measure broad lines and reduce background from cosmic ray proton
interactions with materials around the detector, the double Compton
scatter telescope is useful. The University of California, Riverside
Group used the telescope shown in Figure 4 to measure the gamma rays
from the Vela (Tumer et al., 1984) and Crab (White et al., 1985)
Pulsars. A gamma ray scatter by the Compton interaction from an
electron in the top liquid scintillator tank, continues on and then
Compton scatters from an electron or is absorbed by the photoelectric
effect in the second liquid scintillator tank. Each tank is divided
into 28 cells, each viewed by a separate photomultiplier. The energy
deposits of the electrons are measured in each scintillator. The two
cells where the interactions take place are identified to give the
scattered gamma ray direction, and the time of flight of the gamma ray
between interactions is measured. Plastic scintillators completely
surround each scintillator tank to veto charged particles. Neutrons
and upward moving gamma rays are vetoed by time of flight measured to
0.5 ns. Since each event is accurately timed to 10 μs, phase diagrams
can be measured even for the shortest period (1.5 ms), of any pulsar

yet discovered. Sufficient information is obtained by this telescope to measure the energy of a gamma ray with an uncertainty of 10 to 20%, depending on the angle of scatter. Its direction is uncertain to a circle on the sky. The position of the gamma ray source is determined from the overlap of circles. The telescope has a wide aperture for sky surveys. And because of its large effective area and accurate timing, is especially useful for pulsar measurements. Detectors with lots of hydrogen, such as the double Compton scatter telescope, are subject to a background of 2.2 MeV gamma rays. Cosmic ray interactions in the atmosphere produce neutrons that are slowed by elastic collisions with hydrogen in the detector. When the slow neutrons are captured by protons the 2.2 MeV gamma rays are emitted.

3.4. Pair Spark Chambers

Above a few tens of MeV for low atomic number elements and a few MeV for high, the dominant gamma ray interaction is electron-positron pair production in the electric field of the nucleus of an atom. The threshold for the reaction is 1.02 MeV, the sum of the electron and positron rest masses. From conservation of energy, the photon energy must equal the pair rest mass energies plus their kinetic energies. The positron direction is opposite the electron direction in the center of mass system. When transformed into the laboratory system, the pair is emitted in the photon's forward direction, for photon energies $E_\gamma \gg m_ec^2$ the pair angle is about $m_ec^2E^{-1}$. This has two useful consequences. The direction of the incident gamma ray can be determined from the mean of the electron and positron directions (or from momenta of the electron and positron) and the opening angle is a measure of the gamma ray

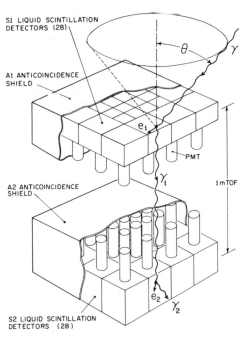

Figure 4. Schematic drawing of the UCR double Compton the scatter telescope.

energy. The latter is further complicated by the scattering of the electron and positron in the high atomic number interaction material. So the scattering itself is also used to measure the energies of the electron and positron.

A schematic diagram of the SAS 2 spark chamber telescope (Derdeyn et al., 1972) is given in Figure 5. It is the first satellite spark chamber telescope, a pioneer in celestial high energy gamma ray observations and set the standards for subsequent measurements. The assembly includes 16 wire grid spark chamber modules above the four central plastic scintillators and 16 below. Each module has two planes of 200 parallel evenly spaced wires strung across the 25 cm x 25 cm opening. Tungsten plates, 0.10 cm thick, separate the

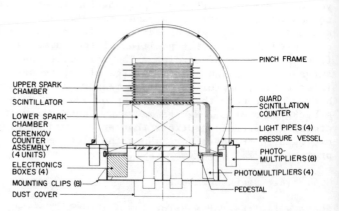

UPPER SPARK CHAMBER
SCINTILLATOR
LOWER SPARK CHAMBER
CERENKOV COUNTER ASSEMBLY (4 UNITS)
ELECTRONICS BOXES (4)
MOUNTING CLIPS (8)
DUST COVER

PINCH FRAME
GUARD SCINTILLATION COUNTER
LIGHT PIPES (4)
PRESSURE VESSEL
PHOTO-MULTIPLIERS (8)
PHOTOMULTIPLIERS (4)
PEDESTAL

Figure 5. Schematic diagram of the SAS-2 digitized spark chamber gamma ray telscope.

spark chamber modules. The spark chamber assembly is triggered by a charged particle that passes through one of the four plastic scintillators and the directional lucite Cerenkov counters immediately below, if there is no coincident pulse in the surrounding plastic scintillator dome. High voltage is then applied to the spark chamber and a memory scan of the ferrite cores at the end of each wire, set by the spark induced current, begins. The effective area of the detector is 50 cm^2 at 100 MeV and the sensitive aperture about 1/4 ster. The efficiency for detecting gamma rays is about 0.25, and the timing accuracy is better than 2 ms. The uncertainty in the gamma ray direction is about 1.5 deg.

3.5. Balloons as Detector Carriers

Gamma rays below about 100 GeV cannot be detected from the surface of the earth. Because the earth's atmosphere is 1000 g cm^{-2} thick and gamma ray mean free paths vary from a few to tens of g cm^{-2}, celestial gamma rays cannot penetrate to a detector on the ground. Since the 1960's, large zero pressure balloons have been used to carry gamma ray detectors to within a few g cm^{-2} of the top of the atmosphere. They are typically made of thin, 1 mil, polyethylene filled with 1 million m^3 helium gas at NTP. Detectors that weigh 1000 kg or more are carried for one to two days. Data are telemetered to the launch site at rates up to 50,000 bits s^{-1}. When the balloon drifts out of telemetry range, the flight is terminated and the payload descends on a parachute. A crush pad under the payload absorbs the shock on landing.

A major limitation of balloon flights has been the short observation times. The longest flights, within telemetry range, are possible at the time of the upper level wind turnabout, at a few g cm^{-2} residual atmosphere, for a couple of weeks in the Spring and Fall.

Then the high level winds are at a minimum and variable. At other times, when the winds are more than 100 km hr^{-1}, the balloon speeds out of telemetry range in a few hours. Transcontinental and transatlantic flights have been tried. Down range telemetry receivers and on board storage of data are useful and have been successful.

Figure 6 shows a sketch of a typical zero pressure balloon launch (National Scientific Balloon Facility User Manual, 1985). The balloon and parachute are laid on the ground with the payload suspended from the launch vehicle. The balloon is filled from tubes, not shown, while it rolls through the spool held in place by the spool vehicle. At launch the balloon is released from the spool and carried by the ground wind over the launch vehicle. The balloon then lifts the payload from the launch vehicle and climbs to drift altitude. After termination the payload is recovered and trucked back to the launch site.

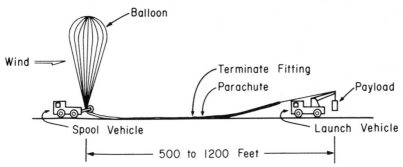

Figure 6. Schematic drawing of a zero pressure scientific balloon on the flight line ready for launch.

3.6. Satellites as Detector Carriers

Satellite observations which include the discovery of the gamma ray galactic plane by OSO 3; the Vela and Crab pulsars, other point sources and the contour of the galactic disk by SAS 2; and the detailed measurements of 25 galactic and extragalactic sources by COS B during seven years of observation have made the major contributions to our knowledge of celestial gamma ray sources. The satellite contributions have been especially important for the high energies of 35 to 5000 MeV. The successes can be attributed to the long observation times, low backgrounds of the spark chambers and location of sources to about a degree. Additional information has been obtained by the NaI scintillators on HEAO 1 at gamma ray energies below about 1 MeV and by the high resolution Ge detector for gamma ray lines on HEAO 3. The NaI detector on OSO 7 discovered gamma ray lines from solar flares and the one on SMM has studied gamma rays from many flares over several years. An artist's drawing of the COS B satellite is shown in Figure 7 with cutaways to reveal some of the inside components. An incident gamma ray penetrates the thermal blanket, 7, from above and interacts in the spark chamber, 2. The produced electron and positron pass through the trigger scintillators, 3, and deposit their energies in the calorimeter, 4. A few of the important parts of the satellite such as the solar cells, 13, nitrogen attitude control tank, 11, neon flush tank, 12, and spin thruster, 9, along with others are also identified. The mass of the satellite is 300 kg, its diameter 140 cm and its height 113 cm. The orbit perigee was 350 km, apogee 100,000 km, inclination 90° and period 37 h. Measurements were taken outside the intense region of the earth's radiation belt.

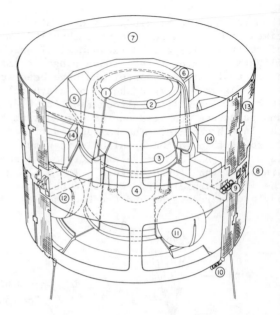

Figure 7. Schematic drawing of the COS-B satellite.

4. GALACTIC SOURCES

4.1. Pulsars

The gamma ray sources most easily identified because of their pulsed period signatures, are the pulsars. Their periods are so precise and variations in time so predictable there can be no mistake in their identifications. The pulsars were discovered with radio waves for which a significant intensity could be built up in light curves of intensity versus phase in a few hundred periods. Phase is measured in fractions of a period. For gamma rays with energies of about 1 MeV to about 1 GeV, it has been difficult to discover pulsars with periods of fractions of seconds. Therefore, searches for gamma ray pulsars have used previously identified radio or x-ray pulsars whose periods and period derivatives were well established. Searches have been made at E > 50 MeV by SAS 2 (Thompson et al. 1983) and COS B (Buccheri, et al. 1983), at energies of 1 to 30 MeV, (Graser and Schonfelder 1983; Sweeney et al, 1987) and 15 KeV to 17 MeV (Knight et al, 1982). However, to date only two gamma ray pulsars have been confirmed. These are the Crab Pulsar PSR 0531+21 and the Vela Pulsar PSR 0833-45. Pulsars reported at energies > 10^{11} eV are given by White in lecture ___, these proceedings..

4.1.1. The Crab Pulsar, PSR 0531+21 (2CG 184+05). The Crab Pulsar,

one of the most studied objects in the sky, has been observed
throughout the electromagnetic spectrum from radio waves to gamma rays
of E > 10^{12} eV covering more than 17 orders of magnitude in energy.
The light curves for 430 MHz radio waves, optical, 1.5-10 keV soft x-
rays, 18-163 keV medium x-rays, 100-400 keV hard x-rays, 1-20 MeV
gamma rays and > 50 MeV gamma rays are shown in Figure 8 of White
(Lecture___, these proceedings). The light curves are similar at all
energies. The first pulse peaks are aligned at the same phase as the
radio waves and the second pulse peaks all follow by the same 0.42 in
phase. However, the shapes of the pulse peaks, their relative heights
and the region between peaks vary somewhat with photon energy. The
inner pulse region (between the peaks) appears highest at energies of
tens and hundreds of keV.

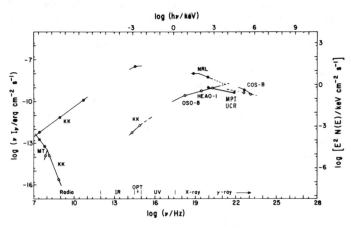

Figure 8. Log log plot of the energy distribution of gamma rays per
decade of energy versus energy of the gamma ray for the Crab on the
right ordinate and upper abscissa. Frequency units are used on the
left ordinate and bottom abscissa. Solid circles represent
observations of the Crab nebula, open circles the Crab pulsar and
solid squares the sum of the nebula and pulsar. Symbols representing
observing groups are: MPI, Graser and Schönfelder, 1982; UCR, White
et al., 1985; COS-B, Lichti et al., 1980; HEAO, Knight, 1981; NRL,
Strickman et al., 1979; OSO-8, Pravdo and Serlemitsos, 1981; KK,
Kundt and Krotscheck, 1980; Manchester and Taylor, 1977.

       The Crab Pulsar photon flux variation with energy has the form
6.17 x 10^{-4} $E^{-2.2}$ photons cm^{-2} s^{-1} MeV^{-1} over at least the energy range
from 50 keV to 5 GeV, five decades of energy (Graser and Schonfelder,
1982). To change from photons to energy, we multiply the photon flux
by E and obtain the power flux in units of energy cm^{-2} s^{-1} MeV^{-1}. To
obtain the right hand ordinate of Figure 8 (Knight, 1981), we multiply
by E again to limit the vertical range of the graph. The ordinate on
the left side is in frequency units. The ordinate range in energy (or

frequency) is 16 decades. In the energy region where this plot is reasonably flat, from about 5 keV to about 5 GeV, the power flux at the earth is about the same over equal intervals of log E; i.e., the power arriving from 10 to 100 keV is about equal to that arriving from 10 to 100 GeV. If the photon flux had varied as $E^{-2.0}$ this would, of course, be exactly true. The power flux in the pulsed radiation is particularly low at radio frequencies of 10^9 Hz, and climbs into the optical region but is still considerably below the value at 10 MeV.

The luminosity of the Crab Pulsar is calculated in any photon energy range by integrating the power flux over the energy interval and multiplying by $4\pi r^2 f$, where r is the distance to the pulsar and f the fraction of the 4π solid angle fed by pulsar beaming. If the pulsar emits its radiation into a solid angle of 1 ster at each of its magnetic pulses, the luminosity of the Crab Pulsar is about 2×10^{35} erg s^{-1} in each of two decades of energy from 5 keV to 5 GeV, with the maximum in the region of 10 MeV. This is about 0.05% of total rotational kinetic energy loss, the spin down energy loss, of the Crab Pulsar.

Since COS B observations extended over 7 years, it was possible to measure changes in the gamma ray light curve for E > 50 MeV over that time period (Wills et al, 1982). The six light curves from August-September 1975 to February-April 1982 along with one from a balloon flight at energies of 1-30 MeV are shown in Figure 9 (White et al., 1985). Visual inspection suggests that the second pulse decreases relative to the first to a low in 1979 then increases again to 1982. Statistical tests verify this variation (Ozel and Mayer-Hasselwander, 1984). A long term periodic variability has been proposed (Ozel, 1988; Kanbach, 1989).

4.1.2. The Vela Pulsar, PSR 0833-45 (2CG 263-02). The Vela Pulsar is the benchmark of gamma ray astronomy from 0.3 to 3,000 MeV. As the strongest of the gamma ray sources it was used by COS B for onboard calibration. Its light curves, shown in Figure 10, White (Lecture __, these proceedings) differ in phase in different parts of the electromagnetic spectrum. The radio signal at 2,295 MHz has only a single pulse (Large et al., 1969). The first pulse of the gamma rays is delayed in phase by 0.12 (Thompson et al., 1977b; Kanbach et al., 1980) and the optical by 0.23 (Wallace et al., 1977) from the radio pulse. The gamma ray phase separation between the first and second pulses is 0.42, the same as for the Crab Pulsar, but is only 0.25 for the optical pulses. Upper limits only exist from measurements of the soft and hard x-rays (Knight et al., 1982).

Results from the University of California, Riverside (UCR) double scatter telescope (Tumer et al., 1984) flown on a balloon at an altitude of 40 km have shown that the light curve from gamma rays of 1 to 30 MeV from double scatters is similar in phase to the one for 50 to 5000 km. Using single scatters the UCR group found no differences down to 0.3 MeV. The Vela Pulsar gamma ray light curve, as for the Crab Pulsar, gives a significant interpulse signal, especially above 50 MeV. There is also a slight tail following the second pulse. The light

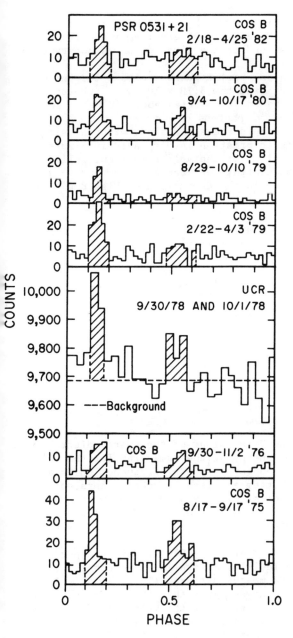

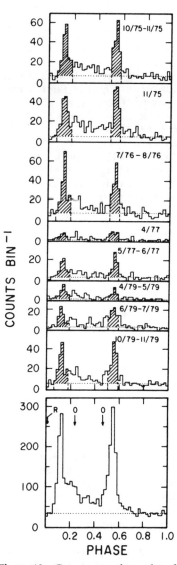

Figure 9. Phase plots of the Crab Pulsar, PSR 0513+21 at various times from 1975 to 1982. The first and second pulses are indicated by the shaded regions.

Figure 10. Gamma-ray phase plot of the Vela pulsar PSR 0833-45 in the energy interval of 50-3000 MeV at the epochs indicated. The shaded areas mark the first and second pulses and the horizontal broken lines show the background levels. The bottom graph is the phase diagram summed over all times. The arrows indicate the phases of the radio (R) and optical (O) peaks.

curves for E > 50 MeV measured by COS B over 6 yr, in contrast to the
Crab Pulsar, have not changed (Figure 10 taken from Hermsen, 1983).
The curves from October 1975 to November 1979 are identical within
statistics. The ratio of the second to the first pulse is constant in
time.

The upper limits in the x-ray region guarantee that the photon
flux distribution must turn over from the $6.70 \times 10^{-4} E^{-1.89}$ photon cm^{-2}
s^{-1} MeV^{-1} (Lichti et al., 1980) found at energies above 50 MeV. Indeed
the UCR group found $3.6 \times 10^{-4} E^{-1.6}$ photons cm^{-2} s^{-1} MeV^{-1} at energies
of 1 to 30 MeV and a possible sharp decrease in slope with the single
scatters down to 0.3 MeV. This information is displayed in Figure 11
(Knight 1981), where the power flux for the Vela Pulsar multiplied by E
is plotted against energy. The contrast between the Crab and Vela
Pulsars is dramatically exhibited in the comparison of Figs 8 with 11
and 9 with 10.

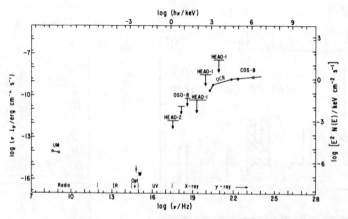

Figure 11. Log log plot for the Vela Pulsar of the energy distribution
of gamma rays per decade versus energy of the gamma ray for the Vela
pulsar on the right ordinate and upper abscissa; frequency units are
used on the left ordinate and bottom abscissa. Symbols representing
observing groups are: UCR, Tumer et al., 1984; U.M., Univ. of
Massachusetts Pulsar List; COS-B, Lichti et al., 1980; Wallace et al.,
1977; Harnden et al., 1977; Knight, 1981; and Pravdo et al., 1976.

Recently the FIGARO II (Sacco et al., 1990) reported upper limits
from a balloon flight from Charleville, Australia on November 25, 1988
significantly lower than the UCR measured fluxes (Tumer et al., 1984)
at energies of 0.2 to 6.0 MeV. They suggest that the different fluxes
may be caused by the difference in states of the Vela Pulsar. The UCR
observations were made 30 days after a Vela glitch, while FIGARO II's
occurred during a quiescent state more than 3 yr after the last
sizeable glitch on July 12, 1985.

At optical energies the Vela Pulsar is the weakest source ever
detected (Wallace et al., 1977) and is a factor of 1000 fainter than

the Crab Pulsar. And the Vela Pulsar reaches maximum power at high energy gamma rays of energy 1 GeV. The luminosity in gamma rays between 10 MeV and 1 GeV, two decades, using the same method and assumptions as for the Crab, is about 2 x 10^{34} erg/s. This is a surprisingly large 0.3% of the spin down energy loss in the rotational energy of the pulsar.

4.2. Supernova Remnant--Crab Nebula

The Crab nebula, a supernova remnant in Taurus, is an expanding mass of gas, spectacular in the visible. The supernova explosion, observed by the Chinese in 1054, was so bright it could be seen in the day for several weeks. Doppler shifts of the gases require speeds up to 1500 km s^{-1}. This velocity and angular extent of the nebula give 2 kpc for the distance to the Crab.

Extensive measurements have been made at low energy gamma rays, 0.3-1 MeV: medium energy, 1-30 MeV; high energy, 30-3000 MeV, and 10^{12} eV. The total gamma ray flux from the Crab Nebula includes both pulsed and steady gamma rays. The total gamma ray energy distribution may be fitted by the power law 3 x 10^{-3} $E^{-2.3}$ photons cm^{-2} s^{-1} MeV^{-1} from 1 keV to 3 GeV (Graser and Schönfelder, 1982). At x-ray energies, most of the flux is steady while at gamma ray energies from 30 to 3000 MeV most is pulsed. The cross-over occurs in the medium energy region from 1 to 30 MeV. The steady radio waves and perhaps more energetic photons are caused by the synchrotron radiation of electrons in the strong magnetic fields of the Nebula. The pulsed radiation is associated with the Crab Pulsar at the center of the Nebula.

5. Galactic Lines

5.1. Galactic Center 0.511 MeV Positron Annihilation Line

The positron annihilation line was discovered by the Rice University Group (Johnson, Harnden and Haymes, 1972) from a balloon flight carried out in November 1970. The energy of the line, measured with a NaI detector that had an aperture of 24 deg FWHM pointed in the direction of the galactic center, was reported as 473±30 keV. The next flight (Johnson and Haymes, 1973) in November 1971 confirmed the result and the combined data gave an energy of 476 ± 24 keV for the line and a flux of (1.8 ± 0.5) x 10^{-3} photons cm^{-2} s^{-1}. The third flight (Haymes et al., 1975) on April 1, 1974 launched from Argentina like the other two gave a line energy of 530 ± 11 keV. All three were consistent with the 511 keV positron annihilation line.

The Rice observations were confirmed by a precision measurement of the Bell Labs-Sandia Group (Leventhal, MacCallum and Stang, 1978; Leventhal et al., 1980; Leventhal et al., 1982; MacCallum and Leventhal, 1985) who made a series of flights from Alice Springs, Australia in November 1977, April 1979, November 1981 and November 1984. Using a germanium crystal of high purity, with a volume of 130 cm^3 and resolution of 3.2 keV FWHM, they measured a flux of (1.22 ±

0.22) x 10^{-3} photons cm^{-2} s^{-1} at 511 keV. Accurate in-flight energy calibrations used positron annihilation in the atmosphere.

While the para state of positronium at rest splits into two monochromatic gamma rays of 511 keV each, the ortho state decays into three gamma rays with a distribution of energies below 511 keV. The measured flux of the ortho state implied that about 90% of the positrons annihilated through orthopositronium although 0% could not be ruled out. Both the Rice and the Bell Labs-Sandia groups measured continuum radiation from the galactic center. The latter group found a flux of 1.86 x 10^{-4} $(E/100)^{-2.31}$ photon cm^{-2} s^{-1} keV^{-1} on their flight in April 1979 while their 511 keV line flux was (2.35 ± 0.71) x 10^{-3} photons cm^{-2} s^{-1}. On the November 1981 and 1984 flights upper limits only of 7 and 9 x 10^{-4} photons cm^{-2} s^{-1} were found. The JPL HEAO 3 satellite group using high resolution germanium detectors also measured the turn off of the galactic center. An observation from September-October 1979 (Riegler et al., 1981) gave a flux of (1.85 ± 0.21) x 10^{-3} photons cm^{-2} s^{-1} and the one from March-April 1980 (Riegler et al., 1985) (0.65 ± 0.25) x 10^{-3} photons cm^{-2} s^{-1}. The variation in flux of the 0.51 MeV line is summarized in Figure 12.

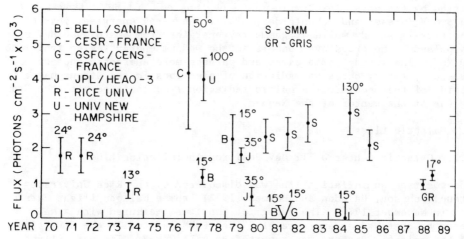

Figure 12. Observations of 511-keV line emission from the direction of the GC. Symbols representing observing groups are: B, Bell/Sandia, Leventhal et al., 1986; C, CESR, France, Albernhe et al., 1981; G, GSFC/CENS-France, Paciesas et al., 1982; J, JPL/HEAO-3, Riegler et al., 1985; R, Rice Univ., Haymes et al., 1975; U, Univ. of New Hampshire, D. Forrest, 1982. The field of view (FOV) of each instrument is indicated. The crosses represent line-flux corrections made for an assumed positronium ($e^+ + e^-$ bound state) fraction of 0.9. The NaI instruments unavoidably include some three-photon positronium continuum in the line. The 1974 Rice measurement was made in a direction ~5° off the GC and needs to be corrected as indicated, to correspond to a point source at the GC. The B, C, G, J and GR observations were made with high-resolution Ge detectors (From Leventhal et al., 1989).

A combination of the above results gave the source dirction as the galactic center ± 4 deg, the annihilation rate equal to 2 x 10^{43} positrons s^{-1} and the luminosity 3 x 10^{37} erg s^{-1}. The decrease in flux by a factor of three in 6 months suggested that both the positron source and the annihilation regions had dimensions less than the velocity of light times 1.5 x10^7 s (6 months) or 10^{18} cm. R. W. Bussard, R. Ramaty and R. J. Drachmann (1979) of NASA Goddard Space Flight Center pointed out that the narrow line width, < 2.5 keV, requires that the gas temperature in the annihilation region be less than 5 x 10^4 K and the 6 month time variation that the gas density be > 10^5 cm^{-3} for the positrons to slow down and annihilate in that time. A number of sources for the production of the positrons and their annihilation have been suggested which include a black hole at the center of the Galaxy.

The annihilation line source at the galactic center was reported again from balloon flights on May 1, 1988 and October 29, 1988 of the Gamma-Ray Imaging Spectrometer (GRIS) by the Bell Labs-Sandia-NASA GSFC Group (Leventhal et al, 1989). They measured fluxes of (9.8 ± 1.9) x 10^{-4} and (12.3 ± 1.6) x 10^{-4} photons cm^{-2} s^{-1}, respectively, with their Ge detector. For the October 29 flight the line center was located at 511.22 ± 0.28 keV and the FWHM was 4.0 ± 0.5 keV indicating that the cosmic annihilation line was well resolved with a width of about 3.6 ± 0.5 keV. This implied a temperature of 10^5 K for the stopping medium. They concluded that the compact object had become active after 1984. They also observed the galactic plane 25° west of the galactic center which gave a distributed source flux of (7 ± 5) x 10^{-4} photons cm^{-2} s^{-1} rad^{-1}.

During the time period 1981 to 1986, the gamma ray spectometer on the Solar Maximum Mission satellite of the SMM group (Share et al., 1988) observed a significant increase in the 511 keV gamma ray flux each year as the Galactic center region passed through its 130° aperture. The year to year variation was less than 30% and the time-averaged flux attributed to a point source at the galactic center was (2.1 ± 0.4) x 10^{-3} photons cm^{-2} s^{-1}. They suggest that these results and the Ge detector results on balloon flights during this same time period could be explained if most of the gamma rays measured by SMM come from an extended region in the Galactic plane. The Galactic plane flux would be (1.6 ± 0.3) x 10^{-3} photons cm^{-2} s^{-1} rad^{-1} if proportional to the measured CO distribution in the Galaxy. On the other hand, the GRIS group state that the CO diffuse distribution alone will account for their results.

5.2. Diffuse Galactic 1.809 MeV Line from ^{26}Al

The JPL HEAO 3 satellite group (Mahoney et al., 1984), from observations in 1979 and 1980 with their narrow line Ge detector, discovered ^{26}Al from the galactic center. The energy of the decay was 1808.49 ± 0.41 keV and the flux from the vicinity of the galactic center (4.8 ± 1.0) x 10^{-4} photons cm^{-2} s^{-1} rad^{-1}. The width of the line was 3.0 keV FWHM. The line energy and flux were verified with the SMM satellite gamma ray group (Share et al., 1985) every year from 1980 through 1985 with a NaI detector that had excellent stability but less sharp energy resolution.

The MPI group (von Ballmoos et al., 1987) observed the Galactic center region (in the field of view of their gamma ray Compton scatter telescope) for 2.6 hr. At gamma ray energies of 1.6 to 2.0 MeV they observed an enhancement in the region of the galactic center. The field of view was about 55° FWHM and the location of the direction of a point source could be located to about 3.5°. When treated as a point source they measure a flux of $(6.7 \pm 2.7) \times 10^{-4}$ photons cm^{-2} s^{-1}. If the source is extended like the COS B galactic plane events at energies > 70 MeV the flux is $(20.9 \pm 8.4) \times 10^{-4}$ photons cm^{-2} s^{-1} rad^{-1}.

The Bell Lab-Sandia Group (Leventhal et al., 1987) combined the results from 4 balloon flights between 1977 and 1984 and found an equivalent point source flux from the Galactic center direction of $(1.3 \pm 0.9) \times 10^{-4}$ photons cm^{-2} s^{-1}. The extended source flux, using the COS B galactic plane distribution as before, gives $(3.9 \pm 2.0/-1.7) \times 10^{-4}$ photons cm^{-2} s^{-1} rad^{-1}. These fluxes along with the others above are summarized in Table 1. Both the MPI and Bell Lab-Sandia groups claim their results are consistent with the HEAO-C and SMM results. It is clear that ^{26}Al has been observed from the galactic plane. Whether from a point source at the galactic center or an extended source along the galactic plane has still not been determined.

The intensity of the line varied with galactic longitude to less than 40% of the galactic center value in the anti-galactic center direction. The observed flux gave a ^{26}Al mass of 3 M$_\odot$ in the interstellar medium, an order of magnitude greater than predicted from supernova production. However, production of ^{26}Al in the novae, red giants and main-sequence stars could probably supply the required amount. This is the first well-verified example of galactic nucleo-synthesis. As ^{26}Al has a long lifetime, 1.04×10^6 y, compared with about 40/yr for novae explosions in the galaxy, the measurement samples the mixture of debris from millions of novae and thus gives a value for the galactic steady state.

TABLE 1. Diffuse Galactic 1.809 MeV line from ^{26}Al. Flux at $\ell = 0°$.

Experiment	Field of View (FWHM)	Point Source Photons cm^{-2}s^{-1}	Extended Source Photons cm^{-2}s^{-1}rad^{-1}
HEAO-C[a]	42°	---	$(4.3\pm0.4) \times 10^{-4}$
SMM[b]	130°	$(4.3\pm0.4) \times 10^{-4}$	$(4.0\pm0.4) \times 10^{-4}$
MPE[c]	10°	$(6.7\pm1.7) \times 10^{-4}$	$(20.9\pm8.4) \times 10^{-4}$
Bell Lab-Sandia[d]			
3 Flights	15°	$(1.3\pm0.9) \times 10^{-4}$	$(3.9^{+2}_{-1.7}) \times 10^{-4}$
1 Flight	87°		

a Mahoney et al. (1985)
b Share et al. (1985)
c von Ballmoos et al. (1987)
d Leventhal et al. (1987)

6. NUCLEOSYNTHESIS OF RADIOACTIVE, GAMMA-RAY EMITTING NUCLEI

The network of nuclear reactions during nucleosynthesis contains many radioactive nuclei. An example is the fusion $^{40}Ca + ^{4}He \rightarrow ^{44}Ti$. The rapid neutron capture r-process passes through a band of radioactive neutron-rich nuclei. When certain nucleosynthesis reactions occur during or just before the explosive supernova or nova phases of stellar evolution, the radioactive nuclei are spewed out and can be detected through the gamma rays emitted during nuclear decay.

In a subsequent lecture Professor White will discuss the discovery of the ^{56}Co lines from the recent supernova SN 1987A. The decay of ^{56}Ni via ^{56}Co into ^{56}Fe is the principal source of the rather abundant iron nuclei in the universe.

The intensities and emission times of gamma rays (measured from the time of supernova explosions) are quite different for Type I and Type II supernovae. The ^{56}Co decay line from a type I supernova is about 100 times more intense than from a Type II. This is due to the short half-life of ^{56}Co (78 days) and the duration of obscuration by the material in the supernova envelope. The thin envelope of a Type I supernova becomes transparent within one half-life while the thick envelope of a Type II obscures the gamma-ray lines of ^{56}Co for several half-lives.

We shall hence explore next the nature of Type II and Type I supernovae. Supernovae of Type II are derived from massive stars (M > 8 $M_\odot$) which undergo gravitational collapse at the end of the nuclear burning cycle when the outward radiation pressure from the core drops. A neutron star of about 1.4 $M_\odot$ forms, while the rest of the mass is ejected to form a dense, absorbing envelope not expected to become transparent to gamma rays for 1 or 2 years.

The progenitors of Type I supernovae probably are accreting white dwarfs, with masses close to the mass of the sun. A star becomes a white dwarf after its hydrogen and helium and its nuclear fuel has burned into carbon and oxygen. It then collapses into a white dwarf, shedding its outer layers. When such stars have an evolving binary companion, they can accrete material until they reach a critical mass close to the Chandrasekhar limit, about 1.4 $M_\odot$. A thermonuclear runaway explosion then occurs close to the center of the star, and the star explodes as a supernova.

Now that we have briefly explored the nature of the supernovae of types I and II, we shall return to the fluxes and light curves of the ^{56}Co line from supernovae. Fig. 13 shows the fluxes and light curves of ^{56}Co for supernovae of types I and II, based on Gehrels et al. (1987). The model for type I supernova is based on the formation of 0.5 $M_\odot$ of ^{56}Ni, and for type II on the formation of 0.1 $M_\odot$ of ^{56}Ni in a star of 15 $M_\odot$. The dashed line shows the effects of upward mixing, based on SN 1987A (Matz et al., 1988 and Gehrels et al., 1988).

Several other gamma-ray lines should be observable with GRO. The ^{57}Co line from SN 1987A should be detectable. This line has been explored by Clayton (1974, 1982) and Arnett (1978). Most ^{57}Fe is considered to be produced from the decay of ^{57}Co. With a half life of 172 days, it can be observed for a relatively long time, (several years). The energy of the line is 0.127 MeV. The estimated flux from

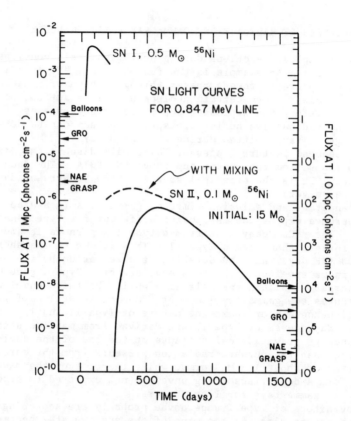

Figure 13. Comparision of time profiles of the ^{56}Co line at 0.847 MeV, for type I and II supernovae. The effects of mixing of material, some of which originates in the inner region, is also shown.

SN 1987A about 1000 to 1500 days after the explosion is (3 to 5) x 10^{-5}/cm^2 s, (Bussard et al., 1989 and Leising and Share, 1990), just above the detection threshold of the GRO OSSE detector.

The 1.16 MeV line from ^{44}(Ti, Sc) is of special interest because ^{44}Ti has a long half-life, about 50 or 60 years. It was explored by Clayton, Colgate and Fishman (1969). It can serve as a tracer of unobserved supernovae that have occurred in our Galaxy during the last two centuries. The estimates for the number of supernovae in two centuries range from 4 to 15 (a frequency of 1 per 13 to 50 years). Its abundance can be estimated from the abundance of its decay product ^{44}Ca. Chan and Lingenfelter (1987) showed that when the supernova remnant has expanded for a couple of centuries, the line shape is asymmetric because the part of the remnant which is farther away (and is responsible for the red-shifted component) contains ^{44}Ti from an earlier period. Hence, its gamma ray emission is more intense due to less ^{44}Ti decay. The line shape thus provides information on the age and mass-velocity structure of the supernova remnant.

Another interesting nuclide because of its long half-life of 3×10^5 years is ^{60}Fe. This nuclide has been discussed by Clayton (1971). Clayton (1973) showed that though the intensity of gamma rays is small due to the long half-life, it can be used to map out the sites of nearby supernovae that are within 0.2 kpc and have occurred during the last 5×10^5 years. However, due to the close distance and large age, these sites would cover a large part of the sky as highly extended sources. The energy of the line is 0.059 MeV from ^{60}Fe, and 1.33 and 1.16 MeV from the decay of its daughter product ^{60}Co.

Other nucleosynthesis lines that should be observable from a Galactic supernova with a GRO-OSSE type detector are ^{22}Na, ^{54}Mn, and ^{60}Co. With a next-generation detector like NAE or GRASP, also ^{58}Co and possibly ^{65}Zn should be observable from supernovae in our Galaxy, as outlined in Fig. 5 and Table 1 of Silberberg, Leising and Murphy (1989) at the previous course of the School at Erice. The measurement of these lines is of considerable interest. Estimates of ^{22}Na depend strongly on the conditions during the final stages of stellar evolution, experimental data on ^{22}Na is needed to establish these conditions. The abundance of ^{65}Zn is of interest. Harris (1988) found that the contribution of s-process is very small, yet the general abundances of ^{64}Zn and ^{66}Zn are appreciable, e.g., $^{64}Zn/^{56}Fe = 10^{-3}$. Could the quasi-equilibrium process spread out the iron peak to some extent beyond the mass number value of 60?

Gamma-ray lines from novae have been explored by Leising and Clayton (1987), see also Silberberg, Leising and Murphy (1989). The line of ^{22}Na is a candidate, and if radioactive nuclei are carried quickly to the surface the short-lived e^+ emitters ^{13}N, ^{14}O, ^{15}O and ^{18}F may yield 0.511 MeV photons.

We shall now briefly explore a topic that probably cannot be studied for many decades, but is of high astrophysical interest; the sites of origin of the r-process nuclei. Suppose they originate in type II supernovae close to the zone of neutron star formation, and are to be observed when the mantle of the expanding supernova has become thin for the transmission of gamma rays. The latter constraint restricts the investigation to neutron-rich nuclei with radioactive half-lives of about 0.5 to 5 years, e.g. ^{194}Os, ^{144}Ce, ^{137}Cs and ^{125}Sb. If about 10 to 20% of iron is derived from type II supernovae, and all of the r-process nuclei are derived from type II, this yields an enhancement factor of 5 to 10 for r-process elements relative to the iron group in type II supernovae. (Most iron in the Galaxy comes from type I supernovae, about 0.6 $M_\odot$ from one belonging to type I, and about 0.1 $M_\odot$ from a type II; the relative numbers of type I and type II in our Galaxy all similar, hence, we obtain the factor 5 to 10 of the previous sentence). Even with this enhancement factor, the relative abundances of the 4 r-process nuclides listed are $\sim 10^{-4}$ relative to ^{57}Co). (The elemental abundances of Cameron (1973) with his r-and s-process subdivision of the stable daughter isotopes were used for the latter estimate of 10^{-4}.) Taking into account the gamma-ray branching ratio during decay, we obtain fluxes of 10^{-8} to 10^{-7} /cm^{2}s for a distance of 10 kpc from the four nuclides discussed earlier, some 3 orders of magnitude below the threshold of observation of GRO, but less than 1 order of magnitude below the threshold of the heavily shielded gamma-ray spectrometer proposed by Gehrels et al. (1990). Eventual observation of gamma-rays from the r-process nuclides no longer looks hopeless! If we assume three more steps of one order of magnitude improvement in gamma-ray line detectors, one step per decade, this would be achieved when some of the students of this Course have become senior research professors.

7. GAMMA RAY BURSTS

The gamma-ray bursts were discussed in the 1988 School on Cosmic Ray Astrophysics by Hurley (1989) and Epstein (1989); students interested in this topic are referred to these reviews. Hence, only a brief summary of some salient features of the observations and interpretations are given.

Gamma-ray bursts were discovered by Klebesadel et al. (1973). About 500 bursts have been observed by now. Yet, these are the least understood observations of gamma ray astrophysics. They last from about 0.1 to 100 seconds, and have fine structure on 1-10 msec scale, as shown in Fig. 2 of Hurley (1989). Attempts have been made to identify the bursts with optical and X-ray counterparts. In general, these searches have been unsuccessful. The March 5, 1979 burst may be associated with a supernova remnant in the large Magellanic cloud, but this may be a chance coincidence. One burst may have an X-ray counterpart. Optical transients associated with gamma ray burst sources have yet to be established.

The energy spectra vary with time during the burst, as shown in Fig. 7 of Hurley (1989). Some energy spectra have absorption features near 50 keV and some have emission features near 400 keV, shown in Fig. 5 of Hurley (1989). These features have been used to suggest that the burst sources (or a subclass of them) are neutron stars. The absorption features could be due to resonance cyclotron absorption of photons in intense magnetic fields ($\gtrsim 10^{12}$ gauss) when the energy of the photon matches that of the first Landau level. The 400 keV emission feature has been interpreted as gamma rays from e^+e^- annihilation, redshifted in the strong gravitational field near the surface of the neutron star.

The distribution of the bursts is isotropic over the sky. This implies that if the sources are within the Galactic disk, with a scale height of about 100 pc, the sources are within a distance of 100 pc, or, as has also been proposed, the gamma-ray burst sources are at cosmological distances ($>10^9$ pc). For these distances, the respective emission energies are 10^{38} erg (for 100 pc) and 10^{52} erg (for 10^9 pc).

If the bursters are within 100 pc, and if there are 10^4 neutron stars within this radius, and if about 100 bursts occur per year, the bursters must be repetitive, about once per century.

The BATSE (Burst and Transient Source Experiment) detector on GRO will be able to test the theory of origin of bursts in neutron stars in the Galactic disk; it will see weaker bursts, hence well beyond 100 pc, and the distribution would start to exhibit a concentration of sources in the Galactic plane.

Several models of gamma ray bursts have been proposed; these were reviewed by Hurley (1989). In the thermonuclear model of Woosley and Taam (1976) a neutron star accretes matter at its magnetic poles. A slow hydrogen flash burns into helium, followed by a fast (10 ms) flash, when the critical density and temperature is reached. Epstein (1989) belives that too many X-rays are formed during the hydrogen flash phase, and that the sources would have been seen with the Einstein X-ray observatory. Epstein (1989) has developed further the suggestion of neutron star quakes or "glitches" proposed by Pacini and Ruderman (1974), with oscillatory motion of the magnetic field, that generates an electric field which accelerates electrons. They Compton-scatter X-rays from the neutron star surface, producing gamma rays. One suggestion for a modification of Epstein's model would be synchrotron radiation by electrons in a 10^{12} gauss field. At such a field strength, the synchrotron radiation photons from electrons of energies of 10 MeV would be gamma rays near energies of 2 MeV.

8. GEMINGA

This gamma-ray source is the second-strongest source, and close to the Galactic plane in the anticenter direction. Yet, it is one of the poorest understood, because its optical and radio counterparts have not yet been identified. Most of the energy output of Geminga is at gamma-ray energies. It was observed with the SAS-2 detector (Thompson et al. (1977)), and was reported to have a periodicity of 60 sec. The COS-B collaboration observed 1000 photons from this source, with a power law spectrum $E^{-1.88}$, from 0.1 to 2 GeV, and pinpointed the location to an accuracy of 24 arcmin. The 60-sec periodicity was at first reported, but later retracted (Masnou et al. 1981). Using data from the Einstein X-ray observatory, Bignami et al. (1983) found a weak X-ray source of ~ 10^{-12} erg/cm^{2}s in the Geminga error box. Bignami et al. (1984) reported this X-ray source, 1E0630+178, also to have periodicity of 60 sec. It was peculiar in not having an obvious optical or radio counterpart. Based on the X-ray spectrum, and absorption in the interstellar gas, Halpern and Tytler (1988) estimate the distance to be about 1000 pc; they also suggest a faint bluish star in the Geminga error box, G" to be the optical counterpart. They point out that it has some resemblance to the Vela pulsar, which also has weak optical and X-ray fluxes, though Vela is also a radio pulsar. Hermsen and Spoelstra (1990) do not agree with this optical identification, they suggest a possible radio and optical counterpart, the radio source 63 W64 with a very hard, flat radio spectrum.

9. CYG X-1, PROBABLE ACCRETING BLACK HOLE

This object was reviewed by Liang (1989) at the previous session of the International School of Cosmic-Ray Astrophysics. He also provided references to the experimental investigations and theoretical interpretations. Hence, only some high-lights will be presented, and the students are referred to the previous volume of the Advanced Study Institute at the library here.

Cygnus X-1 is the closest candidate of a black hole (about 10 $M_\odot$) with an accretion disk, accreting from its binary companion star. The companion is a blue supergiant.

Cyg X-1 is highly variable, with time scales ranging from milliseconds to years. The X-ray flux, 45 to 140 keV varies through three states, γ_1, γ_2 and γ_3, listed in order of increasing X-ray intensity. The duration of the states is irregular, lasting several months; most of the time is probably spent in the γ_2 state. There is an anticorrelation between the X-ray and gamma-ray fluxes. During the γ_1, state, there is a high gamma-ray flux at energies 0.5 - 2 MeV, illustrated in Figs. 3 and 4 of Liang (1989). The X-ray luminosity is about 4×10^{37} erg/s; during the γ_1 state, half the luminosity is in gamma-rays.

The gamma-ray flux is attributed to emission in a hot (kT ~ 400 keV), pair dominated plasma with a density of 5×10^{16} e^+/cm^3, Thomson depth of $\tau_T = 2$, and a radius of about 300 km for the pair cloud. Fig. 6 of Liang (1989) shows an artist's conception of the central pair cloud and the outer X-ray disk. At times other than the γ_1 state, the central region of 300 km cools down, to kT= 100-200 keV, and the plasma is no longer pair dominated. The X-ray spectrum is fitted by the outer X-ray disk model, two versions of which are shown in Fig. 2 of Liang (1989). One version is the thick disk model, with a hot (kT > 100 keV) optically thin inner region, where Comptonized hard X-ray photons are emitted, and a cool optically thick disk where the soft X-ray photons originate. The second version, the disk corona model, also has a hot, optically thin region, but not in the inner region, but as a corona that surrounds the cool optically thick disk. Softer photons are energized to X-ray energies by the inverse Compton collisions with energetic electrons.

10. GAMMA RAYS FROM THE INTERSTELLAR MEDIUM

The interstellar medium, especially the Galactic plane, is a strong source of gamma rays. Cosmic-ray protons and nuclei interact with the atomic nuclei of the interstellar gas and of the interstellar clouds, producing pions. The neutral pions decay promptly into gamma rays, generally 2 gamma rays. Cosmic-ray electrons, when passing through the interstellar gas, generate gamma rays in bremsstrahlung interactions. Cosmic-ray electrons also interact with photons (e.g., star-light photons and 3 K microwave background photons), transferring energy, and boosting the photons up to the energies of gamma rays. These reactions can be summarized as:

1) $p + p \rightarrow p + p + \pi^\circ$, $\pi^\circ \rightarrow 2\gamma$
2) $e^* + Ze \rightarrow e + Ze + \gamma^*$
3) $e^* + \gamma \rightarrow e + \gamma^*$

Here the asterisk denotes high-energy electrons and gamma-ray photons.

Fig. 14 shows the energy spectrum of the galactic gamma radiation for a region near the Galactic center, based on Kniffen et al. (1983). We note that above 100 MeV, the contribution of protons and π^0 decay dominates while below 100 MeV the electron bremsstrahlung contribution dominates. At higher energies, (E> 1 GeV) the estimates of the relative contributions of inverse Compton and bremsstrahlung processes vary by a factor of two.

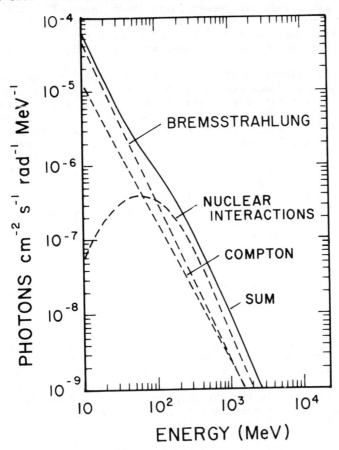

Figure 14. The energy spectrum and its components for the Galactic gamma radiation in the central region of the Galactic disk. The spectra are from the work of Kniffen et al. (1983).

For the calculation of the gamma-ray intensity from a given direction in the Galaxy, one has to know the column density of matter along that direction, and the mean cosmic-ray intensity and spectrum along the same direction. The matter is mainly atomic hydrogen (H_I) and molecular hydrogen H_2. The former is known directly from the H_I 21-cm radio observations, while H_2 is estimated from the distribution of CO molecules, assuming these to be proportional. H_2 and CO are abundant in an inner torus-like region, in a broad band about 5,000 pc from the Galactic center. This region has many large and cold molecular clouds.

At the previous course of the School of Cosmic Ray Astrophysics (1988) Scarsi (1989) in his Figures 3 to 6 presented the gamma-ray intensity distribution as a function of Galactic longitude and latitude. We note that gamma rays are concentrated in an interval in the Galactic plane, ± 60° from the Galactic center, and ± 5° in latitude, i.e., in a relatively thin disk. At the right hand side, between 270° and 180° in longitude, the three strong point sources Vela, Geminga and Crab stand out.

From the distributions of the Galactic gas and the gamma-ray intensity, one can deduce the radial gradient of cosmic rays in the Galaxy. The latest estimate of the radial distribution of cosmic rays is given in Fig. 5 of Bloemen (1989). The gradient is relatively small, the intensity drops only a factor of 2 between 3 and 18 kpc from the Galactic center and Bloemen (1989) concludes that cosmic rays, though at reduced intensity, extend far beyond the Galactic disk. There appears to be an extensive cosmic-ray halo about the Galaxy, as concluded by Bloemen and Dogiel (1990).

The number of "point sources" in the COS-B catalog is 25. Most of these probably are concentrated "diffuse sources", associated with clouds. This association has been stressed by Li Ti Pei and Wolfendale (1981); a review of the gamma-ray sources is given by Bignami and Hermsen (1983).

11. GAMMA-RAY LINES FROM NUCLEAR EXCITATION AND SPALLATION, AND FROM THE SUN

Gamma-ray lines from solar flares were discussed at the 1988 Erice School by Murphy. Details are given in Silberberg, Leising and Murphy (1989). Hence, only a brief review of the lines from solar flares is presented now. The flare particle protons and alpha particles collide on the solar surface, in the chromosphere, generate lines that are directly related to the composition of the interaction site. Predictions of the nuclear interaction rates in flare-particle interactions were made by Lingenfelter and Ramaty (1967). Starting with the large flare of 1972, numerous gamma-ray line observations have been made. Fig. 8 of Silberberg, Leising and Murphy shows the spectrum of the April 27, 1981 flare. We note here the nuclear excitation lines of ^{12}C, ^{16}O, ^{20}Ne, ^{24}Mg, ^{28}Si and ^{56}Fe. Also the lines for neutron capture, e^+ annihilation and of the α-α reaction can be seen. Murphy (1989) presented an interpretation of these lines in terms of elemental abundances in the chromosphere. These abundances differ from that of the photosphere, and resemble that of the solar corona, displaying the suppression of C and O, which have a high first ionization potential. These elements are neutral in the photosphere, and do not move up from the photosphere as readily as ionized atoms in the photosphere.

Gamma-ray lines due to nuclear excitation and spallation have also been observed from the lunar surface and the earth's atmosphere.

Gamma-ray lines due to nuclear excitation and spallation from Galactic sources are much weaker. Positive observations with the GRO-OSSE and COMPTEL detectors appear possible for supernova remnants in dense clouds. Morfill and Meyer (1981) estimate that there may be about 5 such remnants within 5 kpc, and that the 4.4 MeV ^{12}C and 6.1 MeV ^{16}O lines may have intensities of about 6×10^{-5} cm^{-2} s^{-1}.

The intensities of gamma-ray lines from the interstellar medium in the Galactic plane have been estimated theoretically by Ramaty et al. (1979). Higdon (1987) has re-evaluated these fluxes. The possible value of (2 to 8) x 10^{-6} cm^{-2} s^{-1} rad $^{-1}$ is too low for current detectors and appears to require a next-generation detector like NAE or GRASP.

Silberberg and Murphy (1990) found that ^{12}C and ^{16}O lines are enhanced by two orders of magnitude from sites depleted in hydrogen, e.g. the Wolf-Rayet stars. If the latter are in a binary system with an incident beam of particles from a pulsar or a black hole, with a power output of 10^{37} erg s^{-1}, then the intensity of the 4.44 MeV ^{12}C line from a source at a distance of 1 kpc could be 5×10^{-6} photons cm^{-2} s^{-1}, observable with the planned NAE or GRASP detectors.

Such systems may exist in the Galaxy: Many Wolf-Rayet stars are in binary systems with a massive 0 or B star companion. From stellar evolution one would expect the following scenario: The more massive star becomes a giant, starts shedding its outer shell of hydrogen, which is partly accreted onto its neighbor and becomes a supernova and then a residual neutron star. The star that was originally slightly lighter eventually becomes a gigantic Wolf-Rayet star, losing mass to the neutron star and to its Galactic neighborhood. The pulsar beam from the neutron star interacts with the abundant C and O nuclei of the Wolf-Rayet star. Drissen et al. (1986) present evidence that some Wolf-Rayet stars have compact companions, e.g. HD 50896 probably has a neutron star companion, and HD 197406 probably has a massive 12 $M_\odot$ black hole companion.

12. ACTIVE GALACTIC NUCLEI

One of the most important problems in astrophysics is to understand the nature of the compact central power source in active galactic nuclei. These sources have the highest emission rates of energy in the known universe, 10^{42} to 10^{48} ergs/sec, i.e., 10^{8} to 10^{14} times the solar luminosity.

The active galactic nuclei are subdivided into several classes. Radio-galaxies are elliptical galaxies; they are characterized by having pairs of extensive radio lobes, frequently tens of kiloparsecs away from the galaxy. They are at the end positions of jets that are near-perpendicular to the galactic disk. Seyfert galaxies (both class 1 and class 2) are spiral galaxies, which have fast moving clouds. The nuclei of class 2 Seyferts are obscured by dust, which is a powerful re-radiator at infrared wave lengths. Another class of compact nuclei are the BL Lac objects, probably in large elliptical galaxies. These

240

objects are relatively rapidly variable and are characterized by the absence of strong emission lines, i.e., have little gas and dust at the galactic center. The most powerful class of AGN are the quasars, which require up to tens of solar masses per year to be converted into energy.

The active galactic nuclei exhibit a high degree of variability at energies near 1 MeV and a turn-over in the spectrum between about 0.3 and 10 MeV that varies with time.

The AGN are belived to be powered by mass accretion unto ultra-massive black holes of about 10^8 $M_\odot$. It is interesting to note that Cyg X-1 and the Galactic center, both believed to be accreting black holes, (though less massive) are also time variable in this energy interval.

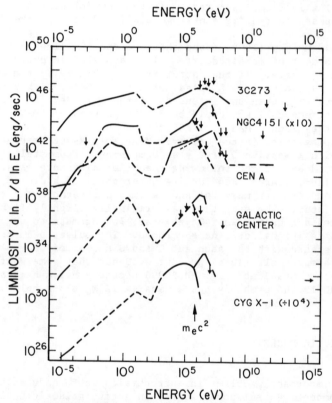

Figure 15. Luminosities as a function of energy for active galactic nuclei. The luminosities of the Galactic center and the black hole candidate Cyg X-1 are also shown.

Fig. 15 illustrates the luminosity spectra as a function of energy for three active galactic nuclei, the Galactic center and Cyg X-1. The luminosity peaks at energies near 1 MeV. The experimental data of the quasar 3C 273 (for gamma rays at 50 to 800 MeV) are from Bignami et al. (1981). For the Seyfert 1 galaxy at energies near 0.5 to 10 MeV, the data are from Perotti et al. (1979), Butler et al. (1981), and during the "low" periods, upper limits from White et al. (1980). Also the

Seyfert 1 galaxy MCG 8-11-11 has been reported by Baker et al. (1981) as a gamma-ray source at energies 0.3 to 10 MeV. For the radio-galaxy Cen A, gamma rays at 0.5 to 10 MeV have been reported by von Ballmoos et al. (1987), and only upper limits by O'Neill et al. (1987). There is still the possibility that only the values quoted as upper limits are correct for NGC 4151 and Cen A, and further measurements by GRO are needed to establish the actual fluxes and time variations from these sources.For Cen A, there is also a measurement at E > 300 GeV by Grindlay et al. (1975). As the single measurement at very high energies, also this value requires confirmation.

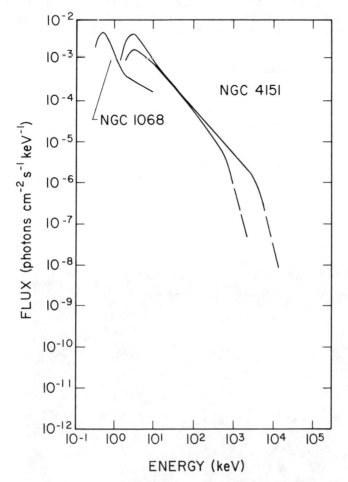

Figure 16. Comparison of X-ray spectra of NGC 1068 and NGC 4151, and the gamma-ray spectrum of NGC 4151. $E > 3 \times 10^2$ keV are gamma rays.

The Seyfert 2 galaxy NGC 1068 is an interesting object. Antonucci and Miller (1985) propose a model with a thick disk of gas and dust seen edge-on. Recently Monier and Halpern (1987) observed X-rays at energies 0.1-3.8 keV, and Elvis and Lawrence (1988) at 2 to 10 keV. The X-ray

flux is an order of magnitude lower than for the Seyfert 1 galaxy NGC
4151, though the total luminosity is similar. (For NGC 1068 the
luminosity peaks in the infra-red.) Monier and Halpern (1987) suggest
that NGC 1068 is consistent with a hidden nucleus that is similar to
that of a Seyfert 1 galaxy, and that the X-rays seen here are due to
photon scattering on electrons at higher galactic latitudes, (scattering
is not from dust, since keV X-rays would be absorbed there). Silberberg
and Shapiro (1990) point out that absorption of gamma rays is much
weaker than of the X-rays; their fig. 1 is reproduced here as Fig. 16.
Extrapolating the spectrum of NGC 1068 beyond 10 keV, the γ-ray
intensity near 1 MeV would be similar to that of NGC 4151, well
observable with GRO. Silberberg and Shapiro (1990) point out that also
the e^+ annihilation line may be observable with GRO.

13. THE GAMMA RAY OBSERVATORY (GRO)

The Gamma Ray Observatory is one of the four "Great Observatories" of
USA for the 1990-s. The other three are the Hubble Space Telescope, the
Advanced X-Ray Astrophysics Facility, AXAF, and the Space Infrared
Telescope Facility, SIRTF.

The Gamma Ray Observatory will be launched in March 1991. It has
four instruments that span the broad energy range from 100 keV to 30
GeV. The instruments are about an order of magnitude more sensitive
than those flown on earlier space missions. They will survey all of the
objects discussed earlier in this lecture.

Fig. 17 shows the four instruments of GRO, called OSSE, COMPTEL,
EGRET and BATSE.

Figure 17. Cut-away schematic of the OSSE, COMPTEL and EGRET
experiments (left to right) of the Gamma Ray Observatory. In the
corners, the BATSE experiment can be seen.

OSSE is the Oriented Scintillation Spectroscopy Experiment of the Naval Research Laboratory, Northwestern University and the Royal Aerospace Establishment. It consists of 4 NaI and CsI phoswich detectors with tungsten collimators.

COMPTEL is an imaging Compton telescope of Max Planck Institute, Laboratory of Space Research in Leiden, University of New Hampshire and Space Science Department of ESA. It consists of an array of liquid scintillator cells and NaI scintillators.

EGRET is the Energetic Gamma Ray Experiment Telescope of Goddard Space Flight Center, Stanford University and Max Planck Institute. It consists of a spark chamber and a big NaI scintillation crystal calorimeter for measuring the energies of the gamma rays.

BATSE is the Burst and Transient Source Experiment of Marshall Space Flight Center. It consists of eight detector modules at the corners of the spacecraft that provide an unobstructed all-sky coverage. Each module consists of a large area thin NaI detector and a smaller area thick NaI detector with good energy resolution for spectroscopic measurements.

The characteristics of the four instruments can be compared from table 2 below.

TABLE 2. Characteristics of the GRO instruments.

BATSE	OSSE	COMPTEL	EGRET
0.02-10	0.1-10	1-30	$30-3 \times 10^3$
(~1event/day)	~10 mCrab	30 mCrab	~10 mCrab
	$\sim 3 \times 10^{-5} cm^{-1} s^{-1}$	$\sim 3 \times 10^{-5} cm^{-2} s^{-1}$	---
8%	8%	8%	15%
1°	10 arcmin	7.5 arcmin	5 arcmin
2 μs (min)	0.1 ms (min)	0.1 ms	0.1 ms
full sky	$3.8° \times 11.4°$	$\sim 45° \times 45°$	$45° \times 51°$

In table 2, the first line gives the energy interval, in units of MeV, the second line gives the flux threshold, the third line gives the line flux threshold, the fourth, fifth and sixth lines give the energy-, position-, and time-resolutions respectively, and the seventh line gives the field of view. On line six, the notation (min) means "minimum", since the time resolution can be selected for different modes of operation.

ACKNOWLEDGEMENTS

R.S. would like to thank ONR for support. The authors are indebted to Professors M. M. Shapiro and J.P. Wefel for organizing the School and for their hospitality in Erice.

REFERENCES

Albernhe, F., et al. (1981) Astron. Astrophys. 94, 214.
Antonucci, R.R. and Miller, J.S. (1985) Ap. J. 297, 621.

Arnett, W.D. (1978) in "Gamma Ray Spectroscopy in Astrophysics", eds. T.L. Cline and R. Ramaty, NASA T.M. 79619, p. 310.

Baker, R.E. et al. (1981) 17th Internat. Cosmic Ray Conf. (Paris), 1, 222.

Bignami, G.F., Caraveo, P.A. and Lamb, R.C. (1983) Ap. J. (Letters) 272, L9.

Bignami, G.F., Caraveo, P.A. and Paul, J.A. (1988), Nature 310, 464.

Bignami, G.F., and Hermsen, W. (1983) Ann. Rev. Astron. Astrophys. 21, 67.

Bignami, G.F. et al. (1981) Astron. Astrophys. 93, 71.

Bloemen, H., (1989) Ann. Rev. Astron. Astrophys. 27, 469.

Bloemen, H. and Dogiel, V.A. (1990) Astron. Astrophys. to be publ.

Buccheri, R., et al. (1983) Astron. Astrophys. 128, 245.

Bussard, R.W., Ramaty, R., and Drachman, R.J. (1979) Ap. J. 228, 928.

Bussard, R.W., Burrows, A. and The, L.S. (1989) in "Proc. Gamma Ray Observatory Science Workshop", ed. W.N. Johnson, p.4-300.

Butler, R.C. et al. (1981) 17th Internat. Cosmic Ray Conf. (Paris), 1, 226.

Cameron, A.G.W. (1973) in "Explosive Nucleosynthesis", eds. D.N. Schramm, and W.D. Arnett, University of Texas, Austin, p.3.

Chan, K.W. and Lingenfelter, R.E. (1987) Proc. 20th Internat. Cosmic Ray Conf. (Moscow) 1, 164.

Clark, G., Garmire, G., and Kraushaar, W. (1968) Ap. J. Lett. 153, L203.

Clayton, D.D. (1971) Nature 234, 291.

Clayton, D.D. (1973) in "Explosive Nucleosynthesis", eds. D.N. Schramm and W.D. Arnett, Univ. Texas, Austin, p. 264.

Clayton, D.D. (1982), in "Essays in Nuclear Astrophysics", eds. C.A. Barnes, D.D. Clayton, and D.N. Schramm, Cambridge Univ. Press, Cambridge.

Clayton, D.D. (1984) Ap. J. 188, 155.

Clayton, D.D., Colgate, S.A. and Fishman, G.J. (1969) Ap.J. 155, 75.

Derdeyn, S.M., et al. (1972) Nuclear Inst. and Meth. 98, 557.

Drissen, L., Lemontagne, R., Moffat, A.F.S., Bastien, P. and Sequin, M. (1986) Ap. J. 304, 188.

Elvis, M. and Lawrence, A. (1988) Ap. J. 331, 161.

Epstein, R.I. (1989) in "Cosmic Gamma Rays, Neutrinos and Related Astrophysics", eds. M.M. Shapiro and J.P. Wefel, Kluwer Acad. Publ., Dordrecht, p. 381.

Fichtel, C.E., et al. (1975) Ap. J. 198, 163.

Forrest, D. (1982) The Galactic Center, eds, G.R. Riegler and R.D. Blandford, AIP New York, p. 160.

Gehrels, N., Candey, R. M. and Matteson, J. L., (1990) in "Astrophysics from the Moon", eds. M. J. Mumma and H. J. Smith, AIP, New York.

Gehrels, N., Leventhal, M. and MacCallum, C.J. (1987) Ap. J. 322, 215.

Gehrels, N., Leventhal, M. and MacCallum, C.J. (1988) in "Nuclear Spectroscopy of Astrophysical Sources", AIP Conf. Proc. 170, eds. N. Gehrels, and G. H. Share, New York, p. 87.

Graser, U., and Schonfelder, V. (1982) Ap. J. 263, 677.

Graser, U., and Schonfelder, V. (1983) Ap. J. 273, 681.

Grindlay, J.E., Helmken, H.F., Hanbury Brown, R., Davis, J. and Allen,
     L.R. (1975) Ap. J. (Letters) 197, L9.
Halpern, J.H. and Tytler, D. (1988) Ap.J. 330, 201.
Harris, M.J. (1988), private communication.
Harnden, F.R., et al. (1979) Bull. Am. Astron. Soc. 11, 424.
Haymes, R.C., et al. (1975) Ap. J. 201, 593.
Hermsen, W., et al. (1983) Space Science Reviews 36, 61.
Hermsen, W., et al. (1977) Nature 269, 494.
Hermsen, W. and Spoelstra, T.A. (1990) Proc. 21st Internat. Cosmic Ray
     Conf. (Adelaide) 1, 208.
Higdon, J.C. (1987) 20th Internat. Cosmic Ray Conf. (Moscow) 1, 160.
Hurley, K. (1989) in "Cosmic Gamma Rays, Neutrinos and Related
     Astrophysics", ed. M.M. Shapiro and J. P. Wefel, Kluwer Acad.
     Publ., Dordrecht, p. 337.
Johnson, W.N., III, Harnden, F.R., Jr., and Haymes, R.C. (1972) Ap.
     J. 172, L1.
Johnson, W.M., III, and Haymes, R.C. (1973) Ap. J. 184, 103.
Kanbach, G. et al. (1980) Astron. Astrophys. 90, 163.
Klebesadel, R.W., Strong, I.B. and Olson, R.A. (1973) Ap.J. (Letters)
     182, L85.
Kniffen, D.A., Fichtel, C.E. and Hartman, R.C. (1983) Proc. 13th
     Internat. Cosmic Ray Conf. (Bangalore) 1, 165.
Knight, F.K. (1981) Ph.D. Dissertation, UCSD-SP-18-13.
Knight, F.K., et al. (1982) Ap. J. 260, 553.
Kundt, W., and Krotschenk, E. (1980) Astron. and Astrophys. 83, 1.
Large, M.I., Vaughan, A.E., and Mills, B.Y. (1968) Nature, 220, 340.
Leising, M.D. (1988) in "Nuclear Spectroscopy of Astrophysical
     Sources", AIP Conf. Proceedings 170, eds. N. Gehrels, and G. S.
     Share, New York, p. 130.
Leising, M.D. and Clayton, D.D. (1987) Ap. J. 323, 159.
Leising, M.D. and Share, G.H. (1990) 21st Internat. Cosmic Ray Conf.
     (Adelaide), Australia, 2, 178.
Leventhal, M., MacCallum, C.J., and Stang, P.D. (1978) Ap. J. Lett.
     225, L11.
Leventhal, M., et al. (1980) Ap. J. 240, 338.
Leventhal, M., et al. (1982) Ap. J. Lett. 260, L1.
Leventhal, M., et al. (1986) Ap. J. 302, 459.
Leventhal, M., et al. (1989) Nature 339, 36.
Li Ti Pei, and Wolfendale, A.W. (1981) Astron. Astrophysics 103, 19.
Liang, E.P. (1989) in "Cosmic Gamma Rays, Neutrinos and Related
     Astrophysics," eds. M.M. Shapiro and J.P. Wefel, Kluwer Acad.
     Publ., Dordrecht, p. 73.
Lichti, G.G., et al. (1980) Adv. Space Explor. 1, 49.
Lingenfelter, R.E., and Ramaty, R. (1967) in "High Energy Nuclear
     Reactions in Astrophysics", ed. B.S.P. Shen, W.A. Benjamin; New
     York, p. 99.
MacCallum, C.J., and Leventhal, M. (1985) Proc. 19th Inter. Cosmic
     Ray Conf. 1, 213.
Mahoney, W.A., et al. (1984) Ap. J. 286, 578.
Manchester, R.N., and Taylor, J.H. (1977) Pulsars, W.H. Freeman,
     Publisher, San Francisco.

246

Masnou, J.L. et al. (1981) Proc. 17th International Cosmic Ray Conf.
(Paris) 1, 177.

Matz, S.M., Share, G.H. and Chupp, E.L. (1988) in "Nuclear
Spectroscopy of Astrophysical Sources", AIP Conf. Proc. 170, eds.
N. Gehrels and G.H. Share, New York, p. 51.

Monier, R. and Halpern, J.P., (1987) Ap. J. (Letters) 315, L17.

Morfill, G.E., and Meyer, P. (1981) 17th Internat. Cosmic Ray Conf.
(Paris) 9, 56.

Murphy, R.J. (1989) in "Cosmic Gamma Rays, Neutrinos and Related
Astrophysics", eds. M.M. Shapiro and   J.P. Wefel, Kluwer Acad.
Publ., Dordrecht, p. 289.

O'Neill, T.J., et al. (1987) Proc. 20th Inter. Cosmic Ray Conf. 1,
206.

O'Neill, T.J., Tumer, O.T., Zych, A.D. and White, R.S., (1987), 20th
Internat. Cosmic Ray Conf. (Moscow) 1, 206.

Ozel, M.E. and Mayer-Hasselwander, H. (1984) Inter. Workshop on "Data
Analysis in Astronomy," Erice, Italy.

Ozel, M.E. (1988) Timing Neutron Stars, H. Ogelman and Heuvel (eds.),
Kluwer Scientific Publications.

Paciesas, W.S., et al. (1982) Ap. J. Lett. 260, L7.

Pacini, F. and Ruderman, M. (1974) Nature 251, 399.

Perotti, F. et al. (1979) Nature 282, 484.

Pravdo, S.H., and Serlemitsos, D.J. (1981) Ap. J. 246, 484.

Pravdo, S.H., et al. (1976) Ap. J. Lett. 208, L67.

Ramaty, R. Kozlovsky, B. and Lingenfelter, R.E. (1979) Ap. J. Suppl.
40, 487.

Riegler, G.R., et al. (1981) Ap. J. Lett. 248, L13.

Riegler, G.R., et al. (1985) Ap. J. Lett. 294, L13.

Sacco, B., et al. (1990) Ap. J. Lett. 349, L21.

Scarsi, L. (1989) in "Cosmic Gamma Rays, Neutrinos, and Related
Astrophysics", eds. M.M. Shapiro and J. P. Wefel, Kluwer Acad.
Publ., Dordrecht, p.1.

Share, G.H., et al. (1985) Ap. J. Lett. 292, L61.

Share, G.H., et al. (1988) Ap. J. 326, 717.

Silberberg, R., Leising, M.D. and Murphy, R.J. (1989) in "Cosmic Gamma
Rays, Neutrinos and Related Astrophysics", eds. M.M. Shapiro and
J.P. Wefel, Kluwer Acad. Publ., Dordrecht, p. 289.

Silberberg, R. and Murphy, R.J. (1990) 21st Internat. Cosmic Ray Conf.
(Adelaide), 1, 162.

Silberberg, R. and Shapiro, M.M. (1990) 20th Internat. Cosmic Ray
Conf. (Adelaide) 1, 158.

Strickman, M.S., Johnson, W.N., and Kurfess, J.D. (1979) Ap. J. Lett.
230, L15.

Sweeney, W.E., et al. (1987) Proc. 20th Inter. Cosmic Ray Conf. 1,
103.

Thompson, D.J., Fichtel, C.E., Hartman, R.C., Kniffen, D.A. and Lamb,
R.C. (1977) Ap.J. 213, 252.

Thompson, D.J., et al. (1977) Astron. Astrophys. 127, 220.

Tueller, J., et al. (1984) Ap. J. 279, 177.

Tumer, O.T., et al. (1984) Nature 310, 214.

von Ballmoos, P., Diehl, R. and Schonfelder, V. (1987) Ap. J. 312, 134.

Wallace, P.T., et al. (1977) Nature 266, 692.

White, R.S., et al. (1980) Nature 284, 608.

White, R.S., et al. (1983) A Plan for Long Duration Scientific Ballooning, Long Duration Balloon Flight Study Committee.

White, R.S., et al. (1985) Ap. J. Lett. 299, L23.

Wills, R.D., et al. (1982) Nature 296, 723.

Woosley, S. and Taam, R. (1976) Nature 263, 101.

VHE AND UHE GAMMA RAY SOURCES

R. S. WHITE
Institute of Geophysics and Planetary Physics
University of California
Riverside, California 92521
U.S.A.

ABSTRACT. The observations of Very High Energy, VHE, and Ultra High Energy, UHE, gamma rays from celestial sources are reviewed. Cerenkov detectors for VHE gamma ray measurements and extended air shower arrays for UHE measurements are described. The x-ray binary pulsar source VHE and UHE observations of Cyg X-3, Her X-1, Vela X-1 and Cen X-3 and of the radio pulsar sources PSR 0531+21 and PSR 0833-45, the Crab and the Vela pulsars, are described in more detail. Possible VHE and UHE gamma ray source catalogs are examined. The current state and future requirements of VHE and UHE gamma ray astronomy are briefly discussed.

1. Introduction

Gamma rays must have their origins in the most energetic interactions in the universe. they may carry clues to the origins of the cosmic rays that are accelerated up to the maximum energies observed in our galaxy. These gamma rays, with energies greater than about 10^{11} eV, 0.1 TeV, are the subject of my lecture today.

The classification of gamma rays by energy range is given in Table 1. Their energies, generic names and detection methods are included. We will concentrate on the very high

TABLE 1. Gamma ray energies (Weekes, 1988).

Energy (eV)	Common Usage	Generic Name*	Detection by
3×10^5-1×10^7	0.5-10 MeV	nuclear lines	NaI, Ge
3×10^5-3×10^7	0.3-30 MeV	ME	NaI, Ge, Compton telescope
3×10^7-10^{10}	20 MeV-10 GeV	HE	Pair spark-chamber
10^{10}-10^{14}	10 GeV-100 TeV	VHE or TeV	Atmospheric Cerenkov
10^{14}-10^{17}	100 TeV-100 PeV	UHE or PeV	Air shower array
10^{17}-10^{20}	100 PeV-100 EeV	EHE or EeV	Air shower array

*   ME - medium energy, HE - high energy, VHE - very high energy, UHE - ultra high energy, EHE - extremely high energy

M. M. Shapiro et al. (eds.), Cosmic Rays, Supernovae and the Interstellar Medium, 249–269.
© 1991 *Kluwer Academic Publishers. Printed in the Netherlands.*

energy, VHE, gamma rays from 0.01 to 100 TeV, the ultra high energy, UHE, from 0.1 to 100 PeV and finally the extremely high energy, EHE, from 0.1 to 100 EeV. One GeV, TeV, PeV and EeV equal 10^9, 10^{12}, 10^{15} and 10^{18} eV, respectively.

Gamma ray astronomy is still in its pioneer stage. Gamma rays cannot be focused like light, radio, infrared, ultraviolet or x-ray photons. Therefore, the signals from the gamma ray sources are usually weak and the backgrounds high. Gamma rays can penetrate only a few tens of gm cm^{-2} of material, so observations must be taken near the top of the atmosphere. Satellites and high flying balloons carry gamma ray detectors and telescopes for observations to 10 GeV. At higher energies, VHE gamma rays may be observed from the ground with large dishes that collect the light from Cerenkov radiation produced by the electron secondaries of the gamma ray interactions high in the atmosphere. The UHE and EeV gamma rays are detected by scintillators spread on the surface of the earth. They measure the energy loss of electrons and muons in extensive air showers (EAS).

At energies above about 10^{10} eV, gamma rays produce electron-positron pairs that grow into showers of electrons and positrons with velocities sufficiently high to produce Cerenkov radiation at visual wavelengths. As seen in Figure 1, the cone of Cerenkov light, about 100 m in diameter at the base, reaches the ground where it may be sampled by dishes that focus the light onto one or more photomultipliers. This method was pioneered by the Crimean Group in the 1960s (Chudakov et al., 1965). The angular resolution of a gamma ray point source is about 1 deg. With observation times of about 25 hr on source and comparable times off source, cosmic ray induced shower Cerenkov radiation backgrounds may be overcome and statistically significant observations reported from celestial sources.

In recent years increased sensitivities have been attained using larger Cerenkov light collectors, decreasing the cosmic ray induced background light and increasing the observation times. To decrease the cosmic ray background the differences in the depth and width of the gamma ray and cosmic ray induced light pools have been used. The variation in time of the Cerenkov light pulse may also be exploited to reduce the cosmic ray background.

Figure 2 is a photograph of two 11 m light collectors located at Sandia Corporation in Albuquerque, New Mexico used by the University of California, Riverside and the Michigan Groups. These dishes of the United States Department of Energy were used during the day for solar engine tests but were available at night for gamma ray astronomy. Their large areas and thus high sensitivities permitted a reduction in the gamma ray threshold energy with the resulting increase in photon to cosmic ray Cerenkov light to reduce background. They are located about 100 m apart and may be used in coincidence or in alternate signal-background modes. The ground collectors have the usual advantages of optical telescope observatories: long observation times, accessibility, ease of control, convenient data retrieval and relatively low cost; they have the disadvantage

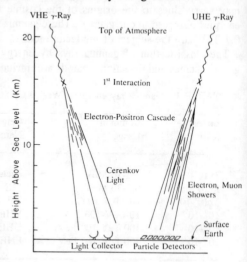

Figure 1. Schematic view of VHE and UHE gamma-ray air showers.

of observation times limited to dark nights without clouds or inclement weather that limit visibility.

When gamma ray energies reach about 10^{14} eV some of the charged particles in the shower, mostly electrons and positrons, have sufficient energy to reach sea level. Mixed in with the electrons are a few muons. Scintillators spread over large areas detect the charged particles in the extended air showers, EAS, by their ionization as shown in Figure 1. Muons interact only weakly with matter, about 10^{-7} that of electrons, so easily penetrate the 10^3 g cm^{-2} of the atmosphere. Electrons go through many generations before reaching the ground. Cosmic ray proton or nucleus induced showers produce a large background. As high energy

Figure 2. The twin 11 m diameter solar collectors at Sandia Laboratories Solar Thermal Test Facility, Albuquerque.

nucleon-nucleus collisions give large numbers of π° mesons that decay into muons while electrons primarily produce showers with secondary electrons and gamma rays with a few muons. The ultra high energy proton showers are expected to be muon rich and the ultra high

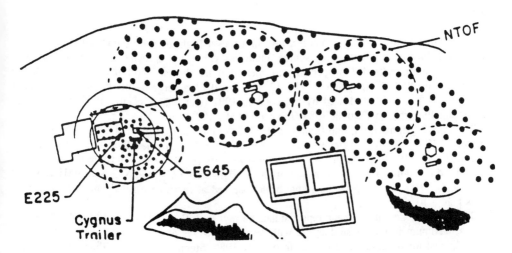

Figure 3. A plan schematic of the CYGNUS array. The data reported were taken with the array shown on the bottom left. Location of the E225 muon detector is indicated. Each small black dot represents an air shower scintillation counter. The array of large black dots shows planned expansion in phases. By the end of 1988 approximately 200 counters were operating (Yodh, private communication).

energy gamma ray showers muon poor. An example of such an array is the Cygnus array given in Figure 3.

The direction of the primary gamma ray is determined from the differences in the arrival times of the shower front at the different detectors. Accuracies of a degree of arc can be obtained for these ultra high energy showers. The first observation of a celestial gamma ray source, Cyg X-3, was reported by Samorski and Stamm (1983) for measurements taken from 1976 to 1980 at Kiel, West Germany. These EAS detectors have the advantage of day-night all weather observations but have much reduced gamma ray fluxes at the higher energies.

2. Reported Gamma Ray Sources

We start the discussion of sources with Table 2, the list of reported VHE, UHE and EeV gamma ray sources. Their locations in Right Ascension and Declination and in galactic latitude and longitude are given along with their distances, periods and thresholds, fluxes and luminosities for VHE, UHE and EeV energies, respectively. Galactic radio pulsars are listed first, followed by x-ray binary pulsars then others, including the Crab Nebula. At the end are the extragalactic sources. For additional information the reader is referred to the review by Weekes (1988) and for the latest results to Fegan (1990), the Rapporteur paper from the 21st ICRC, Adelaide, Australia (1990).

At the outset you are cautioned that most of the results are at significance levels of 3, 4 and 5σ. The significance level is the ratio of the signal, total counts less background counts, divided by the square root of the sum of total counts plus background counts. The probabilities of exceeding these values by statistical fluctuations in the backgrounds are 2.7×10^{-3}, 6.3×10^{-5} and 5.7×10^{-7}, respectively. A few of the most studied sources are discussed below.

2.1. CYGNUS X-3

Cygnus X-3 was discovered with soft x-rays in a rocket flight in 1966 (Giacconi et al., 1967). It was the third most intense x-ray source found in Cygnus and is located close to the cross in the constellation. Its 4.8 hr period was measured by detectors on the UHURU satellite beginning in 1970 (Parsignault et al., 1972). In 1972 a large radio burst was observed (Gregory et al., 1972) followed by a second in 1982 (Geldzahler et al., 1983) and a third, exceptionally large, in October 1983 (Johnston et al., 1985).

The SAS 2 gamma ray group (Lamb et al., 1977) first reported gamma rays with the 4.8 hr period in 1977. Their energies were > 35 MeV. COS B confirmed then rejected the period (Bennett et al., 1977); but with 7 yr data from seven different observation times they are firmly convinced no significant periodic signal or steady signal from Cygnus X-3 is seen (Hermsen et al., 1985). Nor has the periodic signal been observed at radio or optical energies or gamma rays below 10^{11} eV.

The Crimean Cerenkov Group reported gamma rays with $E > 10^{12}$ eV with the 4.8 hr period and a maximum in the phase diagram with respect to x-rays at 0.2 phase. A 5σ significance was claimed for observations summed from 1972-1980 (Stepanian et al., 1982). The Whipple Observatory group confirmed the period but the maximum moved to a phase of 0.75 (Danaher et al., 1981). The Edwards Air Force Base observations confirmed but at a phase of 0.6 (Lamb et al., 1982). The Durham Group at Dugway found the maximum at a phase of 0.62 (Dowthwaite et al., 1983). In 1983 the Kiel Group (Samorski and Stamm, 1983), using

TABLE 2. List of reported VHE and UHE gamma-ray sources to 1990.

Source	RA Dec hr min deg	ℓ deg	b deg	Distance (kpc)	Periods	Thshold (TeV)	VHE Flux (cm⁻²s⁻¹)	Luminosity (erg s⁻¹)	Thshold (PeV)	UHE Flux (cm⁻²s⁻¹)	UHE Luminosity (erg s⁻¹)
Galactic Pulsars											
Radio Pulsars											
Crab	PSR0531+21	2CG184-05		2.0	33 ms	1	4×10^{-12}	6×10^{33}	0.2	4.4×10^{-13}	
Vela	PSR0833-45	2CG263-02		0.5	89 ms	1	3×10^{-12}	3×10^{32}			
6.13 ms	PSR1953+29	2CG065+00		3.5	6.13 ms	2	3×10^{-11}	3×10^{35}			
1.56 ms	PSR1937+21			5	1.56 ms	1	2×10^{-11}	2×10^{35}			
	PSR1802-23	2CG006-00		2.7	112 ms	1	2.3×10^{-10}	3×10^{35}			
					156 ms	1.3	8.6×10^{-12}				
1.61 ms	PSR0355+54				1.607 ms	0.4	4.1×10^{-11}	$<7 \times 10^{34}$	0.5	3.5×10^{-13}	8×10^{34}
	PSR1957+20				9.2 h						
	IE2259+586			3.6	3.49 s	0.4	2×10^{-10}	5×10^{35}			
					6.98 s						
X-ray Binary Pulsars											
Cyg x-3	2031+41			11	12.59	1	5×10^{-11}	3×10^{36}	1	2×10^{-14}	6×10^{36}
					4.8 h						
Her x-1	1656+35	57.6	37.5	5	1.24 s	1	3×10^{-11}	3×10^{35}	0.5	3×10^{-12}	2×10^{37}
Cas -1	4U0115+63			5	3.61 s	1	7×10^{-11}	6×10^{35}			
					24.3 d						
Vela x-1	0900-40	262.8	4.1	1.4	28.3 s	1	2×10^{-11}	2×10^{34}	3	9×10^{-15}	2×10^{34}
	(HD77581)				8.96 d						
Cen x-3				8	4.82 s	0.25	1.3×10^{-10}	1.6×10^{36}			
					2.09 d						
LMC x-4	(in large Magellonic cloud)			50	13.49 s	0.4	1.4×10^{-10}		10	5×10^{-15}	10^{38}
	0532-66				1.41 d						
4U1145-169				1	292 s	0.4	1.3×10^{-10}	1.8×10^{34}	0.5	1×10^{-12}	
					186.5 d						
SMC x-1	(in small Magellonic cloud)				710 ms	0.4					
					3.89 d						
SCD x-1				0.5	0.787 d	0.3	1.2×10^{-10}				
Others											
2GC195+04	0633+19				59 s						
Geminga	(160630+178)										
GalacticPln.											
SN Remnants											
CrabNebula	0531+21	2CG184-05		2.0		1	1×10^{-11}	2×10^{34}	1	10^{-13}	2×10^{35}
Extragalactic											
Radio Galaxies											
Cen A	1324-42			4,400		0.3	4×10^{-11}	3×10^{40}			
NCG5128											
Galaxies											
M31 Andromeda	0041+41										

observations of EAS at E > 10^{15} eV from 1976 to 1980 reported a periodic signal of 4.8 hr but with the phase maximum at 0.35. The maximum was slightly lower, 0.2-0.3, when the Van der Klis ephemeris (Van der Klis and Bonnet-Bidaud, 1981) was used. Their results were confirmed by the Leeds group (Lloyd-Evans et al., 1983) with the phase maximum also at 0.25. Since 1980 both the Cerenkov and EAS observations have reported variations in the results; sometimes they saw the signal but more often not (Lloyd-Evans et al., 1985; Cawley et al., 1985c).

In 1985 the Soudan Group in a mine a mile underground in Minnesota, while looking for the proton decay, claimed a muon signal from the direction of Cyg X-3 (Marshak et al., 1985). This could not be caused by charged particles from Cyg X-3 interacting in the earth's atmosphere because the galactic magnetic field would change the particle's direction; so the primary had to be a neutral particle. Ruled out were neutrons because of their lifetimes, neutrinos because the signal was observed only at angles to the zenith < 90° and gamma rays because the fluxes measured by the VHE and UHE gamma rays were too low. The authors suggested that a new particle or a new interaction producing muons was possible. The results of other underground groups were mixed. The NUSEX Group (Battistoni et al., 1985) supported the results while others, including the FREJUS (C. H. Berger, 1986) and Kamioka Groups (Oyama et al., 1986), were negative.

At the 19th International Cosmic Ray Conference in August 1985, at La Jolla, California, the Durham group announced the discovery of a pulsar in Cyg X-3 (Chadwick et al., 1985d), with a period of 12.5908 ms. Its discovery is most surprising because it was not only the first pulsar discovered in gamma rays but also the first seen with VHE gamma rays of E > 10^{12} and in a time interval of just 7 min.

The intense interest in Cyg X-3 continues unabated. More than 30 papers on Cyg X-3 were presented at the 21st International Cosmic Ray Conference in Adelaide in January this year. Instead of clarifying the status of Cyg X-3, as hoped, these papers seemed to compound the questions about Cyg X-3 and the intensity of debate over its properties.

2.1.1. *Reported 12.59 ms Pulsar.* The Durham Group (Brazier et al., 1990a,b) presented additional analysis of observations from the La Palma Observatory in the Canary Islands during 1988. On the basis of earlier measurements from 1981 to 1985 they estimated a period derivative, $\dot{P}$, and predicted a period, P, for the time of their observations in 1988. Scans around that period produced the predicted P and verified their selection of $\dot{P}$. They give an overall Rayleigh probability of uniformity of phase for the new result of 1.7×10^{-6} that confirmed their initial work.

On the other hand, the Whipple Observatory Group (O'Flaherty et al., 1990) found no evidence for pulsar emission on reanalyzing their 1984-86 data using a search around the Durham value of 12.59 ms. The detector with 39 photomultiplier tubes was used. They included the Durham suggestion of the linear trend in the variation of the period of Cygnus X-3 from 1981 to 1988 and the gamma ray sporadic maximum over the 4.8 h x-ray orbital period. The Whipple Group found no evidence for a large power deviation that might be associated with the 12.59 ms pulsar.

2.1.2. *Orbital Period of 4.8 h.* Many of the papers presented at the 21st ICRC (Proceedings 21st ICRC, volume 2) failed to detect the 4.8 h orbital period of Cyg X-3. These incuded: Utah, 100 TeV (Cassiday et al., 1990a); Los Alamos, 100 TeV (Haines et al. 1990); Kobe, 300 TeV (Asakimori et al., 1990); Whipple, 40 TeV (Gillanders et al., 1990); Utah-Michigan, 100

TeV (Ciampa et al., 1990); Leeds, 1 PeV (Bloomer et al., 1990b); Gran Sasso, 150 PeV (Aglietta et al., 1990); Plateau Rosa, 30 TeV (Dobrzynski et al., 1990) and Haverah Park, 500 TeV (Lawrence, Proser and Watson, 1990). Other groups suggested evidence for the 4.8 h period. The Utah Group (Ko et al., 1990), from a part of Fly's Eye II, for data July-October, 1989, found a 3.3σ excess between phases 0.7 and 0.8. The Nottingham muon detector results (Barley et al., 1990) from the GREX array for 1986-1987 indicated a 3.5 excess between phases 0.5 and 0.7. However, this was only observed in muon-rich data folded with the Mason ephemeris. The Tata group (Sinha et al., 1990a) with the KGF array during April-May 1985 showed a 3.7σ excess at the phase interval 0.5-0.6. The Ohya EAS array (Muraki et al., 1990) at 1 PeV from 1986-1989 used 400 m^2 muon detectors under 30 m of earth. When restricting showers to within 4° of the source, using the ephemeris of van der Klis and Bonnet-Bidaud and accepting only showers in which $N_\mu/N_e \leq 0.01$, they observed a 4.4σ excess in the phase interval 0.25-0.35.

2.1.3. Radio Bursts of 1989, Short Time Emissions and Long Term Steady Fluxes.

Searches continue for gamma rays during the radio bursts that occurred in 1989 and for VHE and UHE emissions of a few hours or days. Mostly null detections of UHE gamma rays resulted from the observations associated with the radio bursts of June 2 and July 21. Likewise nearly all groups reported non-detection of impulsive emission from Cyg X-3 during the later part of the 1980s.

No new results were presented at the 21st ICRC of statistically significant long-term steady fluxes of UHE gamma rays from Cyg X-3. The marginal detections of the early 1980s may have given way to the non-detection by more sensitive detectors in the late 1980s.

2.1.4. EeV Gamma Rays from Cyg X-3.

Since the time dilation factor of EeV neutrons is 10^9, a 15 min lifetime in the lab becomes 30,000 yr in the neutron's frame. EeV neutrons can survive the flight from Cyg X-3, 11 kpc away. So it is reasonable to look for atmospheric showers caused by interactions of these neutrons. The Fly's Eye group reported observations of EeV showers from November 1981-July 1989 (Cassiday et al., 1990b, 1989). Showers with maxima deeper than 700 g cm^{-2} into the atmosphere were selected. This cut eliminated many showers initiated by heavy nuclei, while retaining the neutron induced showers. They reported a flux of 4×10^{-18} $cm^{-2}s^{-1}$ above 2 EeV with a 5.8σ significance. The 4.8 h orbital phase analysis gives a shower concentration between 0.05 and 0.35.

Observations from September 1984-July 1989 of the Akeno Group (Teshima et al., 1990) gave possible verification. For energies > 0.5 EeV the most significant concentration of showers is in the direction near Cyg X-3. The statistical significance is 3.7σ for an angle of 4° around Cyg X-3. No significant 4.8 h modulation was observed.

The Haverah Park observations (Lawrence, Prosser and Watson, 1990; Lawrence et al., 1989) seem to be in disagreement with both groups above. No DC excess > 0.5 EeV from the direction of Cyg X-3 was observed. This gives an upper limit at 95% confidence of 4×10^{-18} $cm^{-2}s^{-1}$, significantly lower than the Fly's Eye and Akeno Groups. Other inconsistencies include the differences of a few degrees between the directions of the maxima of the Fly's Eye and Akeno results and of Cyg X-3. The energy distribution of the Fly's Eye increases with energy above 2 EeV but the Akeno distribution implies no events with energy > 3 EeV. The Fly's Eye reports its strongest signal between the phases of 0.05 and 0.35 but Akeno observed no modulation of the 4.8 h period.

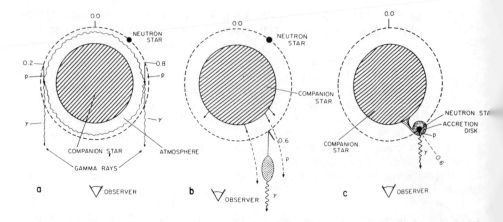

Figure 4. Possible geometries to explain emission of VHE/UHE gamma rays from binary x-ray stars. (a) Companion star atmosphere (0.2 and 0.8); (b) accretion wake or stellar wind; (c) accretion disk (Hillas, 1987).

2.2. HERCULES X-1

In 1973 Her X-1 was found, by the UHURU satellite x-ray group (Giacconi et al., 1973), to be an x-ray pulsar with a period of 1.24 s in an eclipsing binary with an orbital period of 1.7 d. Evidence exists for a 35 d amplitude variation of unknown origin. A hard x-ray line was found with a balloon observation using NaI detectors by the Garching Max Planck Institut and Tubingen X-ray Group (Trumper et al., 1977; 1978) at 58 keV. It was attributed to electron cyclotron emission in the strong magnetic field of $5x10^{12}$ G of a rotating neutron star. The line width was less than 12 keV and the flux was $3x10^3$ photons $cm^{-2}s^{-1}$. Later balloon observations suggested either an emission line at about 52 keV or absorption line at about 38 keV (Voges et al., 1982). Upper limits only were given for a possible second harmonic line. The line has been confirmed by the UCSD-MIT hard x-ray experiment on HEAO 1 (Gruber et al., 1980), the NASA-GSFC Group with a high resolution germanium detector (Tueller et al., 1984), and by several other hard x-ray groups. The companion, HZ Her, has been identified at optical wavelengths (Liller, 1972a,b; Bahcall and Bahcall, 1972a,b). Her X-1 has not been detected as a radio or optical pulsar, a gamma ray pulsar or a steady source between 100 keV and 10^{11} eV.

Her X-1, like the other binary x-ray pulsars Cyg X-3, PSR 1953-29 and 4UO115+63, was reported as a source of pulsed gamma rays above $1.5x10^{11}$ eV by the Whipple Observatory Group (Cawley et al., 1985b), above 10^{12} eV by the Durham (Dugway) Group (Dowthwaite et al., 1984b) and above $3x10^{14}$ eV by the Utah Fly's eye Group (Baltrusaitis, 1985a; Baltrusaitis et al., 1985b). Each group observed short time pulsed gamma rays near the x-ray pulsar frequency of 1.2378s. The Durham Group reported a 3 min interval on April 17, 1983; the Fly's Eye Group a 40 min interval on July 11, 1983 that was observed at the same time by the Durham Group with a negative result; and a 28 min interval on April 4, 1984 and one night's observation on May 5, 1984 by the Whipple Observatory Group.

From 1983 to 1985 observations were reported of periods close to the x-ray value of 1.23776 s. Durham (Dowthwaite et al., 1984; Chadwick et al., 1987), Fly's Eye (Baltrusaitus et al.,

1985), Whipple (Gorham et al., 1986a,b) and Haleakula (Resvanis et al., 1987, 1988). Later measurements of transients in 1986 by Whipple on June 11, 1986 (Lamb et al., 1988), Haleakala on May 13, 1986 (Resvanis et al., 1988) and Cygnus on July 24, 1986 (Dingus et al., 1988) reported periods of 1.2357 s, 0.16% shorter than the x-ray value. If caused by a Doppler shift, the resultant velocity of 480 km s^{-1} around the neutron star was considerably higher than the neutron star's orbital velocity of 169 km s^{-1}. The lower period implied that the VHE and UHE gamma ray production site on Her X-1 was different than for x-rays. No other periods were reported during this time by the 3 groups.

Additional new observations of blue-shifted frequencies were reported for TeV and PeV energies at the 21st ICRC. The Durham Group (Brazier et al., 1990b) reported a 200 s transient at 0.4 TeV on July 16 1988 with a frequency close to their discovery frequency in 1983 and the Bhabha group (Rawat et al., 1990) at 0.2 TeV on June 12, 1988 reported a similar value. They observed at the phase 0.61 and 0.66, respectively, of the 1.7 day orbit and at 0.99 and 0.02 of the 35 d period. The Michigan-Sandia group (Akerlof et al., 1990a) using an imaging cut obtained a value 0.34% lower.

Additional values of 1.236 and 1.23477 s were reported at the 21st ICRC by the Leeds (Bloomer et al., 1990a) and Ooty EAS arrays at PeV energies. The Leeds observations for 20-21 May, 1989 gave 11 events on an expectation of 2.45 while the Ooty observation July 1, August 8-9 and November 21, 1986 gave a chance probability estimated to be 9x10^{-5}. These periods are near those obtained by the Whipple, Haleakula and Cygnus groups. The values of the period for Her X-1 are plotted in Figure 5. The dashed line is drawn at the x-ray period of 1.23776 s. The cluster of lower values in 1986 and early 87 could be caused by a time variation of the VHE and UHE gamma rays. However, because of the scatter of values both before and after this time such a conclusion now seems premature.

Additional caution is urged because of the recent reevaluation of the Her-1 search for the 1.237 s period reported at the 21st ICRC (Reynolds et al., 1990) by the Whipple Group using imaging with their 37 photomultiplier detector. An analysis of 4 years of data from 1984 through 1987, using imaging that successfully detected the Crab Nebula to 9σ, and later with 109 photomultipliers to 18σ, does not see the 1.237 s x-ray period or any other period. In their words "A comprehensive Fourier analysis of the 1984-1987 Whipple Observatory data base for Hercules X-1, on a timescale of 30 minutes, shows evidence for periodic TeV emission near the 1.24 s neutron

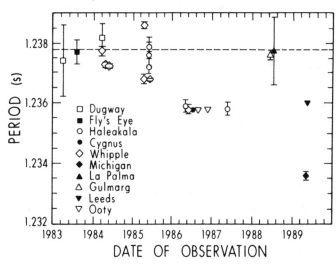

Figure 5. Episodes of blue-shifted emission from Hercules X-1 (1983-89) (Fegan 1990).

star period at the 99% confidence level. This analysis is performed on all showers irrespective of their Cerenkov image properties. However, when this same type of analysis is performed for those showers which resemble gamma-ray showers from the direction of Hercules X-1, there is no evidence for any periodic signal."

2.3. VELA X-1

Vela X-1, like Cyg X-3 and Her X-1, is an eclipsing x-ray binary pulsar with a period of 283 s and orbital period 8.96 d (Boynton et al., 1984). It has been extensively studied in soft and hard x-rays up to about 80 keV. The light curve shows two pulse maxima separated by 0.50 in phase. The NASA Goddard Group (Tueller et al., 1985) with high-purity germanium detectors observed Vela X-1 for 5 hr during a balloon flight from Alice Springs, Australia on December 5, 1984. A strong pulsed signal, with the normal 2 maxima phase plot, was observed from 20 to 80 keV but no lines as strong as 3σ were observed. No cyclotron lines were seen contrary to the line established for Her X-1. The resulting energy distribution was exponential.

Gamma rays below 35 MeV have not been seen and above 35 MeV were not detected by either the SAS 2 or COS B groups. The Adelaide, South Australia EAS group (Protheroe et al., 1984) reported UHE gamma rays of 3×10^{15} from observations taken at the Buckland Park Array during 1979-1981. They found a single pulse at phase 0.63 for the orbital period that was less than 1 bin wide (1/50 in phase). More recently, the Potchefstroom, South Africa Group of North et al. (1987) reported pulsed VHE gamma rays of the pulsar period 282.805 s for the time from April 2 to May 10, 1986. The chance origin was estimated to be 7×10^4. The phase curve was sinusoidal with maxima around 0.15 and 0.84 near eclipse. During a run of 123 min on May 4, they also observed a burst of 1.5 min that was 100% above the mean at the beginning and appeared to be modulated by the 282.805 s period.

The Potchefstroom group with the Nooitgadact telescope during April-May 1987 confirmed the new Gingus x-ray period of 283.14 s (Raubenheimer et al., 1989). Only weak modulation of the orbital period of 8.96 d was found. They again detected the x-ray period from 1988 observations and conclude that Vela X-1 produces persistent pulsed gamma rays (Raubenheimer et al., 1990).

At the 21st ICRC the Durham group (Brazier et al., 1990a) reported observations of Vela X-1 for 103 h on 34 nights between October 30, 1986 and May 19, 1988. The chance probability for the pulsar period not stated (assumed to be the Ginga x-ray satellite value of 283.4 s) was 1.1×10^{-4}. A plot of the pulsar period at various dates is given in Figure 6. Upper limits were presented by the

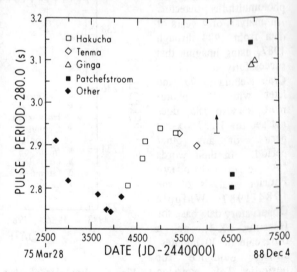

Figure 6. Vela X-1 period history (Brazier et al. 1990a).

Janzos collaboration for observations during March-April 1989 at 1 TeV (Bond et al., 1990). Three UHE groups, Mt. Chacaltaya (Kakimoto et al., 1990) at 30 TeV from September 1987-June 1989, SYS array (Matano et al., 1990) at 0.2 PeV on Mt Chacaltaya for February 1986 to March 1989 and the Leeds-Bartol collaboration (Gaisser et al., 1990) at the South Pole for January 1988-September 1988 at 0.16 PeV also gave upper limits for Vela X-1.

2.4. CEN X-3

Cen X-3 is the prototype of a massive x-ray binary at a distance of 8 kpc. The discovery of its binary system (Schreier et al., 1972) was followed by identification of its companion, an O-type giant star (Krezeminski, 1974). It has a 2.1 d orbital period and a pulsar period of 4.8 s. Over a decade, the orbital period has decreased with apparent significant deviations from a constant rate of decay (Kelley et al., 1983). The overall long-term period decrease is well explained by the tidal interaction between Krezeminski's star and the orbiting neutron star.

VHE gamma rays from Cen X-3 were first reported by the Durham group (Caraminana et al., 1989) using the 0.25 TeV Narrabri telescope with observations between January 1987 and January 1988. Gamma rays were observed at the 0.7-0.8 phase of the orbital period of 2.1 d. The stated chance probability level was 2×10^{-5}. At the 21st ICRC the Durham group (Brazier et al., 1990c) updated and extended their original observations with a total of 200 h on 58 nights between January 1987 and June 7, 1989. They searched a range twice the expected time variation of the Ginga satellite pulsar period of 4.8230 ± 0.002 s for June 1987. Periodicity was identified only for the orbital phase of 0.75-0.85, with a period of 4.823 s at a chance probability of 6×10^{-7}.

At the 21st ICRC the Potchefstroom group (North et al., 1990) reported observations of Cen X-3 during 1986, 88 and 89 with the Potchefstroom TeV telescope. Using the Ginga period closest to their observations they too found that the orbital phase interval 0.7 to 0.8 only gave a significant gamma ray flux. They confirmed the Durham result with a chance probability of 2×10^{-4}. A plot of the pulsar period of Cen X-3 variation with time is given in Figure 7. The 1986 period of 4.8252 s is reasonably close to the Russian satellite Mir x-ray results but the 1988 period of 4.8175 is 6σ below the linear fit. It is 0.16% lower than the x-ray value similar to the low values found for Her X-1.

2.5. THE CRAB PULSAR, PSR0531+21

The Crab Pulsar is one of the most studied objects

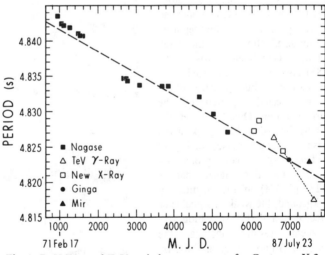

Figure 7. X-Ray and TeV period measurements for Centaurus X-3 (North et al., 1990).

in the sky. It has been observed throughout the electromagnetic spectrum from radio waves of 100 MHz to gamma rays of $E > 10^{12}$ eV covering more than 10^{17} orders of magnitude in photon energies. The light curves for 430 MHz radio waves, optical, 1.5-10 keV soft x-rays, 18-163 keV medium x-rays, 100-400 keV hard x-rays, 1-20 MeV gamma rays and > 50 MeV gamma rays are shown in Figure 8 (Bignami and Hermsen, 1983). The light curves are similar at all energies. The first pulse peaks are aligned at the same phase as the radio waves and the second pulse peaks all follow by the same 0.42 in phase. However, the shapes of the pulse peaks, their relative heights and the region between peaks vary somewhat with photon energy and over the years. The inner pulse region (between the peaks) appears highest at energies of tens and hundreds of keV.

The COS B spark chamber pair spectrometer has unambiguously established PSR0531+21 as a pulsar from 50 to 1000 MeV. The two pulses spaced 0.42 apart in phase have maintained this separation over the 8 years of observation. The relative heights of the main pulse and interpulse in the light curve changed significantly over the eight years.

The Crab pulsar has been a target of VHE and UHE telescopes since the early 1970s. Reviews of this work can be found in Porter and Weekes (1978) and in Ramana Murthy (1980). This era included mostly upper limits and results of low statistical significance from 10^{10} to 10^{14} eV.

From 1980 to 1985 three groups reported radiation from PSR 0531+21. They include Durham (Gibson et al., 1982; Dowthwaite et al., 1984a; Chadwick et al., 1985a); Tata (Bhat et al., 1984); and the California collaboration (Tumer et al., 1985). One group reported that the signal persisted for three months while others saw the signals only occasionally. Whipple Observatory (Cawley et al., 1985a) found no pulsed signal although they reported an unpulsed flux from the Crab Nebula. Tien Shan (Kirov et al., 1985) also reported unpulsed VHE gamma rays. The light curve of the 33 ms period reported by the Durham group (Dowthwaite et al., 1984b) showed a sharp peak at the phase of the radio pulse, see Figure 9. They quote a chance probability of 10^{-5} for this signal that is (0.233 ± 0.054) of the cosmic ray background, the weakest signal ever detected in a VHE observation.

Recent results include the Whipple Group report at the 21st ICRC in January 1990 at Adelaide, Australia of their search for PSR

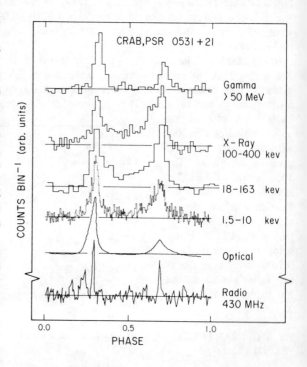

Figure 8. Phase diagram of the pulsed radiation from the Crab pulsar 0531+21 at six different energies from radio waves to gamma rays.

0531+21. Analysis of 25% of the data taken during the winter of 1988-89 from their 109 photomultiplier detector shows no evidence for a pulsed signal in agreement with results from their older 37 element detector (Weekes et al., 1989). The Michigan Sandia group (Akerlof et al., 1990b) and the Tata Pachmarhi group (Bhat et al., 1990) likewise found no Crab pulsar 33 ms period for VHE gamma rays. At 0.2 PeV energies Tata Ooty (Gupta et al., 1990) for observations June 1984 to May 1987 report pulsed gamma rays at the phase of the optical interpulse with a chance probability 1.6x10^{-3}. Note the absolute phases observed by Durham and Tata Ooty differ by 0.5. Several other groups at the 21st ICRC reported negative results for the 33 ms period.

2.6. THE VELA PULSAR, PSR 0833-45 (2CG 263-02)

The 89 ms Vela Pulsar is the benchmark of gamma ray astronomy. As the strongest of the gamma ray sources it was used by COS B for onboard calibration from 50 to 5000 MeV. Its light curves, shown in Figure 10 (Tumer et al., 1984) differ in phase in different parts of the electromagnetic spectrum. The radio signal at 2,295 MHz has only a single pulse (Large et al., 1968). The first pulse of the gamma rays is delayed by 0.12 in phase relative to the radio pulse (Thompson et al., 1977b; Kanbach et al., 1980) and the optical pulse by 0.23 (Wallace et al., 1977). The gamma ray phase separation between the first and second pulses is 0.42, the same as for the Crab Pulsar, but is only 0.25 for the optical pulses. Upper limits only exist from measurements of the soft and hard x-rays (Knight et al., 1982).

The Narrabri Observatory Group (Grindlay et al., 1975a) carried out observations of PSR 0833-45 with Cerenkov light collectors at E > 0.3 PeV during 1972 and 1973. One phase pulse was seen at the 3σ significance level in 1972 but not in 1973 unless the highest pulse height events only were selected. The authors consider their results upper limits only. The Tata Institute group (Bhat et al., 1980), with Cerenkov collectors for 35 hr during February-March 1979, at comparable energies reported the first and second pulses at significance levels of 4.4 and 2.5σ with a phase separation of 0.42 the same as seen at lower energies. This is the only time the double pulse light curve was found for VHE or UHE gamma rays. Neither group measured the absolute phases.

The Tata group later reported (Bhat et al., 1985, 1986) the results of 4 sets of data taken between 1979 and 1985 with absolute phases. When cut to include the lowest energy events only, they found evidence for pulsed gamma rays at the position of the first optical pulse. The energy threshold is high because of the low elevation of PSR 0833-45 at the Ooty site. The significance of the combined detections is 3σ and the flux is not in good agreement with that of the Narrabri group (Grindley et al., 1975). A summary of the fluxes appears in Figure 10.

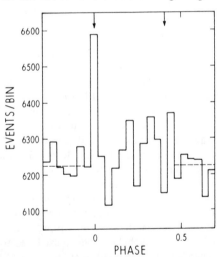

Figure 9. The light curve for all events recorded from PSR 0531+21 in 1982 September-1983 November. The radio main and interpulses are indicated by arrows (Dowthwaite et al., 1984b).

The Vela pulsar spectrum is one of the hardest of all the COS B sources. Extrapolation would suggest a strong source of the VHE gamma rays. However, the measurements in Figure 10 show fluxes or upper limits far below the extrapolated values.

Most recently at the 21st ICRC the Durham group (Brazier et al., 1990d) reported on 40 hr of observations with the Narrabri telescope between January 22 and February 7, 1987 and later observations on March 2 to 10, 1989 following the radio glitch of December 24, 1988. In 1987 they found no evidence for the radio period of 89 s. Their 3σ upper limit for gamma rays > 0.3 TeV was $(6\pm1.5)\times10^{-11}$ cm^{-2}s^{-1} consistent with the measurements of Grindley et al. in the 1970s. Initial analysis after the radio glitch showed no evidence of VHE gamma rays at the radio pulsar period. Clearly, the Vela Pulsar as a source of VHE gamma rays has not lived up to expectations suggested by its strong hard flux at energies of hundreds of MeV.

2.7. CRAB NEBULA (TOTAL GAMMA RAYS)

Our "standard candle", the Crab Nebula, is a supernova remnant in Taurus, an expanding mass of gas that is spectacular in the visible. Doppler shifts of the gas require velocities up to 1500 km s^{-1}. The velocity and angular extent of the nebula give 2 kpc for the distance to the Crab. Extensive measurements have been made at all gamma ray energy regions of Table 3. The total gamma rays from the Crab Nebula include both pulsed and steady radiation. The total gamma ray energy distribution may be fitted by the power law 3 x 10^3 E$^{-2.3}$ photons cm^{-2} s^{-1} MeV^{-1} from 1 keV to 3 GeV (Graser and Schonfelder, 1982). At x-ray energies most of the flux is steady while at gamma ray energies from 30 to 3000 MeV most is pulsed with the cross-over in the medium energy region from 1 to 30 MeV. The steady radio waves and perhaps more energetic photons are caused by the synchrotron radiation of electrons in the strong magnetic fields of the Nebula. The pulsed radiation comes from the Crab Pulsar at the center of the Nebula which also fuels the steady radiation.

A recent interesting possible coincidence occurred among the KGF, BAKSAN and EAS-TOP EAS arrays. The transient was observed on February 23, 1989 by Alexeenko, et al.

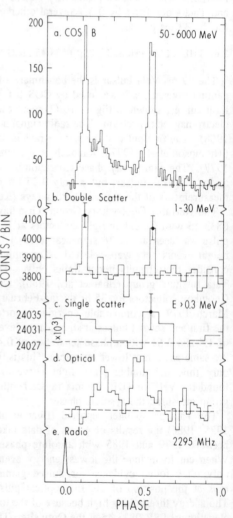

Figure 10. Light curves for gamma rays from PSR 0833-45 of a. COS B, 50-6000 MeV; b. double scatter, 1-30 MeV; c. single scatter, 0.3-1.5 MeV; d. Optical light curve; e. Radio light curve.

(1989) using the BAKSAN array for gamma rays > 0.2 PeV as seen in Figure 11. The 57 events were observed within 2.5° of the Crab Nebula when 31 were expected for a significance of 4.4σ. Also when the Crab was at their zenith the Tata group reported at the 21st ICRC (Sinha et al., 1990b) observations at the KGF array, 35 events within 3.9° of the Crab Nebula when 18 were expected for a significance of 4.1σ. The Gran-Sasso collaboration (in a verbal presentation) reported a maximum of 38 events within 1.59° of the Crab Nebula at its zenith when 25.5 were expected for a significance of 2.3σ. All three observations are plotted in Figure 11. The burst must have lasted for at least 8 h. The 3 independent correlated detections suggested the effect was real with an overall chance probability of 10^{-6}. The HEGRA array at La Palma did not observe an enhancement at 21:00 UT expected if the burst had lasted that long.

TABLE 3. Crab Nebula total VHE gamma ray observations (Fegan, 1990).

Group	Epoch	Dur. (hours)	Sig. σ	Energy (TeV)	Flux $(cm^{-2}s^{-1})$	Reference
Smithsonian	1969-72	150	+3.0	(0.14)	(5.7×10^{-11})	Fazio et al. (1972)
Whipple Coll.	1983-85	40	+4.0	(0.6)	(1.5×10^{-11})	Cawley et al. (1985a)
Whipple Coll.	1986-88	80	+9.0	(0.7)	(1.8×10^{-11})	Weekes et al. (1989)
Whipple Coll.	1988-89	33	+18.3	(0.4)	(7.0×10^{-11})	Lang et al. (1990)
Tien Shan	1979-81	16	+4.4	(2.0)	(5.7×10^{-11})	Mukanov et al. (1983)
Sandia - Mich.	1988-89	30	+5.8	(0.2)	(1.8×10^{-10})	Akerlof et al. (1990b)
U. Cal. Riverside	1988	2	+4.3	(0.6)	(2.5×10^{-11})	Tumer et al. (1990)

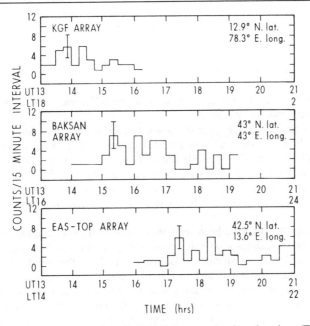

Figure 11. Time profile of the PeV Crab burst at the three locations (Fegan 1990).

The detections of the Crab Nebula to date are given in Table 3 taken from Fegan (1990). For an exhaustive compilation including negative results see Weeks (1988). Examination of Table 3 shows for the first time significances that have increased rapidly responding to effective cosmic ray shower background rejection. The Whipple Collaboration significances increased from 4.0 to 9.0 to 18.3σ during the time periods 1983-85, 1986-88, and 1988-89 while they employed successively more sophisticated imaging of the Cerenkov showers. The 9σ result was obtained with 37 photomultiplier tubes imaging the Cerenkov showers and the 18.3σ with 109 tubes. The orientation of the 37 photomultipliers in the focal plane is shown in Figure 12. A typical recorded event is given in Figure 13a and after calibration and noise reduction in Figure 13b (Weekes et al., 1989). An elipse is

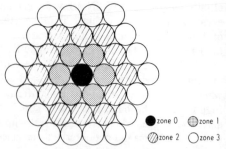

Figure 12. Layout of phototubes in the focal plane of the 10 m optical reflector. Each phototube has a sensitive area defined by a diameter of 0°.4. The full field of view is 3°.5. The center phototube is defined as zone 0; the surrounding ring of six phototubes is zone 1; the ring of 12, zone 2; and the outer ring of 18, zone 3. The latter is not included in the camera trigger (Weekes et al., 1989).

fitted to the image with C at one focus. The other parameters are shown in Figure 13c. When the distributions of the various parameters for simulated showers are plotted as in Figure 13d, the AZWIDTH gives the best separation of gamma ray showers from proton induced showers as it is based on both shape and orientation.

The 18.3σ significance for the Crab Nebula is the major advance in VHE gamma ray astronomy during the 1980s. The Crab Nebula is now a well documented verified compelling bright source that can be used by groups in the world for calibrations.

3. VHE and UHE Source Catalogs

One of the goals of gamma ray astronomy is to establish VHE and UHE source catalogs of statistically compelling gamma ray sources.

Weekes (1988) proposed the VHE gamma ray source catalog current to August 15, 1986 that is given here as Table 4. Thirteen sources are listed in the catalog, 5 pulsars, 6 binary x-ray sources, the Crab Nebula and Cen A. His criterion is that at least one paper in a refereed journal must claim the detection of the source at energies greater than 0.1 TeV. One detection at 3σ is not sufficient. When contradictions arise the source is demoted to a second list of possible VHE gamma ray sources. He points out there is uncertainty about the validity of many of the results.

Some of the catalog sources have been seen above threshold only occasionally as bursts of a few minutes or hours. Sources seen only occasionally could result from lack of sensitivity of the detectors when the source signals occasionally rise above the thresholds. The signals have been reported mostly at the 3, 4 and 5σ levels. There is no obvious reason why gamma ray sources with widely different luminosities at vastly different distances should all conspire to give the same fluxes. If sources are varying over wide ranges where are the 6, 8 and 10σ sources? Failure to confirm sources at previous levels could be blamed on long term downward time variations. However, sources with long term increases in flux as well as decreasing fluxes

a. Typical recorded event

b. After noise reduction

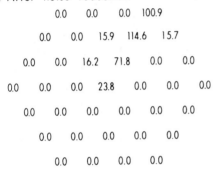

c. Centroid of the image

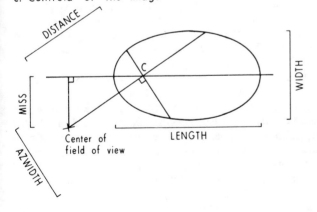

d. Distribution of simulated parameters

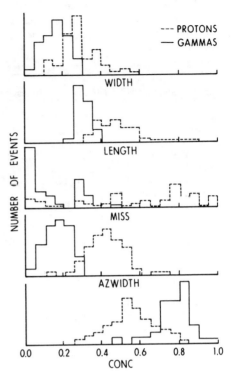

Figure 13. Whipple group AZWIDTH analysis (Weekes et al., 1989).

should make their appearances, especially as detectors have become more sensitive from the 1970s through the 1980s. In order to evaluate variations at radio, visible and x-ray energies it was most helpful to have detectors that measure the low as well as the high fluxes. High sensitivities are required to measure the signals over wide excursions. Without, it is very difficult to establish credibility.

TABLE 4. Very high energy gamma-ray source catalog (Weekes, 1988).

Source	Published detections	Periodicity	Hemisphere	Energy	Flux $(cm^{-1}s^{-1})$	Distance (kpc)	Luminosity $(ergs^{1})$
Pulsars							
Crab	6	33 ms	N	1 TeV	4×10^{-12}	2.0	6×10^{33}
Vela	2	89.2 ms	S	1 TeV	3×10^{-12}	0.5	3×10^{32}
PSR 1937 -21	(1)	1.56 ms	N	1 TeV	2×10^{-11}	5	2×10^{35}
PSR 1953 -29	1	6.13 ms	N	1 TeV	1.2×10^{-12}	3.5	6×10^{35}
PSR 1802 -23	1	112 ms	S	1 TeV	2.3×10^{10}	2.7	3×10^{35}
X-ray Binary Sources							
Cygnus X-3	9	4.8 h	N	1 TeV	5×10^{-11}	>11.4	3×10^{36}
				100 TeV	10^{-13}		
	3			1 PeV	2×10^{-14}		6×10^{36}
Hercules X-1	3	1.24 s	N	1 TeV	3×10^{-11}	5	3×10^{35}
	1			0.5 PeV	3×10^{-12}		2×10^{37}
4U0115 + 63	2	3.61 s	N	1 TeV	7×10^{-11}	5	6×10^{35}
Vela X-1	1	8.96 d	S	1 TeV	2×10^{-11}	1.4	2×10^{34}
	2		S	3 PeV	9×10^{-15}		2×10^{34}
Cen X-3	(1)	2.09 d	S	? PeV	?	10	?
LMC X-4	1	1.41 d	S	10 PeV	5×10^{-15}	50	10^{38}
Supernova remnants							
Crab Nebula	2	steady	N	1 TeV	1×10^{-11}	2	2×10^{34}
	1	variable		1 PeV	1×10^{-13}		2×10^{35}
Radio galaxies							
Cen A	1	steady	S	1 TeV	4×10^{-12}	4400	3×10^{40}

It is possible that the statistical significances of many observations have been overstated. The mathematics is not in question. Even conservative observers may sometimes unconsciously understate the degrees of freedom in their zeal for detecting sources. The observer may fail to take into account that the source with positive results is one on a long list of sources with negative results or that the particular time varying signature may be only one of many that would be considered positive. It is very difficult to assess the statistical significances of short variations with particular characteristics when no objective prior criteria have been established to count the number of ways they would be considered positive. Rarely is the background as thoroughly searched for anomalous effects as the on target observations.

The latest catalog of gamma rays at energies above 0.3 TeV appears in the Rapporteur talk of Fegan at the 21st ICRC at Adelaide in January 1990, given in Table 5. He demands that each discovery observation be independently confirmed and the detailed characteristics of both the discovery and confirmation show broad agreement. His catalog is restricted to 5 sources, the Crab Nebula and 4 binary x-ray pulsars. Fegan suggests that a suitable yardstick of progress in gamma ray astronomy might be the growth-rate of the catalog of established sources and quotes Ramana Murthy's comment at the Durham workshop in 1986. "It is reasonable to expect that by the time of the next workshop (1989-90?) one would have established some sources at significance levels of 10σ or greater and staked claims for several tens of sources at the 5σ level". Instead, the catalog has decreased from 13 to 4 sources; caused partially at least by the different criteria in the selection of sources for the two catalogs. We now have one source, the Crab Nebula, at the 18σ level. Most other sources are still at or below the same 5σ level existing in 1986. Three new candidate VHE and UHE sources 4U1145-619, SMC X-1 and PSR 9355 were reported at the 21st ICRC.

No new positive detections have been reported of the Crab Pulsar, PSR 0531+21, since 1986, despite several searches. Cyg X-3 appears to be on the decline at TeV and PeV energies. The 12.59 ms pulsar in Cyg X-3 has not been confirmed by a second Group at any region of the electromagnetic spectrum in the 5 yr since the initial report. Four groups have attempted but failed to confirm the pulsar period. Her X-1 is reported to be an occasional emitter of blue shifted VHE gamma rays. The imaging technique used so successfully by the Whipple group for the Crab Nebula 18σ detection, failed to detect the normal x-ray period of Her X-1 of June 11, 1986 or the shorter period they earlier reported without imaging. Nor with imaging have they been able to detect the Crab Pulsar, Cyg X-3, 4UO114+63 or IE2259+586.

TABLE 5. Catalog of gamma rays with E > 0.3 TeV (Fegan 1990).

Source	TeV	PeV	EeV	Comment
Crab Nebula	X	X	-	TeV steady, PeV impulsive
Cygnus X-3	X	X	X	Declining at TeV/PeV
Hercules X-1	X	X	-	Episodic, with blue shifting
Vela X-1	X	X?	-	
Cen X-3	X	?	-	

Fegan suggests possible implications of the Whipple results:

a. Some reported detections of gamma rays from x-ray binaries are not genuine but represent statistically improbable random fluctuations.

b. Most reported detections of gamma rays from x-ray binaries are instead particles of mass ≤ 1.3 MeV, required by time dilation, that interact as they pass through the atmosphere. However, such low mass neutral particles would have been measured at accelerators.

c. Photons undergo unexpected interactions at TeV energies. However it appears impossible to change the basic features of gamma-ray showers as long as

$$\sigma(\gamma \to \pi) << \sigma(\gamma \to e^+e^-)$$

Since QCD cannot make photons look like protons, new physics would be required.

The puzzle of the muon content of extended air showers for UHE gamma rays has not yet been solved. Gamma ray showers are expected to have few muons compared to proton induced showers because of the low ratio, about 3×10^{-3}, for the cross sections for the production of pions and electron-positron pairs by gamma rays. At 100 TeV the number of muons should be 30 times greater in hadron than photon produced showers. Tagging showers by muons should eliminate most of the cosmic ray induced showers. However, the original Kiel observation of Cyg X-3 where the muon content was 70% (Samorski and Stamm, 1983), the Los Alamos observations of Cygnus X-3 where cutting events with zero muons eliminated their signal (Dingus et al., 1988) and their observations of the July 24, 1986 bursts from Her X-1 (Alexandreas et al., 1990) where the muon content of their events was substantial compared with that expected from photon-induced showers, violate the conventional wisdom.

To date the Crab Nebula as observed by the Whipple observatory is the only VHE gamma ray source that displays the predicted characteristics of a Celestial gamma ray source. With the more stringent requirements of high significance that increases with elimination of proton induced background and reproducibility over several years, the Crab Nebula remains as the only member of our high reliability catalog of VHE gamma ray sources.

4. The Future

The future of VHE and UHE gamma ray astronomy is long and difficult and is not for the faint-hearted (Fegan, 1990). Observers have no choice but to increase their sensitivities by orders of magnitude. The cosmic ray induced shower backgrounds must be reduced so the weak as well as the strong transients can be measured. Fegan suggests some common-sense procedures and rules that could be followed by practitioners of gamma ray astronomy. These include: (a) simultaneous observational programs wherever possible. (b) Experimentalists adhere to stricter self-imposed hypotheses testing that implies rigorous application of a priori rather than a posteriori statistics. (c) Strict data characterization checks particularly for periodicity testing. (d) All degrees of freedom should be clearly stated before calculating a final probability when data is cut in a variety of ways e.g., multi-parameterization, discrete energy bands, temporal subsets and multi-period analysis.

TeV and PeV gamma rays are certainly emitted by many celestial objects. The question is their luminosities. The challenge to the experimentalists is to design detectors and telescopes with the sensitivities required to measure the fluxes with significances that are acceptable to the scientific community.

5. Acknowledgments

We acknowledge the extended use of the reviews by T. C. Weekes, Physics Reports, 160, 1 & 2 (1988), D. J. Fegan, Rapporteur VHE and UHE gamma rays, Proceedings 21st Inter. Cosmic Ray Conf., Adelaide, Australia (1990), and R. S. White, Encyclopedia of Physical Science and Technology, Vol. 5, 763, Academic Press (1987).

6. References

Aglietta, M., et al. (1990) Proc. 21st Inter. Cosmic Ray Conf. 2, 345.
Akerlof, C., et al. (1990a) Proc. 21st Inter. Cosmic Ray Conf. 2, 95.
Akerlof, C., et al. (1990b) Proc. 21st Inter. Cosmic Ray Conf. 2, 135.
Alexandreas, D. E., et al. (1990) Proc. 21st Inter. Cosmic Ray Conf. 2, 116.
Alexeenko, V. V., et al. (1989) Proc. Int. Workshop on VHE and UHE Gamma Ray Astronomy, Crimea, USSR, p. 187.
Asakimori, K., et al. (1990) Proc. 21st Inter Cosmic Ray Conf. 2, 18.
Bahcall, J. N. and Bahcall, N. A. (1972a), IAU Cir. No. 2427.
Bahcall, J. N. and Bahcall, N. A. (1972b), IAU Circ. No. 2428.
Baltrusaitis, R. M. (1985a) Proc. 19th Inter. Cosmic Ray Conf. 1, 111.
Baltrusaitis, R. M., et al. (1985b) Ap. J. Lett. 293, L69.
Barley, S. K., et al. (1990) Proc. 21st Inter. Cosmic Ray Conf. 2, 43.
Battistoni, G., et al. (1985) Physics Letters 155B, 465.
Bennett, K., et al. (1977) Astron. Astrophys. 59, 273.
Berger, Ch., et al. (1986) Physics Lett. B.
Bhat, P. N., et al. (1980) Astron. Astrophys. 81, L3.
Bhat, P. N., et al. (1984) Adv. Sp. Res. 3, 135.
Bhat, P. N., et al. (1986) Proc. Nato Workshop on V.H.E. Gamma-Ray Astronomy, ed. K. E. Turvey, Reidel, Dordrecht, p. 271.

Bhat, P. N., et al. (1990) Proc. 21st Inter. Cosmic Ray Conf. 2, 148.

Bignami, G. F. and Hermsen, W. (1983) Ann. Rev. Astron. Astrophys. 21, 67.

Bloomer, S. D., et al. (1990a) Proc. 21st Inter. Cosmic Ray Conf. 2, 334.

Bloomer, S. D., et al. (1990b) Proc. 21st Inter. Cosmic Ray Conf. 2, 39.

Bond, I. A., et al. (1990) Proc. 21st Inter. Cosmic Ray Conf. 2, 271.

Boynton, P. E., et al. (1984) Ap. J. Lett 283, L53.

Brazier, K. T. S., et al. (1990a) Proc. 21st Inter. Cosmic Ray Conf. 2, 91.

Brazier, K. T. S., et al. (1990b) Ap. J. 350, 745.

Brazier, K. T. S., et al. (1990c) Proc. 21st Inter. Cosmic Ray Conf. 2, 292.

Brazier, K. T. S., et al. (1990d) Proc. 21st Inter. Cosmic Ray Conf. 2, 379.

Brazier, K. T. S., et al. (1990e) Proc. 21st Inter. Cosmic Ray Conf. 2, 296.

Brazier, K. T. S., et al. (1990f) Proc. 21st Inter. Cosmic Ray Conf. 2, 304.

Caraminana, A. C., et al. (1989) In Timing Neutron Stars, Kluwer, Acad. Press, 369.

Cassiday, G. L., et al. (1989) Phys. Rev. Lett. 62, 4, 383.

Cassiday, G. L., et al. (1990a) Proc. 21st Inter. Cosmic Ray Conf. 2, 14.

Cassiday, G. L., et al. (1990b) Proc. 21st Inter. Cosmic Ray Conf. 2, 60.

Cawley, M. F., et al. (1985a) Proc. 19th Inter. Cosmic Ray Conf. 1, 131.

Cawley, M. F., et al. (1985b) Proc. 19th Inter. Cosmic Ray Conf. 1, 119.

Cawley, M. F., et al. (1985c) Proc. 19th Inter. Cosmic Ray Conf. 1, 87.

Chadwick, P. M., et al. (1985a) Proc. 19th Inter. Cosmic Ray Conf. 1, 155.

Chadwick, P. M., et al. (1985b) Nature 318, 642.

Chadwick, P. M., et al. (1987) in Very High Energy Gamma ray Astronomy, Reidel, Dordrecht, 115.

Chudakov, A. E., et al. (1965) Transl. Consultants Bureau, P. N. Lebedev Phys. Inst. 26, 99.

Ciampa, D., et al. (1990) Proc. 21st Inter. Cosmic Ray Conf. 2, 35.

Danaher, S., et al. (1981) Nature 289, 568.

Dingus, B. L., et al. (1988) Phys. Rev. Lett. 60, 1785.

Dobrzynski, K. et al. (1990) Proc. 21st Inter. Cosmic Ray Conf. 2, 55.

Dowthwaite, J. C., et al. (1983) Astron. Astrophys. 126, 1.

Dowthwaite, J. C., et al. (1984a) Nature 309, 691.

Dowthwaite, J. C., et al. (1984b) Ap. J. Lett. 286, L35.

Fazio, G. G., et al. (1972) Ap. J. Lett. 175, L117.

Fegan, D. J. (1990) Rapporteur VHE and UHE, 21st Inter. Cosmic Ray Conf., Adelaide, Australia.

Gaisser, T. K., et al. (1990) Proc. 21st Inter. Cosmic Ray Conf. 2, 287.

Geldzahler, B. J., et al. (1983) Ap. J. Lett. 273, L65.

Giacconi, R., et al. (1967) Ap. J. Lett. 148, L119.

Giacconi, R., et al. (1983) Ap. J. 184, 227.

Gibson, et al. (1982) Nature 296, 833.

Gillanders, G. H., et al. (1990) Proc. 21st Inter. Cosmic Ray Conf. 2, 23.

Graser, U. and Schonfelder, V. (1982) Ap. J. 263, 677.

Gregory, P. C., et al. (1972) Nature 239, 440

Grindlay, J. E., et al. (1975) Ap. J. 201, 82.

Gruber, D. E., et al. (1980) Ap. J. Lett 240, L127.

Gupta, S. K., et al. (1990) Proc. 21st Inter. Cosmic Ray Conf. 2, 162.

Haines, T. J., et al. (1990) Proc. 21st Inter. Cosmic Ray Conf. 2, 17.

Hermsen, W., et al. (1985) Proc. 19th Inter. Cosmic Ray Conf. 1, 95.

Hillas, A. M. (1987) in Very High Energy Gamma Ray Astronomy, Reidel, Dordrecht, p. 71.

Johnston, K., et al. (1985) Bull. Amer. Ast. Soc. 16 (4), 914.

Kakimoto, F., et al. (1990) Proc. 21st Inter. Cosmic Ray Conf. 2, 358.

Kanbach, G., et al. (1980) Astron. Astrophys. 90, 163.

Kelley, R. L., et al. (1983) Ap. J. 268, 790.

Kirov, I. N., et al. (1985) Proc. 19th Inter. Cosmic Ray Conf. 1, 135.

Ko, S., et al. (1990) Proc. 21st Inter. Cosmic Ray Conf. 2, 131.

GAMMA-RAYS FROM ELECTRON, PROTON BEAM INTERACTIONS WITH MATTER AND/OR RADIATION: APPLICATION TO CYG X-1, GEMINGA AND 3C 273

F. GIOVANNELLI

Istituto di Astrofisica Spaziale, CNR
C.P. 67, I 00044 Frascati, Italy

L. SABAU GRAZIATI

Laboratorio de Astrofísica Espacial y Física Fundamental
Instituto Nacional de Técnica Aeroespacial
E 28850 Torrejon de Ardoz, Madrid, Spain

W. BEDNAREK°^, S. KARAKULA°, W. TKACZYK°

° Institute of Physics, University of Lodz
Ul. Nowotki 149/153, PL 90-236 Lodz, Poland

^ International School for Advanced Studies
Strada Costiera 11, I 31014 Trieste, Italy

ABSTRACT. In this paper we review the most recent studies on the electron-proton beam interactions with the matter and/or radiation. The photon energy spectra from Inverse Compton Scattering (ICS) of an arbitrary background radiation by relativistic electron beams, the photon energy spectra from proton-proton interactions via π° decay, and the spectra of the secondary electrons from $\pi^\pm$ decay, for relativistic proton beams are discussed.
The theoretical spectra have been succesfully used to fit the experimental data of Cyg X-1, Geminga, and 3C 273.

1. Introduction

The discovery of γ-ray point sources stimulated many researches on the mechanisms of high energy photon production. It is generally believed that such energetic photons originate either in hot plasmas ($e^+ e^-$ annihilation, π° decay, bremsstrahlung, etc.) or in the interactions of relativistic particles

271

M. M. Shapiro et al. (eds.), Cosmic Rays, Supernovae and the Interstellar Medium, 271–287.
© 1991 Kluwer Academic Publishers. Printed in the Netherlands.

with matter and/or radiation (π° decay, Inverse Compton Scattering (ICS), secondary electrons from $\pi^\pm$ decay, via $\mu^\pm$ decay, etc.).

Since the mathematics in solving the problems connected with the photon production spectra coming from the mentioned processes is extremely complicated, the first analytical studies and/or the numerical calculations were performed in the very simple case of spherical symmetry, like reviewed by Giovannelli et al. (1991: this Course). But this was only a simple first serious approach in solving these problems, since there is now a great deal of observational evidence for highly anisotropic emission and non-spherical structure in the case of several astronomical objects. Jet-like features have been detected in more than 100 extragalactic sources (Bridle and Perley, 1984) and for a number of sources within our own Galaxy (e.g. SS 433, Sco X-1, Cyg X-3) (see the review paper by Rees, 1985). Superluminal motion has been discovered in the central region of 13 extragalactic radio sources (Cohen and Urwin, 1984; Porcas, 1985; Zensus et al., 1987), which suggests that the particles are moving with Lorentz factor $\gamma \gg 1$, at small angles towards the line of sight. Moreover, X-ray and γ-ray emission have been detected from some sources with jets (e.g. 3C 273, Cen A, M 87).

Relativistic particles emitted by the central engine of such sources should interact with the surrounding radiation and matter. In the case of Active Galactic Nuclei (AGNs), isotropic background radiation can be produced in the surrounding hot plasma (e.g. Frank et al., 1985). In the case of galactic sources, relativistic particles emitted by pulsars or black holes can interact with the radiation and matter of Supernova Remnants (SNRs), or in close binary systems with the thermal radiation and matter from the optical companion. In both cases (AGNs and Galactic sources), anisotropic background radiation can be produced from accretion disks or disk coronae.

In this work, we present the most recent results obtained in the study of the photon energy production spectra for a mono-energetic-one dimensional beam with a Lorentz factor γ and the relative velocity of the beam β, as follows:
 i) the ICS of an electron-beam with the background photons;
ii) the interaction of a proton-beam with the matter.

In order to show the goodness of the calculated theoretical spectra we will show the succesful fits to the experimental data of Cyg X-1, Geminga and 3C 273.

2. The Photon Spectra from ICS of an Electron-Beam with the Background Photons

The comptonization of a photon gas by relativistic electrons has been studied, from an astrophysical point of view, by several authors (Blumenthal and Gould, 1970; Sunyaev and Titarchuk, 1980; Reynolds, 1982; Canfield et al., 1987; Begelman and Sikora, 1987). These authors have usually made some simplifications, such as Thomson limit, highly relativistic electrons, low optical depth, etc., since in the general case the solution is very complicate.

Bednarek et al,(1990a) have calculated the photon energy spectra Q at a selected angle α_1 between the direction of the emitted photons and the beam axis from the ICS of a relativistic electron-beam with an arbitrary background photon spectrum. These spectra are described by the formula:

$$\frac{dN}{d\varepsilon_1\, d\Omega\, dt\, dV} = \frac{n_e}{\gamma^2(1-\beta\cdot\cos\alpha_1)} \iiint c\cdot n'(\varepsilon',\alpha')\, \frac{d^2\sigma}{d\Omega_1'\cdot d\varepsilon_1'}\cdot\frac{d\Omega_1'}{d\Omega^+}\cdot\frac{d\Omega'}{d\Omega_\mu}\cdot d\Omega_\mu\cdot d\varepsilon',$$

where: $\dfrac{d\Omega_1'}{d\Omega^+}=1$, $\dfrac{d\Omega'}{d\Omega_\mu}=1$ Jacobians,

$\dfrac{1}{\gamma^2(1-\beta\cdot\cos\alpha_1)}$ Jacobian of the transformation from the electron rest frame to the observer frame,

$n'(\varepsilon',\alpha')$ - distribution of the background photons in the electron rest frame,

$\dfrac{d^2\sigma}{d\Omega_1'\, d\varepsilon_1'}$ - Klein-Nishina cross-section,

n_e - electron concentration of the beam.

The calculations were made for an isotropic bremsstrahlung and a black body-type background photon spectra normalized to the photon energy density of 1 MeV/cm^3, and for the electron-beam parameters n_e = 1 cm^{-3} and $\gamma \gg 1$.

Figures 1 and 2 show the comptonized black body spectra (T = 10^4 °K and T = 10^7 °K, respectively) for beam's Lorentz factors γ = 10, 10^2, 10^3, and 10^4, and for two values of the angle between the emitted photon direction and the beam axis: α_1 = 0° and 10°. Figure 3 shows the comptonized black body spectra for γ = 10^3 at different angles α_1.

In general, the intensities of these comptonized black body spectra, for small angles α_1 (with respect to 1/γ), are inversely proportional to γ (Figs. 1 and 2). For large angles α_1 (with respect to 1/γ), the intensities are determined by the angle α_1 itself (Fig. 3), and for fixed values of this angle, they are inversely proportional to γ^3 (Figs. 1 and 2). The maximum intensities in the peaks, for fixed angles, are roughly independent of γ, as shown in Fig. 2.

Fig. 4 shows the comptonized thermal bremsstrahlung photon

274

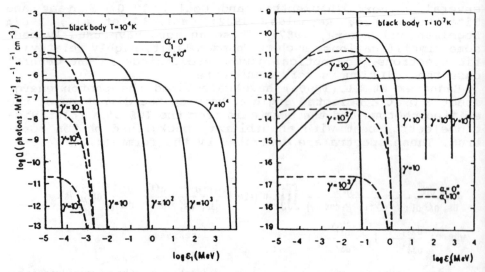

Figures 1 and 2. The comptonized black body spectra for T = 10^4 °K and T = 10^7 °K, respectively, for γ = 10, 10^2, 10^3, 10^4 and α_1 = 0° and 10°.

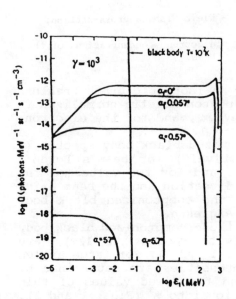

Figure 3. The comptonized black body spectra for γ= 10^3 and T = 10^7 °K.

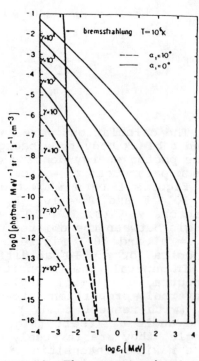

Figure 4. The comptonized Thermal bremsstrahlung photon spectra for T = 10^6 °K.

spectra (T $= 10^6$ °K) for $\gamma = 10$, 10^2, 10^3, and 10^4 and two angles $\alpha_1 = 0$° and 10°. In general, these comptonized bremsstrahlung spectra are similar in shape to the background spectrum because the main contribution to the spectra comes from a very small area around the beam axis (for details, see the paper by Bednarek et al., 1990a). The position of the cut-offs in the comptonized bremsstrahlung spectra are determined like in the case of blck body comptonized spectra, because these features are caused by the kinematics of the ICS. The intensities of the bremsstrahlung comptonized spectra for small angles are proportional to γ, while for large angles, these intensities are proportional to γ^2 (see Fig. 4).

3. The Photon Spectra from the Interaction of a Proton-Beam with the Matter

3.1. THE PHOTON SPECTRA FROM π° DECAY

The relativistic proton beam passing through a hydrogen cloud loses its energy by proton-proton inelastic interactions. The high energy photons can be produced by the decay of π° from the reaction p + p ---- π° + anything. Analyzing such a process, Bednarek et al. (1990a) have obtained the photon spectra (Q) from a monoenergetic beam and hydrogen cloud interaction for a given angle α_1 between the direction of the emitted photons and the beam axis. These spectra are described by the formula:

$$\frac{dN}{dE_\gamma \cdot d\Omega \cdot dt \cdot dV} = \beta \cdot c \cdot n_b \cdot n_H \iiint \frac{d^3\sigma(p_{\pi^0}, \cos\Theta_{\pi^0}, \varphi_{\pi^0})}{dp_{\pi^0} \cdot d(\cos\Theta_{\pi^0}) \cdot d\varphi_{\pi^0}} \cdot P(E_\gamma, \cos\Theta, \varphi) \cdot dp_{\pi^0} \cdot d(\cos\Theta_{\pi^0}) d\varphi_{\pi^0}$$

where: n_H - hydrogen concentration in the cloud,
 n_b - proton concentration in the beam,
 c - light velocity,
 p_{π^0} - π° momentum in the observer frame,
 $\Theta_{\pi^0}, \varphi_{\pi^0}$ angles between the π°emission direction and beam axis in the observer frame,

$$\frac{d^3\sigma(p_{\pi^0}, \cos\Theta_{\pi^0}, \varphi_{\pi^0})}{dp_{\pi^0} \cdot d(\cos\Theta_{\pi^0}) \cdot d\varphi_{\pi^0}} = \frac{p_{\pi^0}^2}{E_{\pi^0}} \left(E_{\pi^0} \cdot \frac{d^3\sigma}{dp^3} \right)$$ - cross section in polar coordinates,

$E_{\pi^0} \cdot \dfrac{d^3\sigma}{dp^3}$ - invariant cross section (Ref. 13),

$P(E_\gamma, \cos\Theta, \varphi)$- energy and angular distributions of photons in the observer frame,

$E_\gamma, \cos\Theta, \varphi$ - energy and angles of the emitted photons in the observer fra̲me.

276

For the details of this analisis, see the paper by Bednarek et al. (1990a). We want to note that in a detailed analysis of the models describing the interaction of a proton-beam with the matter, Dermer (1986) showed that, for a photon energy lower than 3 GeV, the characteristics of this interaction are very well described using an isobar model. For a photon energy greater than 12.5 GeV, this interaction can be described reasonably well using the scaling model of the invariant cross section given by Stephens and Badwar (1981). Bednarek et al. (1990a) studied the interaction of a high energy proton-beam ($\gamma > 10$) with the matter, so they used the latter model.

Figure 5 shows the differential proton spectra from $\pi°$ decay for proton-beam Lorentz factor $\gamma = 10$, 10^2, 10^3, and 10^4 and two values of the angle $\alpha_1 = 0°$ and $10°$. Figure 6 shows the differential photon spectra from $\pi°$ decay for $\gamma = 10^4$ and selected angles $\alpha_1 = 0°$, $0,057°$, $0,57°$, $5.7°$, and $57°$.

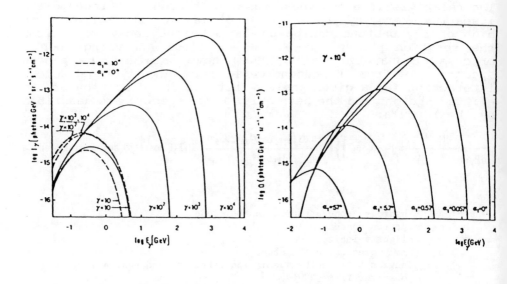

a.   b.

Figure 5. The differential proton spectra from $\pi°$ decay: a) for $\gamma = 10$, 10^2, 10^3, 10^4 and $\alpha_1 = 0°$ and $10°$; b) for $\gamma = 10^4$ and selected values of the angle α_1.

In general the shapes and intensities of these spectra are very sensitive to γ and/or α_1. From Fig. 5a, one can note that for small angles α_1 (with respect to $1/\gamma$), the intensities and the widths of the photon spectra and positions of their maxima grow proportional to γ. For large α_1 (with respect to $1/\gamma$), the shapes and intensities of the photon spectra are practically independent of γ, since the momenta of the π°s, which create these photons, are roughly the same (Bednarek at al., 1990a). In a certain range of the photon energies, the intensities of the spectra, calculated for γ = constant, are comparable in the rising part for different values of α_1 (e.g. for $\gamma = 10^4$, this is roughly valid in the range $-1 \leq \log(E) \leq 2$ and for $0° \leq \alpha_1 \leq 5.7°$: see Fig. 5b). We note that for large angles the position of the maximum intensities of the photon spectra are determined by the values of the angle α_1 and are independent of γ (see Fig. 5a).

All this means that sources with different intensities could give roughly the same experimental results in the low energy region of Fig. 5a, simply because the axis of their beams form a different angle with the line of sight.

3.2. THE PHOTON SPECTRA OF THE SECONDARY ELECTRONS FROM $\pi^\pm$

The interaction of the proton in a relativistic jet with the ambient matter produces charged pions, which then decay, via muons, into secondary electrons ($p + p \longrightarrow \pi\pm \longrightarrow \mu^\pm \longrightarrow e^\pm$). Bednarek and Calvani (1991) have studied the angular dependence of the spectrum of the secondary electrons with respect to the axis of the proton beam. They considered a mono-energetic-one-dimensional proton-beam with a Lorentz factor γ.

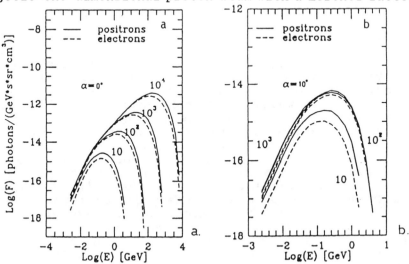

Figure 6. The spectrum of the secondary electrons from $\pi^\pm$.

The beam propagates at an angle α_1 to the line of sight. The spectrum of muons from the decay of pions and the angular dependent spectrum of the secondary electrons, assuming that the muons decay istantaneously, can be found in the paper by Bednarek and Calvani (1991) and the details of the calculations in the paper by Bednarek and Calvani (1990).

The numerical results for the spectrum of the secondary electrons are shown in Figure 6, for Lorentz factors $\gamma = 10$, 10^2, 10^3, and 10^4 of the monoenergetic proton beam and for angle $\alpha_1 = 0°$ and $10°$, and for unit concentrations of the proton beam n_b and of the background matter n_H.

The general behaviour of the spectra of the secondary electrons is very similar to those of the photons from $\pi°$ decay, calculated by Bednarek et al. (1990a). The shape and maximum intensity of the spectra strongly depend on γ and α_1. For small angles α_1 (with respect to $1/\gamma$) and in the relativistic limit ($\gamma \gg 1$), the value of the position of the maxima grow proportionally to γ (Fig. 6a). For large α_1 (with respect to $1/\gamma$), the shape of the spectra and the position of the maxima are practically determined only by the value of α_1, the intensities for different γ being comparable (Fig. 6b).

4. Origin of the High Energy Photons from Cyg X-1, Geminga and 3C 273

We want to show how the calculated photon energy spectra can be succesfully used in fitting the experimental data of three of the most interesting high energy ä-ray sources: Cyg X-1, 2CG 195+04 (Geminga) and 3C 273.

4.1. CYG X-1

Cyg X-1 is the most promising galactic black hole candidate since its general behaviour and morphology are difficult to explain in terms of a neutron star model. Cyg X-1 lies in a binary system, in which the primary star is the blue supergiant HDE 226868. The characteristics and the multifrequency behaviour of this system can be found in the review papers by Oda (1977) and Liang and Nolan (1984).

Up-to-date several suggestions attempting to explain the complex shape and behaviour of the spectrum of Cyg X-1 have been published. At energies below 1 MeV, the spectrum is generally described by a single-temperature inverse Compton model with the electron temperature ranging from 20 to 80 KeV and optical depths from 2 to 5 (Sunyaev and Titarchuk, 1980; Nolan et al., 1981; Steinle et al., 1982). At energies above 1 MeV, the nature of the spectrum seems to be different. In order to explain the origin of this spectrum, some proposals concerning thermal mechanisms have been discussed, namely:

i) annihilation e⁻ e⁺ process in a high temperature plasma
   (Zdziarski, 1980; Ramaty and Meszaros, 1981);
 ii) two temperature Compton model (Pozdnyakov et al., 1983);
iii) bremsstrahlung of electrons created by the decay of
     charged pions (Eilek and Kafatos, 1983).

On the contrary, Bednarek et al. (1990b) suggest that the
photon spectrum of Cyg X-1, in the MeV region, is non-thermal.
In fact, from the radio measurements performed by Woodsworth et al. (1980) a non-thermal nature of the spectrum was unambiguously derived. They proposed a model in which the radio emission comes from relativistic electrons in a stellar wind. So, following the expression of the photon production spectra derived by Bednarek et al. (1990a) and reported in the paragraph 2, Bednarek et al. (1990b) developed a model in which the MeV photon spectrum originates from ICS of the background photons by relativistic electrons.

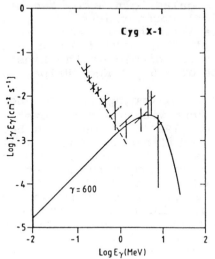

Figure 7. The best fit of the high energy data of Cyg X-1.

The experimental high energy spectrum of Cyg X-1 above 1 MeV (McConnell et al., 1987) can be fitted very well with a comptonized black body spectrum (T = 3 x 10^4 °K), coming from the supergiant companion HDE 226868, by relativistic electrons with Lorentz factor 600, emitted in our direction. Figure 7 shows the best fit to the experimental data of this calculated spectrum at energies above 1 MeV and with the derived spectrum from the single-temperature inverse Compton model (Sunyaev and Titarchuk, 1980) at energies below 1 MeV. The orbital parameters of Cyg X-1/HDE 226868 system have been taken by the papers by Ninkov et al. (1987a; 1987b).

From the observed intensity of the photons above 1 MeV, the lower limit on the emissivity of the relativistic electrons can be estimated. It is equal to 1.5 x 10^{38} electron/s, corresponding to an electron luminosity of 7.0 x 10^{34} erg/s.

4.2 2CG 195+04 (GEMINGA)

Geminga is one of the COS B sources for which many works have been developed in order to find the optical counterpart as well as to interpret the nature of its spectrum at energies greater than 1 MeV. Up to now, two contradictory suggestions exist about the identification of Geminga with known astrophysical objects in other wavelength regions: i) the extragalactic radio source 0630+180, with a flat spectrum, which was optically identified as a quasar with redshift 1.2 (Moffat et al., 1983); ii) the galactic X-ray source 1E 0630+178, detected by the Einstein satellite in the range 0.1 - 4.5 KeV, which was claimed to be a neutron star at a distance of about 100 pc (Bignami et al., 1983). Within the framework of the identification of Geminga with a galactic source, two stars have been proposed as its optical counterparts: a) a 21st magnitude blue star outside the X-ray error circle of the Einstein observatory (Caraveo et al., 1984); b) a 25.14 magnitude blue star inside the error circle of the Einstein observatory, placed at a distance of 0.5 - 1 Kpc (Halpern and Tytler, 1988).

The differential photon spectrum of Geminga in the energy range 100 MeV - 3.2 GeV is consistent with a single power law of the type $\approx E^{-1.8}$ (Masnou et al., 1981). At energies below 100 MeV, the spectrum flattens significantly. This is also suggested by several observations in the softerer regions, such as the hard X-ray and soft γ-ray ranges (Haymes et al., 1979; Graser and Schonfelder, 1982; Baker et al., 1983). On the contrary, at energies above 3.2 GeV, the spectrum steepens as suggested by the highest energy point of COS B (Masnou et al., 1981), by the lack of any significant detection above 10^{11} eV (Helmken and Weekes, 1979; Cawley et al., 1985) and by the upper limit of the photon flux from the direction of Geminga at energies of order 10^{15} eV (Karakula et al., 1985) derived from Tien Shan data (Nikolsky et al., 1984). We want to remark that the only positive detection at energies $\geq 2 \times 10^{12}$ eV, reported by Zyskin and Mukanov (1985), is in contradiction with the former results.

In order to interpret the nature of the spectrum at energies greater than 1 MeV, several proposals have been made, namely:
i) inelastic collisions between cosmic-ray particles and the interstellar gas; relativistic electron bremsstrahlung in the interstellar gas (Cesarsky et al., 1976; Bignami et al., 1976; Abdulwahad and Morrison, 1978);
ii) ICS of background photons by relativistic electrons (e.g. Stecker, 1971; Chupp, 1976).

These two mechanisms have difficulties in explaining the high energy photon emission from Geminga.

Bednarek et al. (1990b) proposed that the high energy photons coming from Geminga originate in the interaction of beamed relativistic particles with the surrounding matter. Such a mechanism of high energy photon production can be realized in close binary systems, where beamed relativistic particles emitted by the collapsed object (e.g. a neutron star) interact with the matter coming from the optical companion.

In the paragraph 3.1 we have described the photon spectra from the interaction of a monoenergetic proton-beam with a hydrogen cloud for a given angle α_1 between the direction of the emitted photons and the beam axis. Figure 8 shows the

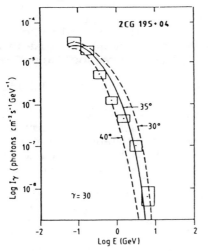

theoretical photon production spectra with the spectral measurements of Geminga from COS B satellite (Masnou et al., 1981). One can see that the photon spectrum calculated for an angle α_1 = 35° and the proton-beam Lorentz factor $\gamma \geq$ 30 fits very well the COS B data. In order to show how the fit is sensitive to the angle α_1, the theoretical curves for 30° and 40° are reported too in Fig. 8, for the same value of Lorentz's factor. From the best fit, one obtains the emissivity of the proton beam equal to:

Figure 8. The best fit of the COS B data of Geminga.

$$N_p = 7.5 \times 10^{-4} \times d^2/X_p \quad (particle/s)$$

where X_p is the column density (in g/cm^2) of the particles crossed by the proton-beam and d the distance to the source. This corresponds to a proton luminosity $L_p = m_p \gamma N_p$, where m_p is the proton rest energy.

So, from the energetical point of view, this model excludes the identification of Geminga with the QSO 0630+180 placed at z = 1.2 (Moffat et al., 1983), and favours that with a galactic source (1E 0630+178) as suggested by Bignami et al. (1983) and by Halpern and Tytler (1988). Overmore, this model is definitively valid in the case that Geminga is a binary system, where a density X_p is expected to be several g/cm^2. In this case a distance of the order of several hundreds parsecs would be acceptable. If Geminga were associated with an isolated neutron star, and then low density in the SNR, as suggested by Halpern and Tytler (1988), this model would require a very large proton emissivity ($N_p \approx 10^{40}/X_p$ particle/s, for d $\approx$ 1 Kpc), which is very unlikely.

4.3. 3C 273

3C 273 is the brightest quasar placed at $\approx$ 860 Mpc with a mass of $\approx$ 2.5 x 10^9 M$_\odot$ (Ulrich, 1981). Its spectrum extends over many decades in energy from radio to γ-ray regions. A small fraction of the soft X-ray emission is connected with the optical part of its jet (Willingale, 1981; Harris and Stern, 1987). The γ-ray emission (E > 50 MeV) was discovered by the SAS II satellite (Swanenburg et al., 1978) and confirmed by COS B satellite (Bignami et al., 1981). Simple attempts (see the paper by Giovannelli et al., 1991: this School) in explaining this emission have been done considering the accretion process of matter onto the central collapsed object, namely:

   i) a thermal process in which the protons may fall adiabati-
      cally onto the black hole;
  ii) a non thermal process in which a shock around a black hole
      is producing a power law spectrum of high energy protons.

   Since there are some experimental evidences that the γ-ray emission could be probably produced in the jet (as implied by the variability of the X-ray flux and stability of γ-ray emission (Bassani and Dean, 1981; 1986)), a model in which γ-rays are produced by relativistic secondary electrons from proton-proton collisions in the optical part of the jet (assuming the isotropization of relativistic protons by weak magnetic fields (Morrison et al., 1984)) has been proposed. Also Anyakoha et al. (1990) studied the production of high energy γ-rays from extragalactic jets, assuming the isotropi-zation of the relativistic protons, but with this assumption is not easy to account the observed orientation of the magnetic field along the axis of the jet (Roser and Meisen-heimer, 1986).

   Bednarek and Calvani (1991) suggested the possibility that γ-rays from 3C 273 are produced in the jet. In particular they developed a non-isotropic model in which the γ-rays are produced by secondary electrons and positrons coming from $\pi^{\pm}$ decay and from π° decay. So, they developed a model in which a monoenergetic, highly collimated proton beam interacts with the matter contained in the jet volume. If the column density of the matter in the jet is high enough, the secondary electrons produced by the $\pi^{\pm}$ decay can emit observable X-rays and γ-rays via bremsstrahlung process. Since the secondary electrons are ultrarelativistic (γ up to 10^3), the emitted radiation will be highly collimated along the direction of the electrons motion (Koch and Motz, 1959). Bednarek and Calvani (1991) used their calculated spectrum of the bremsstrahlung radiation from secondary electrons and from π° decay (Bednarek et al., 1990a) to fit the experimental data of 3C 273. They adopted γ = 6 and α_1 = 35°. The fit is shown in Figure 9. From this fit, it is possible to evaluate the total energy of the relativistic protons in the jet by using the relation:

$$E \approx 10^{18} \gamma d^2 l / \lambda \quad \mathrm{erg}$$

where d is the distance to the quasar, l = dsinß/sinα is the true length of the jet, ß is the angular apparent length of the jet, λ is the column density in the jet (in g/cm^2).

For $\lambda \approx 70$ g/cm^2 (from the best fit), d = 860 Mpc and $\beta \approx$ 20", this energy is E $\approx 2 \times 10^{61}$ erg. The required power emitted in relativistic protons by the core of 3C 273 is P = Ec/1 $\approx 1.5 \times 10^{48}$ erg/s, which corresponds to a mass loss in relativistic protons of ≈ 1.1 M$_\odot$/yr.

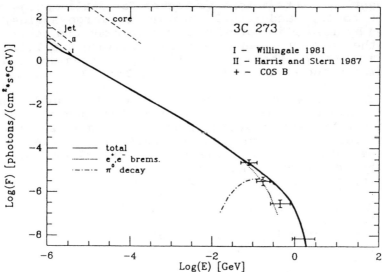

Figure 9. The best fit of the experimental data of 3C 273.

5. Discussion and Conclusions

We have reviewed the most actual situation on the problem of the interactions between relativistic electron and proton beams with the surrounding radiation and matter.

The expression for the inverse Compton photon spectrum has been derived for an arbitrary distribution of photons, various Lorentz's factors of the beam and selected angles between the photon emission direction and the beam axis, by using the Klein-Nishina cross section. Results of numerical calculations have been presented for optically thin thermal bremsstrahlung and black body radiation in the case of isotropic distribution. Such ambient photon distributions probably surround AGNs and close binary systems.

In general for an isotropic distribution of ambient photons, the shape of the comptonized spectra is determined by the shape of the background spectrum, but the mean energy of the comptonized spectra strongly depends on the electron-beam Lorentz factor and on the angle between the line of sight and the beam axis.

Especially in the case of AGNs with directly stable jets, the photon energy spectra from π° decay and from secondary electrons coming from $\pi^\pm$ decay produced in the interaction of the proton-beam with the matter are important. The characteristic shape of the spectra (with their maxima strongly dependent on the beam Lorentz factor for small angles α_1, with respect to $1/\gamma$, and roughly stable for large angles) can be changed by absorption of high energy photons and contributions from other processes such as bremsstrahlung and ICS.

The results of these calculations have been applied to fit succesfully the experimental data of Cyg X-1, Geminga and 3 C 273.

For Cyg X-1 we have shown that its behaviour at energies greater than 1 MeV are compatible with the comptonized spectra if the relativistic electrons, with a Lorentz factor $\gamma = 600$, are emitted in our direction. The hard tail in the MeV region could be caused by comptonization of the black body photons from the supergiant companion HDE 226868. From the observed intensity of the photons above 1 MeV, a lower limit of the relativistic electron emissivity has been derived: it is $N_e \approx 1.5 \times 10^{38}$ erg/s, corresponding to an electron luminosity $L_e \approx 7 \times 10^{34}$ erg/s.

We want to remark that this model expects variations in the intensity of the high energy photon emission according to the orbital period.

For Geminga we have shown that the very high energy photons originate in the interaction of beamed relativistic particles with $\gamma \geq 30$ and the angle between the beam axis and the line of sight $\alpha_1 = 35°$. From the best fit of the calculated photon spectrum from π° decay to the COS B data and with the former parameters, the emissivity of the proton-beam has been derived: it is $N_p \approx 7.5 \times 10^{-4} d^2/X_p$ particle/s, corresponding to a proton luminosity $L_p = m_p \gamma N_p$. From the energetical point of view, this model excludes that Geminga could be an extragalactic source such as the QSO 0630+180, while favours its identification with a binary galactic source, such as 1E 0630+178, placed at $\approx 0.5 - 1$ Kpc.

For 3C 273 we have shown that the entire high energy spectrum, X-rays from the jet and γ-rays, can be explained with a simple model in which these radiations are produced by the interaction of the relativistic proton-beam with the matter in the jet volume. The X-ray spectrum (from the jet) and γ-ray spectrum can be accounted for by bremsstrahlung radiation of the secondary electrons from $\pi^\pm$ decay and by photons from π° decay, assuming a Lorentz factor $\gamma = 6$, for the bulk motion of the proton-beam, and $\alpha_1 = 35°$. From the best fit, the total power emitted in relativistic protons by the central core of 3C 273 is $P = 1.5 \times 10^{48}$ erg/s, corresponding to a mass loss of 1.1 $M_\odot$/yr, with a column density $\lambda = 70$ g/cm^2.

Of course a more realistic model should take into account

the propagation effects of the relativistic protons and secondary electrons as well as the curvature of the jet. In such a case, a steeper theoretical photon spectrum in the γ-ray range and a lower density of the matter in the jet are expected.

References

Abdulwahab, M. and Morrison, P. (1978) Astrophys. J. Letters 221, L33.

Anyakoha, M.W., Okoye, S.E., and Okeke, P.N. (1990) Astro. Lett. and Communications 27, 373.

Baker, R.E., Butler, R.C., Doan, A.J., Hayles, R.I., Ramsden, D., Di Cocco, G., Boella, G., Della Ventura, A., Perotti, F., and Villa, G. (1983) Astron. Astrophys. 117, 38.

Bassani, L. and Dean, A.J. (1981) Nature 294, 332.

Bassani, L. and Dean, A.J. (1986) Astron. Astrophys. 161, 85.

Bednarek, W. and Calvani, M. (1990) preprint.

Bednarek, W. and Calvani, M. (1991) in Frontier Objects in Astrophysics and Particle Physics, (eds. F. Giovannelli and G. Mannocchi), Italian Physical Society, Bologna, Italy (in press).

Bednarek, W., Giovannelli, F., Karakula, S., and Tkaczyk, W. (1990a) Astron. Astrophys 236, 268.

Bednarek, W., Giovannelli, F., Karakula, S., and Tkaczyk, W. (1990b) Astron. Astrophys 236, 175.

Begelman, M.C. and Sikora, M. (1987) Astrophys. J. 322, 650.

Bignami, G.F., Macaccaro, T., and Paizis, T. (1976) Astron. Astrophys. 51, 319.

Bignami, G.F., Caraveo, P.A., and Lamb, R.C. (1983) Astrophys. J. Letters 272, L9.

Blumenthal, R.G. and Gould, R.J. (1970) Rev. Mod. Phys. 42, 237.

Bridle, A.H. and Perley, R.A. (1984) Ann. Rev. Astron. Astrophys. 22, 319.

Canfield, E., Howard, W.M., and Liang, E.P. (1987) Astrophys. J. 323, 565.

Caraveo, P.A., Bignami, G.F., Vigroux, L., and Paul, J.A. (1984) Astrophys. J. Letters 276, L45.

Cawley, M.F., Fegan, D.J., Gibbs, K., Gorham, P.W.., Lamb, R.C., Liebing, D.F., MacKeown, P.K., Porter, N.A., Stenger, W.J., and Weekes, T.C. (1985) Proc. of the 19th Int. Cosmic Ray Conf. (La Jolla) 1, 173.

Cesarsky, C.J., Casse, M., and Paul, J. (1976) Astron. Astrophys. 48, 481.

Chupp, E.L. (1976) "Gamma Ray Astronomy" D. Reidel Publ. Co., Dordrecht, Holland.

Cohen, M.H. and Urwin, S.C. (1984) Proc. of the IAU Symp. No. 110, 95.

Dermer, C.D. (1986) Astron. Astrophys. 157, 223.

Eilek, J.A. and Kafatos M. (1983) Astrophys. J. 271, 804.

Frank, J., King, A.R., and Raine, D.J. (1985) "Accretion Power in Astrophysics", Cambridge University Press, Cambridge, UK.

Giovannelli, F., Sabau Graziati, L., Karakula, S., and Tkaczyk, W. (1991) in Cosmic Rays, Supernovae, and the Interstellar Medium, (eds. M.M. Shapiro, R. Silberberg, J.P. Wefel), Kluwer Academic Publisher, (in press).

Graser, V. and Schonfelder, V. (1982) Astrophys. J. 263, 677.

Halpern, J.P. and Tytler, D. (1988) Astrophys. J. 330, 201.

Harris, D.E. and Stern, C.P. (1987) Astrophys. J. 313, 136.

Haymes, R.C., Meegan, C.A., and Fishman, G.J. (1979) Astron. Astrophys. 79, 88.

Helmken, H.F. and Weekes, T. (1979) Astrophys. J. 228, 531.

Karakula, S., Stamenov, J.N., and Tkaczyk, W. (1985) Proc. of the 19th Int. Cosmic Ray Conf. (La Jolla) 1, 268.

Koch, H.W. and Motz, J. W. (1959) Rev. Mod. Phys. 31, 920.

Liang, E.P. and Nolan, P.L. (1984) Space Sci. Rev. 38, 353.

Masnou, J.L., Bennett, K., Bignami, G.F., Bioemen, J.B.G.M., Buccheri, R., Caraveo, P.A., Hermsen, W., Kanbach, G., Mayer-Hasselwander, H., Paul, J.A., and Wills, R.D. (1981) Proc. of the 17th Int. Cosmic Ray Conf. (Paris) 1, 177.

McConnell, M.L., Owens, A., Chupp, E.L., Dunphy, P.P., Forrest, D.J., and Vestrand, W.T. (1987) Proc. of the 20th Int. Cosmic Ray Conf. (Moscow) 1, 58.

Moffat, A.F.J., Schlickeiser, R., Shara, M.M. Sieber, W., Tuffs, R., and Kuhr, M. (1983) Astrophys. J. Letters 271, L45.

Morrison, P, Roberts, D., and Sadun, A. (1984) Astrophys. J. 280, 483.

Nikolsky, S.I., Stamenov, J.N., and Ushev, S.Z. (1984) Adv. Space Res. 3, 131.

Ninkov, Z., Walker, G.A.H., and Yang, S. (1987a) Astrophys. J. 321, 425.

Ninkov, Z., Walker, G.A.H., and Yang, S. (1987b) Astrophys. J. 321, 438.

Nolan, P.L., Gruber, D.E., Knight, F.K., Matteson, J.L., Rothschild, R.E., Marshall, F.E., Levine, A.M., and Primini, F.A. (1981) Nature 293, 275.

Oda, M. (1977) Space Sci. Rev. 20, 757.

Porcas, R.W. (1985) in Active Galactic Nuclei, (ed. J.E. Dyson), Manchester University Press, Manchester, UK, p. 20.

Pozdnyakov, L.A., Sobol, I.M., and Sunyaev, R.A. (1983) Soviet Sci. Rev. (Sectin E-Astr. Ap. Space Phys. Rev.) 2, 189.

Ramaty, R. and Meszaros, P. (1981) Astrophys. J. 250, 384.

Rees, M. (1985) Proc of the 19th Int. Cosmic Ray Conf. (La Jolla) 9, 1.

Reynolds, S.P. (1982) Astrophys. J. 256, 38.

Roser, H.-J. and Meisenheimer, K. (1986) Astron. Astrophys. 154, 15.

Stecker, F.W. (1971) in Cosmic Gamma Rays, Baltimore: Mono

Book Corp., NASA SP-249.

Steinle, H. Voges, W., Pietsch, W., Reppin, C., Trumper, J., Kendziorra, E., and Staubert, R. (1982) Astron. Astrophys. 107, 350.

Stephens, S.A. and Badhwar, G.D. (1981) Astrophys. Space Sci. 76, 213.

Sunyaev, R.A. and Titarchuk, L.G. (1980) Astron. Astrophys. 86, 121.

Swanenburg, B.N. et al. (1978) Nature 275, 298.

Ulrich, M.H. (1981) Space Sci. Rev. 28, 89.

Willingale, R. (1981) Mon. Not. R. astr. Soc. 194, 359.

Woodsworth, A.W., Higgs, L.A., and Gregory P.C. (1980) Astron Astrophys. 84, 379.

Zdziarski, A.A. (1980) Acta Astron. 30, 371.

Zensus, J.A., Hough, D.H, and Porcas, R.W. (1987) Nature 325, 36.

Zyskin, Yu.L. and Mukanov, D.B. (1985) Soviet Astron. Letter 9, 117.

GAMMA-RAYS AND NEUTRINOS
FROM ACCRETION PROCESSES ONTO COLLAPSED OBJECTS: APPLICATION TO 3C 273

F. GIOVANNELLI

Istituto di Astrofisica Spaziale, CNR
C.P. 67, I 00044 Frascati, Italy

L. SABAU GRAZIATI

Laboratorio de Astrofísica Espacial y Física Fundamental
Instituto Nacional de Técnica Aeroespacial
E 28850 Torrejon de Ardoz, Madrid, Spain

S. KARAKULA, W. TKACZYK

Institute of Physics, University of Lodz
Ul. Nowotki 149/153, PL 90-236 Lodz, Poland

ABSTRACT. In this work we want simply to review the metodology used by the authors in the past in order to develop the very important and difficult problem of the calculation of the energy production spectra of the γ-rays and neutrinos produced in the accretion processes onto collapsed objects. Because of the complexity of the problem we start in describing the physical processes in the case of spherical symmetric accretion.

The results of these calculations will be used to evaluate the upper limit to the number of the black holes in the Galaxy and to fit the γ-ray COS B experimental data of the quasar 3C 273 and to predict the neutrino fluxes from the directions of 3C 273 and the Galactic Center.

M. M. Shapiro et al. (eds.), Cosmic Rays, Supernovae and the Interstellar Medium, 289–306.

1. Introduction

The γ-ray astronomy is a very promising branch of the high energy astrophysics, but unfortunately only few experiments were launched up-to-date, so that the information on this range of energy are rather old and came essentially from SAS II and COS B satellites.

The SAS II and COS B measurements of γ-ray fluxes ($E > 100$ MeV) indicate that their main part originate in the Galaxy, since an excess of the flux from the galactic center is observed.

The possibility that this radiation originates from the interactions of cosmic ray protons and electrons with the diffuse matter and electromagnetic radiation (diffuse component) has been discussed in many papers, but the discovery of discrete γ-ray sources created the doubt that the diffuse component could be probably not predominant.

Up today only 25 γ-ray sources have been discovered and listed in the Second COS B Catalog (Swanenburg et al., 1981). Only few of them were identified with known astrophysical objects. The source 2CG 289+64 was identified with the quasar 3C 273 (Hermsen, 1980; Swanenburg et al., 1981).

Information about the properties of the galactic γ-ray sources and proposed models to produce the γ-ray quanta in such objects were deeply discussed by Bignami and Hermsen (1983).

In the past, studies of the accretion processes of matter onto collapsed objects have been developed, in the case of spherical symmetric geometry, by different authors (Michel, 1972; Kolykhalov and Sunyaev, 1979; Giovannelli et al., 1982a, 1982b).

During the accretion process, the matter may be heated up to temperatures as high as 10^{12} K. In such a hot plasma inelastic collisions of protons may produce π° and $\pi^{\pm}$. The secondary products of the pions decay can be γ-rays, positrons and neutrinos.

In this paper we review the main results obtained by the study of the energy production spectra of the secondary products of the neutral and charged pions decay and their application to evaluate: i) the upper limit to the number of galactic black holes; ii) the expected γ-ray spectrum of the quasar 3C 273; iii) the neutrino flux from the directions of 3C 273 and galactic center.

In order to reach this goals we attented the following steps in calculating:

a) the π° momentum spectrum;
b) the γ-ray spectra from the accretion process:
   - the γ-ray energy production spectra as secondary products of the π° decay;

- the expected γ-ray energy spectra in the case of spherical symmetric accretion;
c) the upper limit to the number of black holes in the Galaxy;
d) the expected γ-ray spectrum of 3C 273;
e) the π^+ momentum production spectrum;
f) the neutrino and antineutrino energy production spectra:
  - the ν_μ, μ^+, $\bar{\nu}_\mu$, ν_e energy production spectra as secondary product of the π^+ decay;
  - the cooling rate coefficient and the attenuation time for the relativistic plasma;
  - the expected neutrino energy spectra;
g) the neutrino luminosity and emissivity from black holes;
h) the neutrino flux from the directions of the:
  - Galactic Center;
  - 3C 273.

2. The γ-Ray Energy Production Spectra in a Relativistic Plasma

We adopt a model in which the matter is spherically accreting onto a collapsed object (Giovannelli et al., 1982a; 1982b). During this accretion process, the matter may be heated up to temperatures as high as 10^{12} °K (Kolykhalov and Sunyaev, 1979). In such a hot plasma, the thermal bremsstrahlung (e-e and e-p) and the π° decay from inelastic collisions of protons are the main sources of γ-rays.

To determine the γ-ray energy production spectra in an isothermal plasma at temperature T, Giovannelli et al. (1982a; 1982b) made the following assumptions:

  i) the plasma is fully ionized;
 ii) the electron and proton momentum distributions are maxwellian;
iii) the electron and proton angular distributions are isotropic;
 iv) the characteristics of the interaction

$$p + p \longrightarrow \pi^\circ + \text{anything}$$

were derived approximating the experimental data of Barashenkov and Tonev (1972).

The numerical calculations were performed for the thermal model and non thermal model as follows:

2.1. THERMAL MODEL

The following steps were attended in order to calculate the γ-ray energy production spectra:

a) the $\pi°$ momentum production spectrum as function of the proton temperature;
b) the γ-ray energy production spectra as secondary products of the $\pi°$ decay;
c) the γ-ray production spectra from bremsstrahlung (e-e and e-p) using Gould's corrected formula (Gould, 1980; Gorecki and Kluzniak, 1981).

The considered range of temperature was $10^{11} - 10^{13}$ K. Figure 1 shows the energy production spectra in the comoving plasma system from $\pi°$ decay and from bremsstrahlung (e-e and e-p) for different selected temperatures (in the range $2.7 \times 10^{11} - 1.1 \times 10^{12}$ K) and unit concentration of the plasma. The spectrum from $\pi°$ decay has the maximum at 67.5 MeV. The production rate is highly directly dependent on the plasma temperature. The width of the spectrum also increases with the temperature. The γ-ray spectra from bremsstrahlung are practically always over those from $\pi°$ decay (for the same temperature of the electrons and protons).

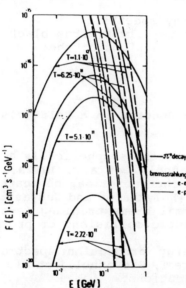

Figure 1. The energy production spectra from $\pi°$ decay and from bremsstrahlung (e-e and e-p).

2.2. NON THERMAL MODEL

The following steps were attended in order to calculate the γ-ray energy production spectra:

a) the γ-ray energy production spectrum resulting from $\pi°$ decay in the case of a power law proton spectrum (Stecker, 1971; Tkaczyk, 1978). The energy spectrum of the protons is cosmic ray like ($A \times E^{-2.6}$) as observable in the solar environment;
b) the γ-ray energy production spectrum from bremsstrahlung (e-p). The electron energy spectrum is a power-law-type which has a break at about 2 GeV (Tkaczyk, 1978):

$$n(E) \propto E^{-1.6} \quad \text{for } E < 2 \text{ GeV}$$
$$n(E) \propto E^{-2.6} \quad \text{for } E \geq 2 \text{ GeV}$$

The ratio between protons and electrons was assumed equal to about 100, since this value was observed in the cosmic ray spectrum near the solar system. For the γ-ray sources correlated with quasars the large ratio $L_\gamma/L_x = 100 - 1000$ was observed (Ulrich, 1981; Moffat et al., 1983). If in that type of sources the X-rays originate from electron bremsstrahlung and γ-rays from protons (π° decay), the electron density should be lower than the proton density. This indicates that the γ-ray sources can originate cosmic rays.

Figure 2 shows the γ-ray production spectra from π° decay and from bremsstrahlung.

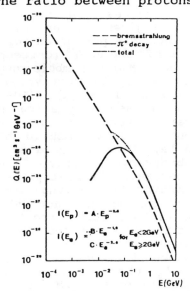

Figure 2. The γ-ray production spectra from π° decay and from bremsstrahlung (solid and dashed lines, respectively).

From the kinematics it is clear that the γ-ray spectrum from π° decay has the maximum at 67.5 MeV, like in the case of the thermal model.

3. The Expected γ-Ray Energy Spectra from Collapsed Objects

In order to determine the expected γ-ray energy spectra from collapsed objects it is necessary to evaluate the temperature, concentration and velocity of the plasma near a black hole. So, the system (Bernoulli, continuity and adiabatic equations) describing the motion of the plasma must be solved (Michel, 1972):

$$\left(\frac{x}{x-1} \theta + 1 \right)^2 \left(1 - \frac{1}{r} + u^2 \right) = const$$

$$n u r^2 = const$$

$$\frac{\theta}{n^{x-1}} = const$$

where:

$\theta = kT/m_p c^2$,
n = concentration ,
$r = R/r_g$, being r_g the gravitational radius,
u = R component of four velocity,
$x = 5/3$.

To determine the temperature as function of the distance from a black hole, different selected values of u_0^2 were taken

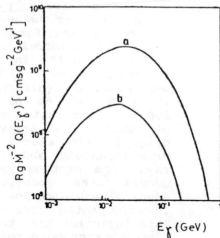

Figure 3. The γ-ra energy spectrum at infinity.

for a given r_0. The calculations were performed for $u_0^2 = 2.6 \times 10^{-5}$ and 6×10^{-5} (corresponding to Mach's numbers roughly 1 and 2, respectively) by Giovannelli et al. (1982b). In the case of spherical symmetric accretion of matter onto a Schwarzschild black hole, they calculated the observable γ-ray energy spectrum at infinity, transforming the comoving spectrum and taking into account all the relativistic effects such as the gravitational and Doppler's redshifts. Figure 3 shows the energy spectrum $Q(E_\gamma)$ observed at infinity, multiplied by $R_g/\dot{M}^2$, for Mach's numbers 1 and 2 (curves a and b, respectively), being $\dot{M}$ the mass accretion rate, which forms, together with the gravitational radius R_g, the couple of parameters of the accretion model.

It is important to emphasize that in this model the shape of the expected γ-ray energy spectrum, for a given Mach's number, does not depend on the mass of the collapsed object and on the mass accretion rate. The luminosity of such objects is proportional to the ratio $\dot{M}^2/R_g$.

There is a question not yet completely settled: under which conditions can the protons reach a sufficiently high energy to produce neutral and charged pions via proton-proton reaction, taking into account the radiative losses and the general relativistic effects?

The answer is far to be definitive. Therefore the problem of the conditions of the plasma around a black hole deserves further discussions. From our point of view, we have considered two possibilities:

i) a thermal process in which the protons may fall adiabatically, while the radiative losses could limit the electron temperature to lower values. This means that the electrons and protons are thermally decoupled near a black hole;

ii) a non thermal process in which a shock around a black hole is producing a power law spectrum of high energy protons.

Since the electrons may loose a large quantity of energy, they cannot be directly accelerated. The secondary electrons produced via π° decay have an equilibrium spectrum. It can be determined by using the magnetic field, the energy density of

the electromagnetic radiation and the dimensions of the source
(Protheroe and Kazanas, 1983).

We have not solved the equilibrium equation. We simply
assumed that the electrons have a cosmic-ray-type spectrum.

4. The Upper Limit to the Number of Black Holes in the Galaxy

Assuming that a typical black hole can have a mass of about 10
M_o and an accretion rate of about 10^{-8} M_o/yr, it is possible to
derive the luminosity L(E > 100 MeV) and the emissivity N(E >
100 MeV) for the two selected values of Mach's numbers:

Mach's N.	Luminosity (erg/s)	Emissivity (photon/s)
1	6.3×10^{33}	2.1×10^{37}
2	2.8×10^{32}	7.3×10^{35}

From SAS II measurements, the Galaxy emissivity of photons
with energies E > 100 MeV is 1.3×10^{42} photon/s (Strong et
al., 1976). Assuming that all the Galaxy emissivity arises
from this kind of collapsed objects, their number should be
10^5 or 10^6 for Mach's numbers 1 and 2, respectively, corresponding roughly to a fraction 10^{-6} or 10^{-5} of the stellar
population of the Galaxy.

5. The expected γ-Ray Energy Spectrum of 3C 273

We have attempted the fit to the experimental data of the
quasar 3C 273 with the simple adiabatic accretion model in the
case of a thermal proton momentum spectrum. The X-ray data are
coming from the experiments of Worral et al. (1979), Primini
et al. (1979), Pietsch et al. (1981), Bezler et al. (1984).
The γ-ray data are coming from COS B satellite (Bignami et
al., 1981; Pollock et al., 1981). The adopted values for the
parameters of 3C 273 are: mass M = 2.5×10^9 M_o and distance d
= 860 Mpc (Ulrich, 1981). A two temperature plasma model has
been used.

We have considered two possibilities:

i) the X-ray and γ-ray sources are separated: in this case
the photon-photon interaction does not exist. The best fit to
the experimental data with the thermal model gives an electron
maximum temperature of 1.35×10^{11} K with an electron temperature profile described by $T_e = T_p$, for R > $10R_g$ (R is the
distance to the collapsed object) and by $T_e = T_p(R = 10R_g)$=

constant, for $R \leq 10R_g$. The best fit gives $\dot{M}^2/M_8 = 3.2 \times 10^3$ $(M_\odot/yr)^2$ (M_8 is the mass of the collapsed object in unit of $10^8\ M_\odot$). So, the derived mass accretion rate is $\dot{M} = 280\ M_\odot/yr$. The critical distance at which $T_e < T_p$ is about $10R_g$, corresponding to 7.5×10^{15} cm (Karakuła et al., 1984); ii) the X-ray and γ-ray originate in the same hot region surrounding the collapsed object: in this case the photon-photon interaction must be considered. So, it is necessary to compute the γ-ray spectra expected from π° decay for different selected radii (R_s) of the X-ray source from 10^{18} to 10^{16} cm (Tkaczyk et al., 1984), taking into account that the dimensions of the central compact object in 3C 273 has a lower limit of $> 1.5 \times 10^{15}$ cm (Elvis et al., 1980; Bignami et al., 1981) and an upper limit of $\leq 4 \times 10^{17}$ cm (White and Ricketts, 1979).

The expected bremsstrahlung energy spectra for electron temperature profiles having different selected values of the maximum temperature (T_{max}) have been calculated too.

Fig. 4 shows the X-ray and γ-ray energy spectra together with the experimental data already mentioned. The observed X-ray power-law index (1.5) is obtained with the theoretical spectra for $T_{max.} = 5 \times 10^9$ K. From this normalization it is possible to derive a mass accretion rate $M = 730$ $M_\odot/yr$.

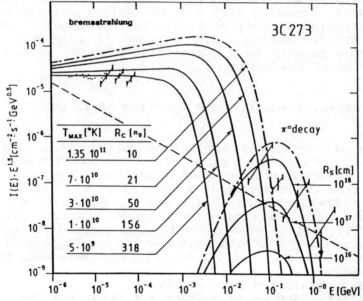

Figure 4. The expected X-ray and γ-ray energy spectra over-lapped to the experimental data of 3C 273.

It is evident that the COS B data are now below the energy

spectrum predicted from π° decay, without the photon-photon interaction (dot-dashed line), but above the curve predicted by the energy γ-ray spectrum from the central hot region of 3C 273 surrounded by the X-ray source with radius of 10^{17} cm. This radius is comparable with the distance of $316R_{g6}$ corresponding to 2.4×10^{17} cm, obtained for $T_{max} = 5 \times 10^9$ K.

So, from our model, best fitting the experimental data, we can conclude that the radius of the X-ray emitting region must be few times 10^{17} cm, which is in excellent agreement with that derived by White and Ricketts (1979) from the X-ray variability of 3C 273 detected with Ariel V Sky Survey Instrument ($\leq 4 \times 10^{17}$ cm). The non thermal model does not fit the experimental data (dashed line in Fig. 4).

6. The Neutrino and Antineutrino Energy Production Spectra

The production of neutrinos in hot plasmas was studied by Marscher et al. (1980) and they concluded that the neutrino emission is the only means by which the raw properties of optically thick sources can be observed. The existence of high temperature plasmas in astrophysical objects was firstly demonstrated by high resolution observations of apparent superluminal expanding radio sources (Cohen et al., 1977). The most likely explanation for this phenomenon involves highly relativistic bulk motions of the radio emitting components (Marscher and Scott, 1980). To explain the existence of a relativistic fluid one usually assumes that one small volume of the plasma is initially heated to ultra-high temperatures. In such a case the thermal energy is converted into the bulk kinetic energy of the fluid. Another suggestion on the existence of ultra-relativistic plasmas in cosmic space was given by Cavallo and Rees (1978); in their work, they expected γ-ray bursts from such sources.

Giovannelli et al. (1983a) considered only the reaction

$$p + p \longrightarrow \pi^+ + anything$$
$$\longrightarrow \mu^+ + \nu_\mu$$
$$\longrightarrow e^+ + \bar{\nu}_\mu + \nu_e$$

since the other $p + p \longrightarrow \pi^- + anything$ is much less significant (Ramaty and Lingenfelter, 1966; Lingenfelter and Ramaty, 1967; Eilek, 1980).

The numerical calculations were performed in the following way:

i) the π^+ momentum production spectrum in the temperature range $10^{11} - 10^{13}$ K;

ii) the ν_μ, μ^+, $\bar{\nu}_\mu$, ν_e energy production spectra as secondary

298

products of the π^+ decay;
iii) the cooling rate coefficient and the energy attenuation time for the relativistic plasma;
iv) the expected neutrinos spectrum in the case of spherically symmetric accretion of matter onto a black hole.

6.1. THE π^+ MOMENTUM SPECTRUM

In order to determine the momentum spectrum of π^+ produced in an isothermal plasma at temperature T, the following assumptions were made (Giovannelli et al., 1983a): a) the plasma is fully ionized; b) the proton momentum distribution is maxwellian; c) the proton angular distribution is isotropic. The calculations were performed for different selected temperatures and unit concentration of the plasma. Figure 5 shows the π^+ momentum production spectrum. Its shape is easily understandable: the maximum number of π^+ is produced at energies slightly higher than the rest energy of π^+. The maxwellian momentum distribution of the parent protons causes the cut-off at high momenta. The threshold energy for the proton-proton reaction is apparent in the cut-off at low momenta. The production efficiency is highly sensitive to the plasma temperature.

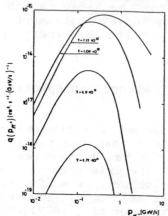

Figure 5. The π^+ momentum production spectrum.

6.2. THE ENERGY PRODUCTION SPECTRUM OF THE NEUTRINOS FROM π^+ DECAY

In a hot plasma, the neutrinos can be created by the π^+ decay ($\pi^+ \longrightarrow \nu_\mu + \mu^+$). Since this is a two body decay, its kinematics is simple. The neutrino energy production spectra for different selected temperatures and for unit concentration of the plasma are shown in Figure 6. The maximum of the spectra is at 31 MeV.

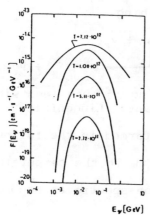

Figure 6. The neutrino energy production spectra.

6.3. THE μ^+ ENERGY PRODUCTION SPECTRUM

Since the neutrinos can be created in μ^+ decay, it is neces-
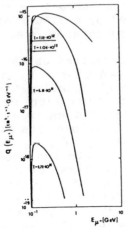
sary to find the energy spectrum of the parent muons. The muon energy production spectrum at different selected temperatures and for unit concentration of the plasma is shown in Figure 7.

Figure 7. The μ^+ energy production spectrum.

6.4. THE μ^+ DECAY AS SOURCE OF NEUTRINOS AND ANTINEUTRINOS

Since the reaction $\mu^+ \longrightarrow e^+ + \bar{\nu}_\mu + \nu_e$ is a three-body decay, its kinematics is more complex. Giovannelli et al. (1983a) solved this problem. The antineutrino and neutrino energy production spectra do not differ substancially from those of the neutrinos from π^+ decay. So, practically, the three kinds of neutrinos contribute in the same way in cooling the plasma.

6.5. THE COOLING RATE COEFFICIENT AND THE ENERGY ATTENUATION TIME

The cooling rate coefficient R(T) is defined as the product of
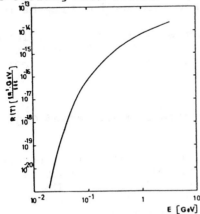
the neutrino energy production spectrum and the energy, integrated over all the energies. So, the cooling rate coefficient is a function of the plasma temperature and concentration. Then, from the astrophysical point of view it is important to evaluate the plasma energy losses owing to neutrino emission. The calculations were done for unit concentration of the plasma, so the results can be easily used for any concentration of the plasma simply multiplying R(T) by n^2. Figure 8 shows the cooling rate coefficient

Figure 8. The cooling rate coefficient.

300

(divided by n^2) versus the proton plasma kinetic energy. It varies from about 10^5 for a variation of the temperature by a factor 10, in the energy range 10^{11} - 10^{12} K, while it increases much slower (about two orders of magnitudes) in the range 10^{12} - 10^{13} K. This fact can be explained by a slower growth of the pion production efficiency at temperatures greater than 10^{12} °K.

The energy attenuation time τ is defined as the time required by the plasma to change its own energy by a factor e = 2.718... Figure 9 shows the energy attenuation time (for unit concentration) versus the mean kinetic energy of the plasma, which loses its energy because of ν_μ, $\bar{\nu}_\mu$, ν_e emission. To evaluate the energy attenuation time for any concentration of the plasma, it is necessary to divide τ by the number of protons in a cubic centimeter. The energy attenuation time is mainly depending on R(T); so, increasing the temperature of the plasma, the energy attenuation time rapidly decreases for any concentration. Since the neutrino emission is not the only way to cool the plasma, we expect a shorter attenuation time. In fact, if we consider that

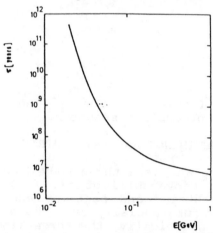

Figure 9. The energy attenuation time.

γ-ray emission from a hot plasma (Giovannelli et al., 1982a; 1982b) carries out a quantity of energy comparable with that carried out by neutrinos, the energy attenuation time becomes about a factor two shorter.

Then, the relativistic plasma can survive for a time longer than the energy attenuation time only if it is permanently heated by some mechanisms, such as the accretion of matter onto a collapsed object.

7. The Expected Neutrino Energy Spectra from Collapsed Objects

We have considered an accretion model with two different temperatures. The temperature of the electron plasma is much less than that of the proton plasma ($T_e \ll T_p$). The proton plasma temperature, density and velocity were found as a solution of the system of Bernoulli, continuity and adiabatic equations (Giovannelli et al., 1983b), which describes the plasma adiabatic compression near a black hole (Michel, 1972).

This model is valid when the parameters of the accretion process (mass of the black hole and mass accretion rate) secure that the collisions are frequent enough so that the particle momentum distributions are maxwellian. As in the case of the calculation of the γ-ray energy production spectra, different values of the R-component of the four velocity were taken for a given initial point r_0, in order to determine the temperature of the plasma as a function of the distance to the black hole.

Numerical calculations were performed for $u_0^2 = 2.6 \times 10^{-5}$ and 6×10^{-5}, corresponding to Mach's numbers 1 and 2, respectively (Giovannelli et al., 1983b).

In the case of spherically symmetric accretion of matter onto a Schwarzschild black hole, the observed neutrino spectrum at infinity (obtained by transforming the neutrino energy spectrum comoving with the plasma, taking into account all the relativistic effects, such as the gravitational and Doppler's redshifts) can be written in the same way as for the γ-ray spectrum (Kolykhalov and Sunyaev, 1979; Giovannelli et al., 1982b). Fig. 10 shows the observed neutrino spectra at infinity (multiplied by R_g/M^2; curves a and b correspond to Mach's numbers 1 and 2, respectively) from the π^+ decay ($\pi^+ \longrightarrow \mu^+ + \nu_\mu$). The observed antineutrino and electron-neutrino spectra at infinity from μ^+ decay ($\mu^+ \longrightarrow e^+ + \bar\nu_\mu + \nu_e$) have practically the same shapes and slightly different values of the intensities than those of the neutrinos (Giovannelli et al., 1983b). The maxima of the observed energy spectra of the neutrinos, antineutrinos and electron-neutrinos are shifted toward low energies when compared with the maxima of the corresponding production spectra (Giovannelli et al., 1983a) because

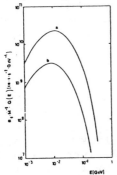

Figure 10. The observed neutrino spectra at infinity.

of the Doppler and gravitational redshifts. Table 1 summarizes the maximum values of the energies for the neutrino, antineutrino and electron-neutrino energy production spectra and for the expected energy spectra. Looking at the Table 1 one can see that the best observational conditions are in the the region around 10 MeV. In this region, around

E_{max}		F(E) (MeV)	Q(E) (MeV)	
			a	b
$\pi^+ \longrightarrow \mu^+ \cdot \nu_\mu$	ν_μ	31	13.3	8.9
$\mu^+ \longrightarrow e^+ \cdot \bar\nu \cdot \nu_e$	$\bar\nu_\mu$	40	15.5	10.0
	ν_e	40	15.8	10.0

Table 1. The maximum values of the energies for ν_μ, ν_μ and ν^e energy production spectra.

the maximum energies, the intensities of the antineutrinos and electron-neutrinos are practically the same, while they differ a little from that of the neutrinos.

The use of these results is very easy. In fact, it is necessary only to divide the values from the Fig. 10 by the selected values of R_g and M^2 in order to obtain the actual spectrum.

8. The Neutrino Luminosity and Emissivity from Black Holes

The luminosity and emissivity of a black hole of 10 M_0 and mass accretion rate $\dot{M} = 10^{-8}$ M_0/yr were calculated for Mach's numbers 1 and 2 (Giovannelli et al., 1983b). The results are reported in Table 2. One can see that the luminosity of this black hole is practically the same for every kind of neutrinos. The total energy carried out by all the neutrinos from the accreting matter onto such a black hole is 3.8 $\times 10^{34}$ erg/s or 2.4 $\times 10^{33}$ erg/s and the emissivity is 4.3 $\times 10^{38}$ neutrino/s or 4.3 $\times 10^{37}$ neutrino/s, for Mach's numbers 1 and 2, respectively. The γ-ray luminosity of this black hole, which can be derived from the papers by Giovannelli et al. (1981; 1982b), is 7.5 $\times 10^{33}$ erg/s or 4 $\times 10^{32}$ erg/s for Mach's numbers 1 and 2, respectively.

		$u_e^2 \cdot 10^5$	L (erg/s)	N (s^{-1})
$\pi^+ \longrightarrow \mu^+ + \nu_\mu$	ν_μ	2.6	$1.18 \cdot 10^{34}$	$1.56 \cdot 10^{38}$
		6.0	$8.14 \cdot 10^{32}$	$1.53 \cdot 10^{37}$
$\mu^+ \longrightarrow e^+ + \bar{\nu}_\mu + \nu_e$	$\bar{\nu}_\mu$	2.6	$1.22 \cdot 10^{34}$	$1.38 \cdot 10^{38}$
		6.0	$8.51 \cdot 10^{32}$	$1.34 \cdot 10^{37}$
	ν_e	2.6	$1.40 \cdot 10^{34}$	$1.41 \cdot 10^{38}$
		6.0	$1.00 \cdot 10^{33}$	$1.40 \cdot 10^{37}$

Table 2. The luminosity and emissivity of a 10 M_0 black hole with $\dot{M} = 10^{-8}$ M_0/yr.

So, the energy carried out during the accretion of matter onto collapsed objects by all the neutrinos is about five times greater than the energy carried out by the γ-rays.

Taking into account the upper limits to the number of galactic black holes (10^5 or 10^6 for Mach's number 1 or 2, respectively) derived from the γ-ray flux under the hypothesis that the γ-rays originate from π° decay, the upper limits for the neutrino luminosity and emissivity of our Galaxy are:

Mach's N.	Luminosity (erg/s)	Emissivity (neutrino/s)
1	3.8×10^{39}	4.3×10^{43}
2	2.4×10^{39}	4.3×10^{43}

9. The Neutrino Flux from the Galactic Center and from 3C 273

It is possible to use these calculations in order to get information on the expected fluxes of neutrinos from the Center of the Galaxy and from the quasar 3C 273 as follows:
 i) using the upper limit to the number of black holes, derived from the γ-ray flux, and assuming that all these black holes are concentrated in the galactic center, it is

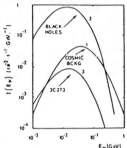

possible to predict the neutrino flux from this direction;
 ii) using the mass accretion rate derived for 3C 273 (few hundreds M_o/yr) and its mass ($2.5 \times 10^9 M_o$) it is possible to predict the neutrino flux expected from this quasar. Figure 11 shows the neutrino flux expected from the direction of the galactic center (curve 1: the cosmic background;

Figure 11. The neutrino flux expected from the Galactic Center and from 3C 273.

curve 2: the flux of the black holes) and from 3C 273 (curve 3).

10. Conclusions

We have shown that the decay of neutral and charged pions produced in a hot plasma may be the source of high energy γ-rays and neutrinos.
　We calculated the γ-ray energy production spectra and the neutrino energy production spectra in a relativistic accreting plasma onto a collapsed object under the simple hypothesis, namely: i) the plasma is fully ionized; ii) the electron and proton angular distribution is maxwellian; iii) the electron and proton angular distribution is isotropic.
　Then, solving the Bernoulli, continuity and adiabatic equations, which form a system of equations describing the plasma motion around a black hole, we evaluated the temperature, concentration and velocity of the plasma near the black hole.
　Using a two temperature plasma model, we have succesfully fitted the model to the COS B experimental data of 3C 273 considering two possibilities: i) the X-rays and γ-rays originate in different regions; ii) the X-rays and γ-rays originate in the same place, so the photon-photon interaction must be considered.
　In the first case the best fit of our thermal model gives a maximum electron temperature of 1.35×10^{11} K. The derived

mass accretion rate is $\dot{M}$ = 280 M_o/yr. The critical distance at which $T_e < T_p$ is about $10R_g$, corresponding to 7.5 x 10^{15} cm.

In the second case the best fit to the experimental data gives a maximum temperature of the electrons equal to 5 x 10^9 K and a radius of the X-ray region surrounding the collapsed object of a few times 10^{17} cm, which is in agreement with the evaluation made by White and Ricketts (1979) who gave a dimension of $\leq$ 4 x 10^{17} cm, derived from variations of the X-ray measurements in the KeV region, and with the lower limit of > 1.5 x 10^{15} cm, derived from short time scale variability in the soft X-ray region (Bignami et al., 1981). From the fit we derive also a value of the mass accretion rate of 730 M_o/yr, which is not far to be reasonable, being the mass of the central black hole of 3C 273 extremely high (2.5 x 10^9 M_o).

From the γ-ray flux, measured by SAS II satellite, under the hypothesis that γ-rays originate from π^o decay, we have evaluated the upper limit to the number of galactic black holes, which is of order 10^5 or 10^6 (depending on the Mach's number: 1 or 2, respectively). Using this upper limit, we evaluated the upper limits to the neutrino luminosity and emissivity, which are of about 3.8 x 10^{39} erg/s and 4.3 x 10^{43} neutrino/s.

The energy carried out during the accretion of matter onto a typical galactic black hole is about five times greater than the energy carried out by the γ-rays. So, the detection of neutrinos from such objects is very unprobable.

References

Barashenkov, W.S. and Tonev, W.D. (1972) Wzaimodejstvija wysokoenergeticheskih chastic i atomnyh jader s jadrami, Moscow.

Bignami, G.F., Bennet, K., Buccheri, R., Caraveo, P.A., Hermsen, W., Kanbach, G., Lichti, G.G., Masnou, J.L., Mayer-Hasselwander, H.A., Paul, J.A., Sacco, B., Scarsi, L., Swanenburg, B.N., and Wills, R.D. (1981) Astron. Astrophys. 93, 71.

Bignami, G.F. and Hermsen, W. (1983) Ann. Rev. Astron. Astrophys. 21, 67.

Bezler, M., Kendziorra, E., Staubert, R., Hasinger, G., Pietsch, W., Reppin, C., Trumper, J., and Voges, W. (1984) Astron. Astrophys. 136, 351.

Cavallo, G. and Rees, J.M. (1978) Mon. Not. R. astr. Soc. 183, 359.

Cohen, M.H., Kellerman, K.I., Shaffer, D.B., Linfield, R.P., Moffet, A.T., Romney, J.D., Seielstad, G.A., Paulini-Toth, I.I.K., Preuss, E., Witzel, A., Schilizzi, R.T., and Geldzahler, B. (1977) Nature 268, 405.

Eilek, J.A. (1980) Astrophys. J. 236, 664.

Elvis, M., Feigelson, E., Griffiths, R.E., Henry, J.P., and Tananbaum, H. (1980) in High-lights of Astronomy, (ed. H. van der Laan).

Giovannelli, F., Karakula, S., and Tkaczyk, W. (1981) in Origin of Cosmic Rays, (eds. G. Setti, G. Spada, and A.W. Wolfendale), IAU Symp. No. 94, p. 335.

Giovannelli, F., Karakula, S., and Tkaczyk, W. (1982a) Astron. Astrophys. 107, 376.

Giovannelli, F., Karakula, S., and Tkaczyk, W. (1982b) Acta Astron. 32, 121.

Giovannelli, F., Karakula, S., and Tkaczyk, W. (1983a) Astron. Astrophys. 125, 121.

Giovannelli, F., Karakula, S., and Tkaczyk, W. (1983b) Astron. Astrophys. 125, 126.

Gorecki, A. and Kluzniak, W. (1981) Acta Astron. 31, 457.

Gould, R.J. (1980) Astrophys. J. 238, 1026.

Hermsen, W. (1980) Ph.D. Thesis, University of Leiden, Holland.

Karakula, S., Tkaczyk, W., and Giovannelli, F. (1984) Adv. Space Res. Vol. 3, No. 10-12, p. 335.

Kolykhalov, P.I. and Sunyaev, R.A. (1979) Soviet Astron. 23, 183.

Lingenfelter, R.E. and Ramaty, R. (1967) High Energy Nuclear Reactions in Astrophysics, (ed. B. Shen), Benjamin, New York.

Marscher, A.P. and Scott, J.S. (1980) Publ. Astron. Soc. Pacific 92, 127.

Marscher, A.P., Vestrand, W.T., and Scott, J.S. (1980) Astrophys. J. 241, 1166.

Michel, F.C. (1972) Astrophys. Space Sci. 15, 153.

Moffat, A.F.J., Schlickeiser, R., Shara, M.M. Sieber, W., Tuffs, R., and Kuhr, M. (1983) Astrophys. J. Letters 271, L45.

Pietsch, W., Reppin, C., Trumper, J., Voges, W., Lewin, W., Kendziorra, E., and Staubert, R. (1981) Astron. Astrophys. 94, 234.

Pollock, A.M.T., Bignami, G.F., Hermsen, W., Kanbach, G., Lichti, G.G., Masnou, J.L., Swanenburg, B.N., and Wills, R.D. (1981) Astron. Astrophys. 94, 116.

Primini, F.A., Cooke, B.A., Dobson, C.A., Howe, S.K., Scheepmaker, A., Wheaton, W.A., and Lewin, W.H.G. (1979) Nature 278, 234.

Protheroe, R.J. and Kazanas, D. (1983) Astrophys. J. 265, 620.

Ramaty, R. and Lingenfelter, R.E. (1966) J. Geophys. Res. 71, 3687.

Stecker, F.W. (1971) in Cosmic Gamma Rays, Baltimore: Mono Book Corp., NASA SP-249.

Strong, A.W., Wolfendale, A.W., and Worral, D.M. (1976) Mon. Not. R. astr. Soc. 175, 23P.

Swanenburg, B.N., Bennet, K, Bignami, G.F., Buccheri, R., Caraveo, P., Hermsen, W., Kanbach, G., Lichti, G.G., Masnou,

J.L., Mayer-Hasselwander, H.A., Paul, J.A., Sacco, B., Scarsi, L., and Wills, R.D. (1981) Astrophys. J. Letters 243, L69.

Tkaczyk, W. (1978) Postepy Astronomii Tom XXVI, Zeszyt 2.

Tkaczyk, W. Karakula, S., and Giovannelli, F. (1984) in X-Ray Astronomy '84, (eds. M. Oda and R. Giacconi), Institute of Space and Astronautical Science,Tokyo, p. 499.

Ulrich, M.H. (1981) Space Sci. Rev. 28, 89.

White, G.L. and Ricketts, M.J. (1979) Mon. Not. R. astr. Soc. 187, 757.

Worral, D.M., Mushotzky, R.F., Boldt, E.A., Holt, S.S., and Serlemitsos, P.J. (1979) Astrophys. J. 232, 683.

NEARBY GALAXIES IN HIGH ENERGY GAMMA RAYS

Mehmet Emin Özel
University of Cukurova and
Tubitak Marmara Research Institute, Gebze
Turkiye

1. Introduction

At present, there are no definitive results from nearby galaxies at photon energies
above about 50 MeV. High energy gamma ray measurements of our neighboring
galaxies have the potential of revealing the presence of cosmic rays as well as their
density and distribution properties. These observations will have the extra advantage
of being free of the complications of making the observations from within the galaxy,
as is the case for our Milky Way (MW) Galaxy. In addition, such results are
expected to provide new insight into many aspects of our own galaxy.

High energy gamma ray experiments of the '70's have provided upper limits (and
very few positive detections) for a number of objects beyond the MW. The new
generation of instruments that will be put into operation in the '90's are expected to
have the ability to detect new objects in the extragalactic class. Especially, NASA's
Gamma Ray Observatory, with its effective area approximately a factor of 20 larger
than that of the previous experiments SAS-2 and COS-B, should be able to definitely
see the LMC and SMC and, probably, M31, the nearest spiral galaxy (Ozel and
Fichtel, 1988, Ozel and Berkhuijsen, 1987 and references therein), and M82, the
nearest active galaxy (Akyuz et al., 1991), enriching the "zoo" of high energy gamma
ray emitting extragalactic objects known.

2. Method of Calculation

Calculation of gamma ray intensities expected from these and similar objects are
based on the information about their diffuse matter content, obtained through HI and
CO measurements, as well as on reasonable extrapolations of the intensity of cosmic
rays (electrons, protons, nuclei) from solar neighborhood measurements. As CR's
travel in space, they interact with diffuse matter, photon fields and magnetic fields to
create gamma rays. A general discussion of the relevant processes - neutral pion
production, bremsstrahlung, inverse Compton and synchrotron - together with
intensity estimates and references is given by Fichtel and Trombka (1981). The
resulting final intensity distribution and the energy spectrum for the diffuse gamma
radiation in our Galaxy match the observations quite well.

307

M. M. Shapiro et al. (eds.), Cosmic Rays, Supernovae and the Interstellar Medium, 307–311.
© 1991 *Kluwer Academic Publishers. Printed in the Netherlands.*

308

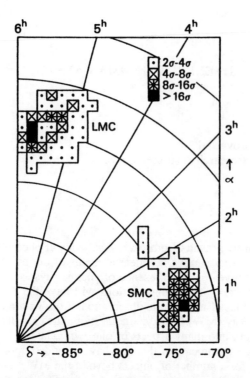

Figure 1. Distribution of the calculated number of gamma rays with E>100 MeV by EGRET, in terms of the statistical significance above the total diffuse background (uniform CR density).

For the calculations reported here, it was assumed that the approach just mentioned is valid and that corrections and refinements made in recent work, as noted in Ozel and Fichtel (1988), are included. The source function above 100 MeV was taken as 2.0×10^{-25} $n(HI2)$ r gamma rays/(cm^3-sec) where $n(HI2)$ is the number of hydrogen nuclei, atomic and molecular, per cm^3 and r is the ratio of the cosmic ray density in the object to that in the solar vicinity.

The density distribution of cosmic rays in a galaxy is, in fact, the quantity that, hopefully, the gamma ray measurements will reveal. For the present purpose however, certain hypotheses need to be made so that the predicted gamma ray intensity can be calculated. This provides not only an indication of the level of gamma ray emission that might be expected, but also a basis for testing the theoretical assumptions such as the ratio of electrons to nucleonic component in CR, or the correlation scale between cosmic ray and matter densities.

3. Detection Possibilities

The four galaxies (LMC, SMC, M31, M82) which are considered in this note are the ones that seem to have characteristics to make them candidates for gamma ray emission at levels detectable by Gamma Ray Observatory's EGRET instrument which will be the most sensitive instrument to be flown in the photon energy range above 20 MeV. EGRET will detect photons of energy up to 30 GeV with a typical angular resolution of about 1/2 deg or better, a considerable improvement over previous experiments (including that of GAMMA-1). The typical EGRET sensitivity level expected is about (2 to 4) x 10^{-8} photons/cm^2-s for 4 weeks of observations away from the galactic disk (Ozel and Fichtel, 1988).

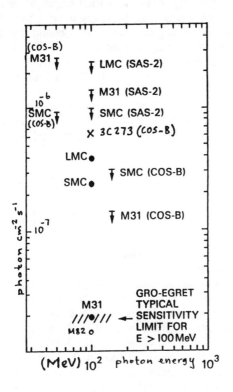

Fig. 2. Existing upper limits and expected integral fluxes from LMC, SMC, M31, and M82. EGRET's sensitivity limit for a four week observation is also indicated.

4. Results and Discussion

The Magellanic Clouds are the prime extragalactic target of coming gamma ray observations not only because their expected gamma ray intensities are above the estimated instrument sensitivity thresholds, but also because they offer the possibility of understanding the distribution of cosmic rays (CR) in a galaxy other than our own. For a CR density that is constant over the Clouds (and equal to that near the solar neighborhood, corrected for solar modulation effects), the expected distribution of gamma ray intensity over the Clouds is predicted and given in Fig. 1 (from Ozel and Fichtel, 1988).

For M31 and M82, high energy gamma ray detections seem possible only if the average cosmic ray intensity is larger than that of the solar neighborhood (Ozel and Berkhuijsen, 1987, Akyuz et al., 1991). Expected gamma ray intensity levels for all four galaxies for a constant CR intensity value and presently available upper limits, together with the estimated EGRET sensitivity threshold, are summarized in Fig. 2.

Among the four galaxies under consideration, LMC has the advantage of being our nearest neighbor observed at a relatively small inclination angle. Recently, the CR density distribution in the LMC was calculated quantitatively using a model based on the concept of dynamic balance, where the magnetic fields and cosmic rays are confined to the Galaxy by the weight of the gas threaded by the field, as discussed by Parker (1969, 1977) and Bierman and Davis (1960). A range of coupling scales between CRs and matter are investigated (Fichtel et al., 1991). A brief summary of these results is given below.

To start with, it has been assumed that the nonthermal component of the observed radio emission is synchrotron emission by electrons with a shape $N(E) = KE^{-t}$ moving in a magnetic field strength H as given by (Ginzburg and Syrovatskii, 1964):

$$I(f) = 1.35 \times 10^{-22}\, a(t) \cdot L \cdot K \cdot H^{\alpha}\, (6.26 \times 10^{18}/f)^{\beta} \text{ erg/(cm}^2\text{-s-sr-Hz)} \qquad (1)$$

Here a(t) is about 0.1 for our case, L is the range where electrons and H are present, f is the observing frequency and the exponents $\alpha = (t+1)/2$ and $\beta = (t-1)/2$. From this equation, if I(f) and its frequency dependence are known and H and L can be estimated, then K may be determined. It is also assumed that the ratio of electrons to nucleons in CR's is 100, as it is in the MW.

Specifically, if K' and H' are the local (i.e. solar) values in our Galaxy, and w(x)K' is the value in the LMC, the corresponding H value in the LMC is $[w(x)]^{1/2}H'$ to maintain the near-equality of CR and magnetic fields (magnetic pressure $\propto H^2$). The nonthermal component of the radio emission from the LMC is estimated to have a slope of 0.57 ± 0.07 which is very similar to the value from the MW galaxy, 0.62 ± 0.04. The value of the total (ordered plus random components) Galactic mean field, H' is calculated to be about 11 μG. For L, the appropriate size is about 1 kpc and K' = 2.6×10^{-15} electrons-cm^3-ergs^{t-1} (Fichtel et al., 1991). Then,

$$w(x) \cong 0.45\, I(f, -18)^{1/2}\, f(8)^{1/3} \qquad (2)$$

where I(f, -18) is in units of 10^{-18} erg/(cm^2-sr-Hz) and f(8) is the frequency in units of 10^8 Hz. With this equation, it is possible to estimate the CR intensity level as a function of position, x, in the LMC using the synchrotron data. One such map of the

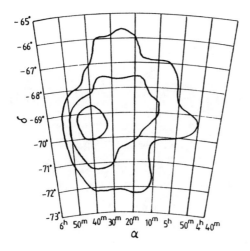

Fig. 3. Contour levels for the predicted CR energy density, relative to those in our Galaxy, based on the 408 MHz data of Haslam et al., (1982). Contour levels on the Figure correspond to w=0.71, 0.86 and 1.23 (from Fichtel et al., 1991).

cosmic ray intensity distribution in the LMC is given in Fig. 3. CR maps are also calculated for different coupling scales with diffuse matter. For a 2.5 kpc coupling scale, the results are quite similar to Fig. 3 (Fichtel et al., 1991). The expected gamma ray intensity from such cosmic ray map models, combined with the reported atomic and molecular diffuse matter distributions, are presented elsewhere (Fichtel et al., 1991). Any differences between Fig. 1 and observations, when combined with the CR distribution models considered, should reveal much about the extent and distribution of cosmic rays and cosmic ray sources in the LMC as well as about the hypotheses that go into the calculations.

7. References

Akyuz, A., Brouillet, N., Ozel, M. E., 1991, submitted, Astr. Astrophys.
Bierman, L., Davis, L., 1960, Zeitschrift fur Astrophysik, 51, 19.
Fichtel, C., Trombka, I., 1981, "Gamma Ray Astrophysics," NASA SP-453.
Fichtel, C., Ozel, M. E., Stone, R., Sreekumar, P., 1991, Ap. J., in press.
Ginzburg, V., Syrovatskii, I., 1964, "The Origin of Cosmic Rays," MacMillan.
Haslam, et al., 1982, Astronomy and Astrophys. Suppl., 47, 1.
Ozel, M. E., Berkhuijsen, E., 1987, Astron. Astrophys., 172, 378.
Ozel, M. E., Fichtel, C., 1988, Ap. J., 335, 135.
Parker, E. N., 1969, Space Sci. Rev., 9, 654.
Parker, E. N., 1977, NASA CP-002, 283.

COSMIC RAYS AT THE HIGHEST ENERGIES

A.W. WOLFENDALE
Physics Department
University of Durham
South Road
Durham DH1 3LE
UK.

and J. WDOWCZYK
Institute of Nuclear Studies
Uniwersytecka 5
Lodz 1
Poland

ABSTRACT. The case is made for there being an extragalactic component of cosmic rays, having an energy density locally of about 10^{-5}eV cm^{-3} and dominating over Galactic particles at energies above about 2 x 10^{19}eV. The interaction of the extragalactic particles, assumed to be protons, with the cosmic microwave background is considered under different assumptions as to the sources of the particles. Electromagnetic cascades ensue from the interactions, leading to potentially detectable fluxes of gamma rays, most particularly at energies near 10^9eV, 10^{14}eV and above 10^{19}eV. Estimates of the fluxes are given.

1 Introduction

If the arguments put forward in this paper are correct, then cosmic rays have a distinct cosmological connotation. It is tempting, then, to refer to the famous remarks made by JJ and G.P. Thomson in the 1928 edition of their book "Conduction of Electricity through Gases" and to express the view that their prophesy may well be true. The remarks followed the discovery of cosmic rays by Victor Hess in which he correctly attributed the deflections in his balloon-borne electrometer as due to a radiation from outside the atmosphere and of cosmic origin.

It would be one of the romances of science if these obscure and prosaic minute leakages of electricity from well-insulated bodies should be the means by which the most fundamental problems in the evolution of the cosmos came to be investigated.

313

M. M. Shapiro et al. (eds.), Cosmic Rays, Supernovae and the Interstellar Medium, 313–323.
© 1991 *Kluwer Academic Publishers. Printed in the Netherlands.*

This attitude gained momentum over the following years. For example, Eddington was to write

"If I am right, cosmic radiation is a museum - a collection of relics of remote antiquity".

The implication of the whole of cosmic rays being extragalactic and filling the whole cosmos is clear; cosmology indeed.

Eddington's remarks were conditioned by the experimental fact that no significant directional anisotropies had been seen despite careful searches. However, as time progressed, small directional anisotropies did appear, which grew with energy above 10^{14}eV or so, and these results, together with other observations, led to the idea that the particles were Galactic, rather than extragalactic. In consequence, the cosmological significance of cosmic rays ceased to be considered.

The authors' view is that there is now a rebirth of cosmological interest in the subject, at the very highest energies, and this is the main subject of the present paper.

It is first necessary to consider the situation at those energies where a Galactic origin can be reasonably assumed.

2 Galactic Origin to 2 x 10^{19}eV.

Gamma ray astronomy has demonstrated that the bulk of cosmic rays - those below $\simeq$ 10^{10}eV - are of Galactic origin and that their 'sources' are supernova remnant shocks in the ISM (see e.g. Ramana Murthy and Wolfendale, 1986). SNR are commonly considered to be likely sources to 10^{14}eV or so and pulsars may contribute up to this limit and to higher energies, too. The best evidence for a Galactic origin up to at least 10^{18}eV probably comes from the observed anisotropy of arrival directions although it must be stated that such measurements are difficult and the accurate form of the anisotropy versus energy plot is still not completely clear (see Murakami et al., 1990, for a recent summary).

It is well known that as one approaches 10^{20}eV the magnetic rigidity of cosmic ray protons becomes so high that the trajectories should become almost straight lines in the Galaxy and insofar as the majority of the Galactic sources are likely to be in the Galactic Plane an enhancement in intensity from the plane should result. We (Wdowczyk and Wolfendale 1984, Szabelski et al., 1986) searched for this enhancement in the world's EAS data with the result shown in Figure 1. More recently (Matsubara et al. 1990) there has been confirmation of the increase in enhancement from the Akeno EAS array, as indicated in the Figure. If the particles were of Galactic origin at all energies we would expect f_E to saturate at $\simeq 1$. In fact, it will be observed that there is a dramatic change at the highest energies, $E \geq 2$ x 10^{19}eV, to a Galactic Plane avoidance. Such behaviour can be interpreted in terms of a transition to a dominance by extragalactic particles at the very highest energies.

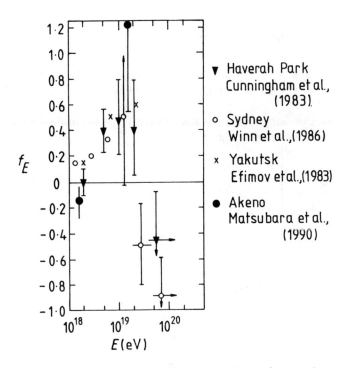

Figure 1. Dependence of the Galactic enhancement factor, f_E, on primary energy as derived by us from the data listed (with the exception of the Akeno results which were given by the authors using our formalism). The adopted form for the dependence of cosmic ray intensity on Galactic latitude, b, is $I(b) = I_o[(1-f_E) + f_E \exp-b^2]$. Clearly, $f_E = 0$ implies isotropy and $f_E = 1$ implies the maximum Galactic enhancement. f_E less than zero implies an extragalactic origin but with extragalactic anisotropy, possibly connected with the VIRGO supercluster.

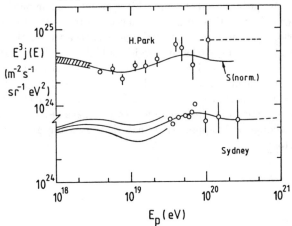

Figure 2. The spectral shape at the highest energies from the Sydney and Haverah Park observations. The Sydney spectrum has been normalised to that from Haverah Park at 10^{19}eV in the upper graph (from the summary by Wdowczyk and Wolfendale, 1989).

3 Extragalactic Origin above 2 x 10^{19}eV.

In addition to the behaviour of the Galactic enhancement factor there is the well known behaviour of the spectral shape, viz the apparent flattening above $\sim 10^{19}$eV. Figure 2 indicates the situation.

A possible reason for the change of slope is again that there is a transition from Galactic to extragalactic origin, as indicated in Figure 3.

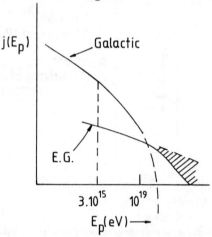

Figure 3. Diagrammatic representation of the transition from Galactic to extragalactic origin. The shaded area indicates the energy taken out of the EG beam by interactions of the protons with the 2.7K CMB radiation.

A natural situation, which fits the observations, is that the EG spectrum has the spectral form $j(E) \propto E^{-2}$, such as would occur for shock acceleration in EG space.

Before examining the consequences of such a model it is useful to examine the energetics of EG origin. Figure 4 shows the situation. It appears that there are several EG mechanisms which could give the necessary energy in total although it is true to say that the actual process by which individual cosmic rays achieve energies as high as 10^{20}eV or above is still most unclear. Of those indicated the collisions of galaxies seems to offer promise and further work would be valuable; one mechanism would be the reconnection of magnetic field lines between colliding spiral galaxies, each with its spiral - aligned magnetic field. The fact that there is some evidence for an excess of radio emission from the space between near-colliding galaxies offers promise although it is appreciated that there is a big gulf between GeV electrons and 10^{20}eV protons.

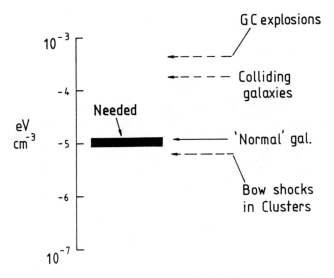

Figure 4. The energetics of EG phenomena. Dashed lines indicate total energy available, of which only a fraction would go into cosmic rays. In the case of 'normal galaxies' it is necessary to assume that our Galaxy is deficient in output above $\simeq 10^{18}$eV at the present time compared with the average normal galaxy.

4 Cosmological Effects : General Principles

Probably the most important physical phenomenon in contemporary cosmology is the cosmic microwave background radiation and in turn it is the interactions of the EG cosmic rays with this radiation that provides the most important aspect of interest in EG cosmic rays. The phenomenon has been well documented (e.g. Wdowczyk et al., 1972, Wdowczyk and Wolfendale, 1990, Halzen et al., 1990). The initial interaction of the protons with the 2.7K photons generate γ-rays (from π^o- mesons) and electrons (from $\pi \rightarrow \mu \rightarrow$ e decays) which in turn cause cascades which propagate through the universe to produce a γ-ray spectrum of particular form at the earth. This spectral shape has within it the cosmological parameters. It will be appreciated that red shift effects require that the production spectrum of the protons must extend to even higher energies ($\sim 10^{22}$eV) when production is important at large z-values.

318

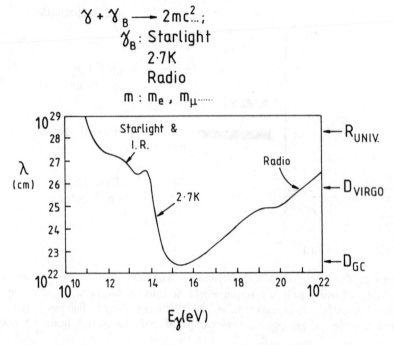

Figure 5. Mean free path for $\gamma - \gamma$ collisions. The great dip in λ is caused by interactions with the 2.7K CMB radiation. Important distances are indicated on the right hand side.

Two situations (at least) can be envisaged. In the first, EG cosmic rays are Universal and fill the Universe uniformly (the Universal Model). In the second, EG cosmic rays are concentrated in Galaxy clusters and super-clusters, such as VIRGO (the SC model). The predicted effects are somewhat different.

The propagation of the EG gamma rays is conditioned by the energy-dependence of the mean free path for $\gamma - \gamma$ collisions. Figure 5 shows this energy dependence.

It should be noted that there are uncertainties about the average energy densities in extragalactic space in the starlight and radio wavelength bands. Furthermore, these energy densities (and associated collision mean free paths) will be higher in galaxy clusters than elsewhere. Nevertheless, these uncertainties are ignored in what follows.

The nature of the cascade is shown in Figure 6. It will be appreciated that when allowance is made for an increase of EG cosmic ray output in the past at large z, the calculations assume a degree of complexity.

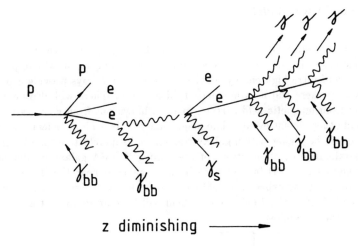

z diminishing ⟶

Figure 6. Nature of the cascade. γ_{bb} denotes CMB photons and γ_s starlight photons.

5 The Universal Origin Model

Figure 7 shows an accurate representation of the EG spectrum and the energy going into the cascade. Three conditions are indicated. 'NC' : no cosmological increase in EG cosmic ray output at early epochs. The other two relate to cosmological enhancements.

Two variants for the cosmological case have been taken; the output varies as $(1+z)^{\beta-5/2}$ back to z_m and we have given production spectra which give rise to the measured spectra for $\beta = 3.7$ and $z_m = 4$ and 9.

The ensuing cascades give the equilibrium γ-ray spectrum shown in Figure 8. The main effect of the cosmological increase at high z is to increase the predicted flux at the lowest energies.

There are, in fact, three regimes where the predicted gamma ray fluxes might be detectable:

(i) Above 10^{19}eV, where the γ/p ratio approaches 10%,

(ii) Near 10^{14}eV, where $\gamma/p \sim 10^{-5}$, and

(iii) Near 10^{8}eV, where the predicted flux is already near the observed flux from SAS II.

Concerning (i) and (ii), the new EAS arrays under construction and coming into service should be able to detect the gamma rays.

Turning to (iii), already the SAS II observations set a limit on z_m, specifically $z_m \leq 5$. Data from GAMMA I and GRO should enable stronger limits to be put on these important cosmological quantities, β and z_m.

6 The Supercluster Model

The majority of cosmic ray protons escape from the galaxies in which they are generated and extragalactic space therefore contains a finite cosmic ray component irrespective of any dramatic source of ultra-high energy particles. These cosmic rays provide a pressure and associated with it there will be a magnetic field pressure. There will also be a field pressure resulting from magnetic-field carrying plasma blown out from galaxies by supernova explosions and other violent events. The magnitude of this field is unclear but it is almost certain that it will be higher within galaxy clusters and superclusters than in extragalactic space in general. Indeed, observations of the 'strong' COMA galaxy cluster have shown rather large fields ($\simeq 2\mu$ G) in the space between galaxies near the cluster centre. For our own environment, we expect the field to be lower but still significant: several $10^{-2}\mu$G (Wdowczyk and Wolfendale, 1990). Such a field will have an important effect on particle propagation in the Supercluster.

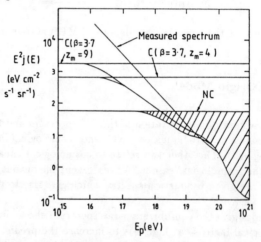

Figure 7. Energy spectra for injection (horizontal lines) which give the measured spectra above 10^{19}eV. NC denotes no cosmological increase and the shaded area represents the energy going into the electromagnetic cascade (see text for details).

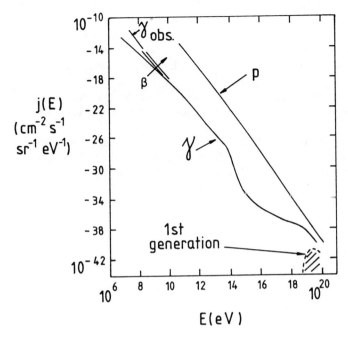

Figure 8. The predicted energy spectrum of cosmological gamma rays coming from the cascades initiated by the EG proton - 2.7K CMB photons. At the highest energies the 'first generation' contribution is to be regarded as the lower limit to the flux; the upper limit is only achieved for a very low extragalactic magnetic field.

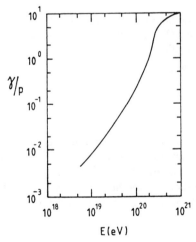

Figure 9. The predicted γ/p ratio for the VIRGO diffusion model for one steradian towards the VIRGO cluster.

In the paper just referred to we have adopted the model of Giler et al. (1980) in which protons are accelerated in the Core of VIRGO - in galaxies such as M87, with its prominent jet for example. The protons then diffuse outwards and some arrive at earth. In the calculations the parameters are adjusted so that the observed proton flux is achieved and the γ-ray flux from the p-γ_{bb} collisions is calculated. The predicted γ/p ratio is shown in Figure 9.

It will be noted that the ratio is quite large and, indeed, for the parameters adopted in the calculations there are more gamma rays than protons predicted at energies above about 2×10^{20}eV.

The energy region centred on 10^{14}eV is also of interest and here the experimental possibilities are more favourable than for the Universal model in view of the clear anisotropy expected (i.e. peak intensity towards VIRGO). Figure 10 shows the situation.

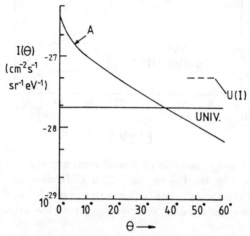

Figure 10. Predicted gamma ray intensity at 10^{14}eV as a function of the angle, θ, with respect to the VIRGO direction. 'UNIV' denotes γ-rays from all individual galaxies, assumed to be like our Galaxy, averaged spatially and assuming that they behave independently.

7 Conclusions

Although it is premature to claim that the link of cosmic rays to Cosmology has been renewed the results are encouraging. A straightforward model involving an EG origin for cosmic rays observed at earth above 2×10^{19}eV has been formulated and this has been used to make specific predictions in the field of gamma ray astronomy. New results over the next decade from both ground- and space-based detectors should allow confirmation or dismissal.

REFERENCES

Cunningham, G. et al., 1983, Proc. 18th ICRC, Bangalore, 2, 157.

Efimov, N.N., Mikhailov, A.A. and Pravdin, M.I., 1983, Proc. 18th ICRC, Bangalore, 2, 149.

Giler, M., Wdowczyk, J. and Wolfendale, A.W., 1980, J. Phys. G. 6, 1561.

Halzen, F., Protheroe, R.J., Stanev, T., and Vankov, H.P., 1990, Phys. Rev. D, 41, 343.

Martsubara, Y. et al., 1990, 21st ICRC, Adelaide, 3, 201.

Murakami, K. et al., 1990, 21st ICRC, Adelaide, 3, 192.

Ramana Murthy, P.V. and Wolfendale, A.W., 1986, Gamma Ray Astronomy (Cambridge University Press).

Szabelski, J. et al., 1986, J. Phys. G. 12, 1433.

Wdowczyk, J. et al., 1972, J. Phys. A., 5, 1419.

Wdowczyk, J. and Wolfendale, A.W., 1984, J. Phys. G., 10, 1453; 1989, Ann. Rev. Nucl. Part Sci., 39, 43; 1990, Astrophys. J., 349, 35.

Winn, M.M. et al., 1986, J. Phys. G. 12, 653; J. Phys. G. 12, 675.

PARTICIPANTS

AKYÜZ, Aysun
Çukurova University
Physics Department
Balcali
01330 Adana
TURKEY

AVERNA, Daniela
Istituto d'Astronomia
Universita di Catania
Viale A. Doria, 6
95100 Catania
ITALIA

BAYKAL, Altan
Middle East Technical University
Ankara
TURKEY

BEALL, James H.
Naval Research Laboratory
Code 4120
Washington, DC 20375
USA

BEAMAN, John
Physics Department
University of Leeds
Woodhouse Lane
LS2 9JT Leeds
ENGLAND

BENIT, Jean
IAS
Batiment 120 Universite d'Orsay
91405 Orsay
FRANCE

BLOUNT, Octavia L.
Department of Physics
Drexel University
32nd Chestnut Street
Philadelphia, PA 19140
USA

de BOER, Hans
Space Research Center
Niels Bohr Weg 2
Leiden
HOLLAND

BORIONE, Alexandre
University of Chicago
Enrico Fermi Institute
933 E. 56th Street
Chicago, IL 60637
USA

BROWN, Laurie M.
Dept. of Physics & Astronomy
Northwestern University
Evanston, IL 60208
USA

BUCKLEY, James
University of Chicago
Enrico Fermi Institute
933 E. 56th Street
Chicago, IL 60637
USA

BÜTIKOFER, Rolf
Universität Bern
Physikalisches Institut
Sidler Str. 5
3012 Bern
SWITZERLAND

BZOWSKI, Maciej
Space Research Center
Ordona 21
PL 01-237 Warsaw
POLAND

CAMPOS FAUTH, Anderson
Unicamp-Inst. Fisica
Dep. Raios Cosmicos
CX. Postal 6165
13081 Campinas
BRAZIL

CARRAMIÑANA, Alberto
University of Durham
Physics Department
South Road
DH1 3LE Durham
U.K.

CEI, Fabrizio
INFN Pisa
V. Vecchia Livornese
56100 S. Perio A Grado (PI)
ITALY

CHRISTIAN, Thomas
University of Siegen
Physics Department
Adolf-Reichwein Straße
5900 Siegen
GERMANY

DELPERAL, Luis
Universidad Complutense deMadrid
Dpt. Atomic, Mol. & Nucl. Physics
28040 Madrid
SPAIN

DOGIEL, Vladimir
P.N. Lebedev Physical Inst.
Leninsky pr.53
117924 Moscow
USSR

DOLL, Paul
Kernforschung Karlsruhe
Leopoldshafen
7500 Karlsruhe
GERMANY

DRÖGE, Wolfgang
University of Kiel
Institut für Kernphysik
Olshausenstraße 40
D-2300 Kiel
GERMANY

DRURY, Luke O'Connor
Dublin Inst. Adv. Studies
5 Merrion Square
Dublin 2
IRELAND

FERNANDEZ, Paloma
University of Kiel
Institut für Kernphysik
Olshausenstraße 40
D-2300 Kiel
GERMANY

GANDHI, Vivek
Tata Inst. of Fundamental Research
HECR Group
Homi Bhabha Road
400 005 Bombay
INDIA

GIOVANNELLI, Franco
Istituto di Astrofisica Spaziale
CNR
Via E. Fermi 21
00044 Frascati
ITALY

GREEN, David
Dominion Radio Astrophys. Obser.
P.O. Box 248
Penticton, B.C. V2A 6K3
CANADA

GREENBERG, J. Mayo
University of Leiden
Laboratory of Astrophysics
Nielsbohrweg 2
Leiden 2300 RA
HOLLAND

GROVE, J. Eric
Code 4150
Naval Research Laboratory
Washington, DC 20375
USA

GUPTA, Sunil K.
Tata Inst. of Fundamental Research
HECR Group
Homi Bhabha Road
400 005 Bombay
INDIA

HALVERSON, Peter G.
University of California at Irvine
Physics Department
Irvine, CA 92717
USA

HAUSTEIN, Volker
II Institüt für Experimental Physik
Universität Hamburg
Lurupev Chaussee 149
200 HH 50 Hamburg
GERMANY

HEINDL, William
Caltech
Physics 220-47
Pasadena, CA 91125
USA

HESSE, Andreas
University Siegen
Physics Department
Hammerstraße 9
5963 Wenden
GERMANY

HOF, Michael
University Siegen
Physics Department
Adolf-Reichwein Straße
5900 Siegen
GERMANY

HULL, Alan
Physics Department
University of Leeds
Woodhouse Lane
LS2 9JT Leeds
ENGLAND

LIJOWSKI, Michal
Louisiana State University
Dept. of Physics & Astronomy
Nicholson Hall 202
Baton Rouge, LA 70803-4001
USA

KANDEMIR, Gulçin
Istanbul Technical University
Physics Department
Maslak
80626 Istanbul
TURKEY

MACEDO, Paulo G.
University of Porto
Applied Mathematics Department
R. das Taipas, 135
4000 Porto
PORTUGAL

KARLE, Albrecht
MPI für Physik und Astrophysik
Werner-Heisenberg Inst. für Physik
Föhringer Ring 6
8000 München 40
GERMANY

MARKOVSKY, Leigh
University of Wisconsin
Physics Department
1150 University Ave.
Madison, WI 53710
USA

KIM, Tae Yeon
Department of Physics
Korea University
136-701 Seoul
KOREA

MAURICIO, Paulo
University of Porto
Applied Mathematics Department
R. das Taipas, 135
4000 Porto
PORTUGAL

KIZILYALLI, H. Mümtaz
Ankara University
Physics Department
Fen Fak.
06100 Ankara
TURKEY

MERCK, Martin
MPI für Physik und Astrophysik
Physik B
Föhringer Ring 6
8000 München 40
GERMANY

LANGER, Winfried
University Siegen
Physics Department
Adolf-Reichwein Straße
5900 Siegen
GERMANY

MORRIS, Daniel
University of New Hampshire
Space Science Center
Science & Engineering Res. Bldg.
Durham, NH 03824
USA

MÜYESSEROGLU, Zekeriya
Ankara Univ. Faculty of Sciences
Astronomy & Space Science Dept.
Dögol cad.
06100 Ankara
TURKEY

de NIEM, Detlef
Institut für Kosmosforschung
Bereich 8
Rudower Chausse 5
1199 Berlin
EAST GERMANY

NORCI, Laura
MPI Garching
D8046 Garching bei München
GERMANY

NUTTER, Scott
Indiana University
Physics Department
Bloomington, IN 47405
USA

O'CONNOR, Daniel
University of Hawaii
Physics Department
2505 Corrca Road
Honolulu, HI 96822
USA

ÖZEL, Mehmet E.
Çukurova University
Physics Department
Balcali
01330 Adana
TURKEY

PAJOT, Philippe
Service d'Astrophysique (bat:528)
CEN-Saclay
91191 Gif-sur-Yvette Cedex
FRANCE

PROSSER, David
Physics Department
University of Leeds
Woodhouse Lane
LS2 9JT Leeds
ENGLAND

PROVOROV, Aleksey
Institute for Nuclear Research
Deep Underwater Neutrino Det.
60th Oct. Anniversary Prospect, 7A
117312 Moscow
USSR

PTUSKIN, Vladimir S.
Inst. of Terr. Magnetism, Ionosphere
& Radio Wave Propagation.
USSR Academy of Sciences
Cosmic Ray Department
142 092 Troitsk
USSR

ROCHE, Paul
Southampton University
Physics Department
University Road
S09 5NH Southampton
UK

RODRIGUEZ FRIAS, Dolores
Universidad Complutense de Madrid
Dept. of Atomic, Molecular &
Nuclear Physics
28040 Madrid
SPAIN

330

ROULIAS, Dimitris
University of Athens
Physics Dept., Astrophys. Lab.
Panepistimiopolis, Zografos
15783 Athens
GREECE

SAKURAI, Kunitomo
Institute of Physics
Kanagawa University
Rokkaku-bashi
221 Yokohama
JAPAN

SAMBRUNA, Rita Maria
Dipartimento di Fisica
Sezione Astrofisica
viale Celoria 16
Milano
ITALY

SCHOPPER, Erwin
University of Frankfurt
Physics Department
August Euler Straße 6
D6000 Frankfurt
GERMANY

SELAM, Selim
Ankara Univ. Faculty of Sciences
Astronomy & Space Science Dept.
Dögol cad. Besevler
06100 Ankara
TURKEY

SHAPIRO, Maurice
University of Maryland
Physics & Astronomy Department
205 Yoakum Parkway #1720
Alexandria, VA 22304
USA

SILBERBERG, Rein
Code 4150
Naval Research Lab.
Washington, DC 20375
USA

SIMON, Manfred
University Siegen
Physics Department
Adolf-Reichwein Straße
5900 Siegen
GERMANY

SMITH, R. Chris
Harvard University
Center for Astrophysics
60 Garden Street
Cambridge, MA 02138
USA

del SORDO, Stefano
IFCAI CNR
via M. Stabile 172
90100 Palermo
ITALY

SPENCER, Steven
University of Sydney
Astrophysics Department
2006 Sydney
AUSTRALIA

STANEV, Todor
Bartol Research Inst.
University of Delaware
Newark, DE 19711
USA

TIMMERMANN, Ralf
MPI Für Kernphysik
Kosmophysik Department
Saupfercheckweg 1
6900 Heidelberg
GERMANY

TRENIKHIM, Alexey
Institute for Nuclear Research
Deep Underwater Neutrino Det.
60th Oct. Anniversary Prospect, 7A
117312 Moscow
USSR

UYANIKER, Bülent
METU
Physics Department
06531 Ankara
TURKEY

VARENDORFF, Martin
Max-Planck Institute
Gamma Astronomie Dept.
Giessenbachstraße
8057 Garching
GERMANY

WANDEL, Amri
Wiezmann Inst. of Science
Nuclear Physics Department
76 100 Rehovot
ISRAEL

WEFEL, John P.
Louisiana State University
Dept. of Physics and Astronomy
Nicholson Hall 202
Baton Rouge, LA 70803-4001
USA

WHITE, R. Stephen
University of California, Riverside
Physics Department
Riverside, CA 92521
USA

WOLFENDALE, Arnold W.
University of Durham
Physics Department
South Road
DH1 3LE Durham
U.K.

AUTHOR INDEX

Abdulwahab, M., 280, 285
Adams, R.A., 25
Adamson, A.J., 68
Agarwal, V.K., 59, 67
Aglietta, M., 255, 268
Ahlen, S.P., 138, 151
Ait-Ouamer, F., 176
Akerlof, C., 257, 261, 263, 267
Akyuz, A., 307, 310, 311
Albernhe, F., 228, 244
Alexandreas, D.E., 267, 268
Alexeenko, V.V., 262, 268
Allamandola, L.J., 67, 68
Allen, L.R., 235
Amari, S., 159, 161
Anders, E., 46, 52, 64, 68, 100, 103, 104, 108, 109, 116, 161
Antonucci, R.R., 241, 243
Anyakoha, M.W., 282, 285
Appleton, P.N., 117
Archarya, B.S., 53
Arcoragi, J.P., 117, 122
Arnett, W.D., 188, 203, 231, 244
Arnould, M., 54, 117
Asakimori, K., 254, 268
Aschenbach, B., 103, 188
Augustyniak, W.M., 85
Averna, D., 81, 84, 85
Axford, 16, 25, 87, 96, 249
Axon, D.J., 117

Baas, F., 67, 68
Badhwar, G.D., 276, 287
Bahcall, J.N., 256, 268
Bahcall, N.A., 256, 268
Baker, R.E., 241, 244, 280, 285
Balasubrahmanyan, V.K., 53, 54, 117
Baltrusaitis, R.M., 256, 268
Bandiera, R., 188, 203
Barashenkov, W.S., 291, 304
Barbier, L.M., 53
Barley, S.K., 255, 268
Bartel, N., 105, 116
Basina, Yu.V., 50, 53

Basini, G., 54
Bassani, L., 282, 285
Bastien, P., 244
Battistoni, G., 254, 268
Beall, J.H., 187, 190, 192, 193, 196, 202, 203, 205
Bednarek, W., 203, 271, 273, 275, 276, 277, 278, 279, 280, 282, 285, 286
Begelman, M.C., 190, 203, 273, 285
Bell, A.R., 87, 96
Bennett, K., 252, 268, 286, 304, 305
Berezhko, E.G., 87, 96
Berezinsky, V.S., 179, 181, 183, 184, 185, 186
Berger, Ch., 254, 268
Berkhuijsen, E.M., 134, 164, 166, 307, 310, 311
Beuerman, K., 117, 134
Bezler, M., 295, 304
Bhat, C.L., 67, 70, 74, 75, 79, 95, 96
Bhat, P.N., 260, 261, 268
Bierman, L., 310, 311
Biermann, P.L., 94, 96, 97, 105, 108, 116, 117, 178, 185
Bignami, G.F., 235, 238, 240, 244, 260, 269, 280, 281, 282, 285, 286, 290, 295, 296, 304, 305
Binns, W.R., 7, 25, 31, 37, 46, 48, 52, 53, 55, 100, 116
Bionta, R.M., 167, 177
Biswas, S., 31, 33, 35, 52
Black, J.H., 68
Blanford, G.E., Jr., 36, 52
Blandford, R.D., 73, 87, 96, 134, 185
Bloemen, J.B.G.M., 68, 69, 75, 76, 77, 79, 123, 134, 238, 244
Bloomer, S.D., 255, 256, 269
Bludman, S.A., 194, 203
Blumenthal, R.G., 273, 285
Boella, G., 285
Bogomolov, E.A., 138, 151
Bohlin, R.C., 158, 161
Boland, W., 82, 85
Boldt, E.A., 306
Bond, I.A., 186, 259, 269
Bonnet-Bidaud, J.M., 254, 255, 270
Bonometti, R.J., 116
Boon, J.J., 67
Boring, J.W., 85
Bowen, T., 25
Boyd, T.J.M., 196, 204
Boynton, P.E., 258, 269

Bradt, H.L., 25, 120, 134
Braun, R., 207, 212
Brazier, K.T.S., 254, 257, 258, 259, 262, 269
Brecher, K., 208
Bregman, J.N., 130, 134
Breitschwerdt, D., 130, 134
Breizman, B., 196, 206
Breneman, H.H., 159, 161
Brewster, N.C., 55
Bridle, A.H., 272, 285
Briggs, R., 67
Broadbent, A., 77, 78, 79
Bronfman, 75, 76
Brouillet, N., 311
Brown, R.L., 204
Brown, W.L., 81, 83, 85
Browne, E., 54
Buccheri, R., 222, 244, 286, 304, 305
Buffington, A., 24, 25, 53
Burbidge, E.M., 25
Burbidge, G.R., 3, 7, 25
Burnett, T.H., 43, 52, 105, 107, 110, 111, 116
Burns, M., 204
Burrows, A., 189, 205, 244
Bussard, R.W., 189, 205, 229, 232, 244
Burchart, I., 68
Butler, R.C., 240, 244, 285
Byrnak, B., 52
Bzowski, M., 72, 79

Calvani, M., 277, 278, 282, 285
Cameron, A.G.W., 18, 64, 67, 68, 99, 100, 103, 116, 233, 244
Candey, R.M., 244
Canfield, E., 273, 285
Canizares, C.R., 203, 205
Caraminana, A.C., 259, 269
Caraveo, P.A., 244, 280, 285, 286, 304, 305
Casse, M., 16, 25, 54, 101, 116, 117, 154, 161, 254, 255, 269, 285
Cassiday, G.L., 254, 255, 269
Caswell, J.L., 164, 166, 167
Catchpole, R.M., 186
Cavallo, G., 74, 79, 297, 304
Cawley, M.F., 254, 256, 260, 263, 269, 280, 285
Cesarsky, C.J., 27, 101, 116, 132, 134, 150, 151, 177, 181, 185, 280, 285
Chadwick, P.M., 254, 256, 260, 269
Chan, K.W., 168, 171, 172, 176, 232, 244
Chevalier, R.A., 189, 190, 205
Chikova, L.O., 53

Chlewicki, G., 67
Christian, E.R., 53
Chudakov, A.E., 250, 269
Chupp, E.L., 23, 25, 246, 280, 285, 286
Ciampa, D., 255, 269
Clark, D.H., 163, 164, 166
Clark, G., 215, 244
Clay, R.W., 270
Clayton, D.D., 62, 79, 231, 232, 233, 244, 245
Cohen, M.H., 272, 285, 297, 304
Cohen, N.L., 116
Colgate, S.A., 232, 244
Connor, S., 67
Cook, B.A., 305
Cook, W.R., 172, 173, 175, 176
Coroniti, F.V., 186
Cowen, V.G., 25
Cowie, L.L., 73
Cowsik, R., 122, 123, 131, 135, 150, 152
Creutz, E., 26
Cropper, M., 189, 204
Crutcher, R.M., 72, 79
Cunningham, G., 315, 323

Dake, S., 52
Danaher, S., 252, 269
Dawson, J., 195, 204
Davies, L., 120, 121, 135
Davis, J., 245
Davis, L., 310, 311
Dean, A.J., 282, 285
De Jong, T., 82, 85
Della Ventura, A., 285
De Loore, C., 117
DeNoyer, L.K., 210, 212
Derdeyn, S.M., 219, 244
Dermer, C.D., 276, 286
Derrickson, J.H., 52
d'Hendecourt, L.B., 67, 68
DiCocco, G., 285
Dickel, J.R., 210, 212
Dickman, R.L., 67
Diehl, R., 247
Dingus, B.L., 257, 267, 269
Dobrzynski, K., 255, 269
Dobson, C.A., 305
Dogiel, V.A., 238, 244
Doom, C., 117
Dotani, D., 167, 176, 189, 205
Dowthwaite, J.C., 252, 256, 260, 261, 269
Draine, B.T., 78, 79

Drissen, L., 239, 244
Drachman, R.J., 229, 244
Drury, L.O'C., 72, 79, 87, 93, 94, 96, 185, 207, 208
Duley, W.W., 68
Dunphy, P.P., 286
Durgaprasad, N., 31, 33, 35, 52
Dutta, A., 52
Dvoryanchikov, Ya.V., 52
Dwarakanath, K.S., 212
Dwek, E., 79
Dwyer, R.D., 32, 33, 52

Eardley, D.M., 205
Ebihara, M., 46, 52, 64, 68, 100, 116
Efimov, N.N., 315, 323
Eichler, D.S., 16, 25, 87, 95, 96, 136, 185
Eijkel, G.B., 67
Eilek, J.A., 279, 286, 297, 304
Ellison, D.C., 95, 96, 157, 161, 205
Elvis, M., 241, 244, 296, 305
Engelmann, J.J., 32, 33, 52, 54, 100, 104, 116, 136
Epstein, R.I., 214, 234, 235, 244
Esposito, J.A., 53

Fateeva, I.M., 53
Fazio, G.G., 263, 269
Fedorov, A.N., 53
Fegan, D.J., 252, 257, 263, 264, 266, 267, 268, 269, 285
Feigelson, E.D., 202, 204, 315
Felten, J.E., 192, 204
Ferrando, P., 31, 32, 33, 35, 53, 54, 123, 132, 135, 136
Ferris, J.P., 59, 67
Fichtel, C.E., 215, 244, 245, 246, 307, 308, 309, 310, 311
Fickle, R.K., 55
Fisher, A.J., 54
Fishman, G.J., 189, 205, 232, 244, 286
Fisk, L.A., 87, 96
Fitzpatrick, E.L., 68
Fleischer, R.L., 6, 25, 26, 27
Forrest, D.J., 228, 244, 286
Foti, G., 85
Fountain, W.F., 52
Fowler, P.H., 46, 53
Fowler, W.A., 25
Frank, J., 272, 286
Fransson, C., 204
Freedman, I., 130, 135

Freidlander, M.W., 52
Freier, P.S., 25, 55
Frerking, M.A., 65, 68
Freund, H.P., 194, 195, 204
Frisch, P.C., 72, 79
Fryxell, B., 188, 203
Fuki, M., 52
Fuller, G.M., 108, 117
Furst, E., 165, 167, 208, 212

Gagarin, Yu.F., 31, 35, 36, 53
Gaisser, T.K., 150, 152, 181, 186, 190, 205, 259, 269
Garcia-Munoz, M., 31, 33, 35, 38, 49, 53, 54, 116, 120, 123, 127, 128, 135, 136, 147, 148, 152
Garmire, G., 215, 244
Garrard, T.L., 44, 45, 48, 49, 52, 53, 55, 116
Gay, A.M., 53
Geballs, T.R., 68
Gehrels, N., 168, 170, 171, 174, 176, 231, 233, 244
Geldzahler, B.J., 190, 202, 252, 256, 269, 304
Gerhardy, P.R., 270
Giacconi, R., 252, 256, 269
Gibbs, K., 285
Gibner, P.S., 52
Gibson, A.J., 260, 269
Gillanders, G.H., 254, 269
Giler, M., 79, 115, 116, 132, 133, 134, 135, 322, 323
Gilmozzi, R., 190, 203, 205
Ginzburg, V.L., 3, 11, 15, 26, 119, 120, 122, 125, 127, 131, 132, 135, 178,185, 186, 310, 311
Giovannelli, F., 204, 271, 272, 282, 285, 286, 289, 290, 291, 294,297, 298, 299, 300, 301, 302, 305, 306
Godfrey, B.B., 194, 195, 199, 205
Golden, R.L., 25, 29, 55, 138, 150, 152
Goldreich, P., 190, 205
Goldstein, M.V., 116, 196, 206
Golinskaya, R., 53
Gordeev, Yu.P., 53
Gorecki, A., 292, 305
Gorenstein, M.V., 116
Goret, P., 52, 101, 116, 154, 161
Gorham, P.W., 257, 285
Goswami, J.N., 52
Gould, R.J., 273, 285, 292, 305
Graham, D.A., 212
Graser, U., 222, 223, 227, 244, 262, 269, 280,

296
Grebenev, S.A., 188, 204
Green, D.A., 72, 75, 79, 162, 165, 166, 207, 208, 218
Greenberg, J.M., 57, 67, 68, 81, 82, 83, 84, 85
Gregory, J.C., 52
Gregory, P.C., 252, 269, 288
Greiner, D.E., 227, 228, 236
Grevesse, N., 64, 68, 100, 103, 104, 108, 109, 116
Griffiths, R.E., 305
Grigorieva, L.B., 53
Grigorov, N.L., 40, 53
Grindlay, J.E., 241, 245, 261, 263, 269
Grove, J.E., 45, 50, 53
Grunsfeld, J.M., 39, 41, 53, 55, 105, 110, 111, 112
Gruber, D.E., 256, 269, 286
Guillory, J., 205
Gunn, G.E., 186
Gupta, M., 43, 53, 100, 104, 116
Gupta, S.K., 261, 269
Guzik, T.G., 33, 51, 53, 115, 116, 135

Habe, A., 130, 135
Haber, I., 204
Hagen, F.A., 54
Hagen, W., 67
Haines, T.J. 254, 269
Halpern, J.H., 235, 241, 242, 245, 246, 280, 281, 286
Halzen, F., 317, 323
Hanbury-Brown, R., 245
Harding, A.K., 186, 189, 204
Harnden, F.R., 226, 227, 245
Harris, D.E., 282, 283, 286
Harris, M.J., 233, 245
Hartman, R.C., 215, 245, 246
Hasinger, G., 304
Haslam, C.G.T., 208, 210, 212, 311
Hauser, M.G., 76, 77, 79
Havnes, O., 101, 116
Hawkins, I., 159, 161
Hayakawa, S., 3, 20, 25, 26, 110, 131, 135
Hayashi, T., 52
Hayes, B.T., 53
Hayles, R.I., 285
Haymes, R.C., 216, 217, 227, 228, 245, 280, 286
Hein, L.A., 53
Heinbach, U., 53, 132, 134, 135, 147, 148, 149, 152

Heinrich, W., 53, 79, 136
Helmken, H.F., 245, 280, 286
Henkel, M., 31, 32, 35, 53
Henry, J.P., 305
Herbst, W., 68
Hermsen, W., 215, 226, 235, 238, 244, 245, 252, 260, 279, 286, 290, 304, 305
Hesse, A., 53
Higdon, J.C., 239, 245
Higgs, L.A., 287
Hill, J.L., 161
Hillas, A.M., 24, 25, 256, 269
Hirata, K., 167, 176
Holman, G.D., 205
Holynski, R., 52
Holt, S.S., 306
Honda, M., 185, 186
Hong, S.S., 67
Hough, D.H., 287
Howard, W.M., 285
Howe, S.K., 305
Hoyle, F., 25, 87, 96
Hubbard, E.L., 25
Hudson, P.D., 87, 96
Humphreys, R.M., 108, 116
Hurley, K., 214, 234, 235, 245

Ichimura, M., 53
Ikeuchi, S., 130, 135
Ionson, J.A., 205
Ipavich, F.M., 130, 135
Israel, M.H., 52, 53, 55, 116, 153, 154, 161
Issa, 76, 79, 96
Ito, K., 25, 135
Itoh, M., 188, 204
Ivanenko, I.P., 30, 34, 53
Iwai, J., 52

Jackson, J.D., 190, 196, 204
Jenkins, E.B., 161
Jesse, W.P., 3, 25
Johnson, R.E., 85
Johnson, W.N., 216, 217, 227, 245, 246
Johnston, K., 204, 252, 269
Jokipii, J.R., 87, 96, 130, 135
Jones, F., 130, 135, 139
Jones, M.D., 52, 105, 116
Jones, W.V., 52
Julian, W.H., 189, 204
Juliusson, E., 52
Jurak, A., 52
Kafatos, M., 279, 286

Kahn, S.M., 212
Kainer, S., 205
Kamioka, E., 53
Kakimoto, F., 259, 269
Kamionkowski, M.P., 52
Kanbach, G., 127, 134, 135, 224, 235, 261, 269, 286, 304, 305
Karakula, S., 203, 271, 280, 285, 286, 289, 296, 305, 306
Karovska, M., 189, 204
Kato, T., 204
Kawamura, T., 40, 42, 53
Kazakova, A.E., 53
Kazanas, D., 204, 295, 305
Kearsey, S., 135
Keen, N.J., 209, 212
Kelley, R.L., 259, 269
Kellerman, K.I., 304
Kendziorra, E., 287, 304, 305
Kennel, C.F., 216
Kerr, F.J., 79
Kertzman, M.P., 52
Khazan, Ya.M., 135
Khilyuta, I.G., 52
Kidd, J.M., 25
King, A.R., 286
Kirii, K., 53
Kirov, I.N., 260, 269
Kirshner, R.P., 167, 176
Kish, J.C., 39, 57, 115, 127, 128, 136
Klarmann, J., 52, 53, 55, 116
Klebesadel, R.W., 234, 245
Klein, R.I., 188, 204
Kluzniak, W., 292, 305
Kniffen, D.A., 215, 237, 245, 246
Knight, F.K., 222, 223, 224, 226, 245, 261, 270, 286
Ko, S., 255, 269
Kobayashi, T., 53
Koch, Ch., 53, 152
Koch, H.W., 282, 286
Koch-Miramond, L., 52, 54, 136
Kocharov, G.E., 22, 74, 79
Kolykhalov, P.I., 290, 291, 301, 305
Konstantinov, A.N., 79
Kozlov, V.D., 53
Kozlovsky, B., 246
Krauschaar, W., 215, 244
Kriss, G.A., 202, 204
Kristian, J., 175, 176, 204
Krombel, K.E., 43, 53, 100, 104, 116
Kronberg, P.P., 105, 116

Krotschenk, E., 223, 235
Krymsky, G.F., 87, 96
Krzeminski, W., 259, 270
Ku, W.H.-M., 207, 212
Kuhr, M., 286, 305
Kumpan, I.P., 53
Kundt, W., 223, 245
Kurfess, J.D., 246

Lagage, P.O., 177, 181, 185
Lal, N., 53, 135
Lamb, R.C., 244, 246, 252, 261, 270, 285
Lang, M.J., 263, 270
Langer, N., 108, 116
Langer, W.D., 68
Lanzerotti, L.J., 81, 83, 85
Large, M.I., 224, 245, 261, 270
Larimer, R.M., 54
Lawrence, A., 241, 244
Lawrence, M.A., 255, 270
Leahy, D.A., 165, 166
Lebrun, F., 70, 95, 96
Lederer, C.M., 169, 176
Lee, H.M., 78, 79
Lee, M.A., 82, 85
Lee, Y.C., 194, 205
Leer, E., 87, 96
Leising, M.D., 172, 176, 188, 204, 232, 233, 238, 245, 246
Lemontagne, R., 245
Lerche, I., 131, 135
Leske, R.A., 32, 33, 35, 54
Lesko, K.T., 54
Letaw, J.R., 26, 117, 136
Levchenko, V.A., 79
Leventhal, M., 217, 227, 228, 229, 230, 244, 245
Levine, A.M., 286
Lewin, W.H.G., 305
Lezniak, J.A., 35, 54, 120, 135
L'Heureux, J., 53, 55
Li Ti Pei, 238, 245
Liang, E.P., 214, 235, 236, 245, 278, 285, 286
Lichti, G.G., 223, 226, 245, 304, 305
Liebling, D.F., 285
Lightman, R.P., 205
Liller, W., 256, 270
Linfield, R.P., 304
Lingenfelter, R.E., 168, 171, 172, 176, 232, 238, 244, 245, 246, 297, 305
Linsley, J., 107, 116
Litvinova, I.Yu, 171, 176

Lloyd-Evans, J., 25, 254, 270
Lo, K.Y., 204
Lofgren, E.J., 25
Long, K.S., 212
Longair, M.S., 26
Lord, J.J., 52
Lovelace, R.V.E., 204
Lund, N., 15, 25, 31, 44, 45, 52, 54, 100, 110, 111, 116
Luzietti, B., 53
Lyaguchin, V.I., 53

Macaccaro, T., 285
MacAuslan, J., 204
MacCallum, C.J., 217, 227, 244, 245
MacKeown, P.K., 285
MacLaren, I., 67, 75, 77, 78, 79
Maeder, A., 103, 108, 109, 116, 117
Maehl, R.C., 35, 54
Mahoney, W.A., 175, 176, 229, 230, 245
Makino, F., 188, 202, 204
Maloney, P., 68
Manchester, R.N., 223, 244
Mandritskaya, K.V., 55
Marcaide, J.M., 116
Marcantonio, K.K., 85
Margolis, S.H., 53, 120, 135
Markiewicz, W.J., 96
Marscher, A.P., 297, 305
Marshak, M.L., 254, 270
Marshall, F.E., 286
Masheder, M.R.W., 53
Mason, G.M., 135
Masnou, J.L., 235, 246, 280, 281, 286, 304, 305
Massa, D., 68
Masse, P., 52, 54, 136
Matano, T., 259, 270
Mathis, K.D., 79, 136, 152
Mathis, J.S., 81, 85
Matsubara, Y., 314, 315, 323
Matsutani, H., 53
Matteson, J.L., 244, 286
Matz, S.M., 171, 176, 188, 204, 231, 246
Mayer, C.J., 67, 79, 96
Mayer-Hasselwander, H., 224, 246, 286, 304, 306
McConnell, M.L., 279, 286
McDonald, F.B., 53, 135
McElroy, B., 108, 116
McFadzean, A.D., 68
McKee, C.F., 130, 135

McKenzie, J.F., 134
McLafferty, F.W., 67
Meegan, C.A., 286
Meisenheimer, K., 282, 286
Mendoza-Gomez, C.X., 67
Meszaros, P., 279, 286
Metzger, M., 55
Mewaldt, R.A., 31, 37, 38, 39, 43, 49, 53, 54, 116, 158, 159, 161
Meyer, J.P., 16, 25, 44, 45, 54, 100, 101, 102, 103, 116, 134, 135
Meyer, P., 27, 32, 33, 52, 53, 55, 239, 246
Meynet, G., 103, 108, 116
Michel, F.C., 290, 293, 300, 305
Middleditch, J., 190, 204
Mikhailov, A.A., 323
Miller, J.S., 241, 243
Mills, B.Y., 245, 270
Milne, D.K., 164, 166
Mischenko, L.G., 53
Mitra, B., 52
Miyamura, O., 52
Moats, A., 24, 25
Mobius, E., 95, 96
Moffat, A.F.J., 244, 280, 281, 286, 293, 305
Moffat, P.H., 210, 212
Moffet, A.T., 304
Monier, R., 241, 242, 246
Morales, G.J., 194, 205
Montmerle, T., 150, 151
Morfill, G.E., 82, 85, 239, 246
Morrison, P., 25, 192, 204, 280, 282, 285, 286
Moses, R.T., 53
Motz, J.W., 282, 286
Mukanov, J.B., 263, 270, 280, 287
Muller, D., 53, 55, 105, 111, 115
Muller, E., 188, 203
Murakami, K., 314, 323
Muraki, Y., 255, 270
Murphy, R.J., 233, 238, 239, 246
Mushotzky, R.F., 306
Nadyozhin, D.K., 171, 176
Nakamura, T., 186
Nakazawa, K., 53
Nanjyo, H., 53
Newport, B.J., 52
Ney, E.P., 25
Ng, L.R., 140, 141, 142, 144, 145, 150, 152
Nikanorov, V.M., 53
Nikolsky, S.I., 280, 286
Ninkov, Z., 279, 286
Nishimura, J., 153, 162

Nolan, P.L., 278, 286
Noll, A., 53
Nordsiek, K.H., 81, 85
Norman, C.A., 67
Norman, E.B., 45, 54
North, A.R., 258, 259, 270
Northcliffe, L.C., 102, 117

Oberman, C., 195, 204
Oda, H., 52
Oda, M., 153, 161, 186
O'Dell, F., 6, 11, 25
Ogata, T., 52
Ogelman, H., 215
Okeke, P.N., 285
Okoye, S.E., 285
Olson, R.A., 245
O'Flaherty, K., 254
O'Neill, T.J., 241, 246
Oppenheimer, F., 25
Ormes, J.F., 25, 53, 54, 117
Osborne, D.L., 116
Osborne, J.L., 33, 54, 123, 132, 133, 135
Ostriker, J.P., 87, 96, 130, 134, 135, 204
Ovchinnikova, A.Yu., 53
Owens, A.J., 130, 135, 286
Oyama, Y., 254, 270
Ozel, M.E., 215, 224, 246, 307, 308, 309, 310, 311

Paciesas, W.S., 228, 246
Pacini, F., 186, 188, 203, 235, 246
Paizis, T., 285
Palmadesso, P., 204
Pal, Y., 135
Palumbo, G.G.C., 79
Panagia, N., 117, 205
Papadopoulos, K., 194, 195, 204, 205
Papina, L.P., 53
Parker, E.N., 87, 96, 310, 311
Parnell, T.A., 52
Parsignault, D., 252, 270
Paschmann, G., 96
Paul, J.A., 95, 96, 244, 285, 286, 304, 306
Paulini-Toth, I.I.K., 304
Pedlar, A., 117
Pennypacker, C.R., 25
Penzias, A.A., 67
Perkins, D.H., 26
Perley, R.A., 272, 285
Perotti, F., 240, 246, 285
Peters, B., 20, 25, 52, 120, 134

Phillips, M.M., 189, 205
Phillips, S., 127, 135
Pietsch, W., 287, 295, 304, 305
Pinto, P.A., 168, 173, 174, 175, 176, 186, 188, 205
Pirronello, V., 81, 84, 85
Pisarski, 212
Platonov, V.V., 53
Pollock, A.M.T., 295, 305
Pomeroy, S.S., 52
Porcas, R.W., 272, 286, 287
Porter, N.A., 260, 270, 285
Powell, C.F., 26
Pozdnyakov, L.A., 279, 286
Prantzos, N., 50, 54, 103, 104, 108, 112, 117
Pravdin, M.I., 323
Pravdo, S.H., 223, 226, 246
Preston, P.A., 116
Preus, E., 304
Price, P.B., 25, 26, 27
Prilutski, O.F., 186
Primini, F.A., 286, 295, 305
Prishchep, V.L., 125, 130, 135, 136
Prosser, D.C., 255, 270
Protheroe, R.J., 52, 258, 270, 285, 305, 323
Ptuskin, V.S., 33, 49, 54, 119, 120, 121, 123, 124, 125, 127, 128, 129, 130, 132, 133, 135, 136, 179, 181, 185

Quest, K., 88, 96

Raine, D.J., 286
Raisbeck, G.M., 72, 79, 124, 136
Raizer, Yu.P., 87, 96
Ramadurai, S., 52
Ramana Murthy, P.V., 23, 25, 52, 69, 260, 266, 314, 323
Ramaty, R., 229, 238, 239, 244, 245, 246, 279, 286, 297, 305
Ramsden, D., 285
Rao, M.V.S., 52
Rapoport, I.D., 53
Rasmussen, I.L., 52, 53
Ratner, M.I., 116
Raubenheimer, B.C., 258, 270
Rawat, H.S., 257, 270
Rees, M.J., 186, 272, 286, 297, 304
Reich, P., 106
Reich, W., 164, 166, 208, 212
Reif, K., 166
Reimann, C.T., 85
Reppin, C., 176, 287, 204, 205

Rester, C., 175, 176
Resvanis, L., 257, 270
Reynolds, P.T., 257, 270
Reynolds, R.J., 123, 136
Reynolds, S.P., 205, 273, 286
Richardson, K.M., 67, 79
Ricketts, M.J., 296, 297, 304, 306
Riegler, G.R., 228, 246
Roberts, D., 286
Roberts, F.E., 52
Rogers, A.E.E., 116
Romney, J.D., 304
Rosenbluth, M.N., 194, 203
Rose, W.K., 190, 192, 193, 196, 201, 202, 205
Roser, H.-J., 282, 286
Rotenberg, M., 52
Rothschild, R.E., 286
Rowland, H.L., 204
Rudaz, S., 151, 152
Ruderman, M., 235, 246
Rukhadze, A.A., 192, 205
Rukhlin, V.G., 192, 205
Rumpl, W., 81, 85
Ryabova, N.G., 51
Ryan, M.J., 40, 41, 54, 110, 111, 116
Ryutov, D., 194, 204

Sabau Graziatti, L., 271, 286, 289
Sacco, B., 226, 246, 304, 306
Sadun, A., 286
Sagdeev, R.Z. 176
Saito, M., 53
Sakurai, K., 46, 153, 154, 155, 156, 157, 158, 160, 161
Salamon, M.H., 24, 25
Salter, C.J., 212
Salvati, M., 117, 186, 188, 203
Samonov, G.A., 53
Samorski, M., 24, 25, 252, 267, 270
Sanders, D.B., 76, 123, 136
Sanderson, J.J., 196, 204
Sandie, W.G., 173, 175, 176
Sastry, Ch.V., 208, 212
Sato, H., 182, 186
Savage, B.D., 161
Sazhina, G.P., 55
Scarsi, L., 238, 246, 304, 306
Schamel, H., 194, 205
Schatzman, E., 87, 96
Scheepmaker, A., 305
Schein, M., 3, 25

Scheuer, P.A.G., 207, 212
Schilizzi, R.T., 304
Schilling, R.F., 102, 117
Schindler, S.M., 25, 53
Schlickeiser, R., 131, 135, 286, 305
Schonfelder, V., 222, 223, 237, 244, 247, 262, 269, 280, 286
Schott, G.A., 191, 205
Schramm, D.N., 108, 117
Schreier, E., 259, 270
Schrier, D.A., 39, 55, 117
Schutte, W., 59, 67
Schwab, F.R., 116
Scott, J.S., 195, 196, 205, 297, 305
Scoville, N.Z., 77, 123, 136
Seielstad, G.A., 304
Sequin, M., 244
Serlemitsos, D.J., 223, 246, 306
Shaffer, D.B., 189, 201, 204, 304
Shanahan, W.R., 193, 194, 204
Shapiro, I.I., 116
Shapiro, M.M., 1, 10, 11, 12, 16, 20, 25, 26, 27, 31, 33, 44, 54, 101, 117, 119, 120, 122, 123, 136, 153, 242, 246
Shapiro, S.L., 205
Shara, M.M., 286, 305
Share, G.H., 172, 175, 176, 188, 204, 229, 230, 232, 245, 246
Shes-toperov, V.Ya., 53
Shevgaonkar, R.K., 212
Shibata, T., 52, 53
Shibuta, K., 53
Shiryaeva, V.Ya., 53
Sieber, W., 286, 305
Sikora, M., 273, 285
Silberberg, R., 11, 15, 20, 25, 26, 27, 30, 31, 33, 44, 45, 50, 54, 97, 98, 99, 102, 104, 116, 120, 122, 123, 134, 136, 214, 233, 238, 239, 242, 246
Simmons, E., 85
Simon, M., 53, 72, 79, 117, 131, 132, 134, 135, 136, 137, 147, 148, 149, 152
Simpson, J.A., 10, 21, 26, 27, 31, 32, 33, 35, 44, 49, 53, 54, 116, 127, 135, 136, 153, 158, 161
Singh, R.K., 52
Sinha, S., 255, 263, 270
Sitte, K., 27
Sivaprasad, K., 52
Skadron, G., 87, 97
Skilling, J., 127, 132, 136
Smith, B., 205, 215

Smith, L.F., 108, 115
Smith, M.D., 210, 212
Smolensky, L.G., 53
Snow, T.P., 161
Sobinyakov, V.A., 53
Sobol, I.M., 286
Sodroski, T.J., 76, 79
Soker, N., 189, 204
Sokolskaya, N.V., 55
Solovyev, A.V., 53
Sood, R.K., 188, 205
Soutoul, A., 33, 35, 52, 54, 120, 121, 122, 123, 124, 127, 128, 129, 132, 135, 136
Spillantini, P., 50, 54
Spitzer, L., 62, 67, 130, 136, 161, 205
Spoelstra, T.A., 235, 245
Sramek, R.A., 105, 116, 117, 205
Sreekumar, P., 311
Stamenov, J.N., 286
Stamm, W., 24, 25, 252, 267, 270
Stanev, T., 177, 183, 184, 186, 189, 204, 323
Stang, P.D., 227, 245
Staubert, R., 188, 287, 304, 305
Stecker, F.W., 27, 151, 152, 280, 286, 292, 305
Steinle, H., 278, 287
Stenger, W.J., 285
Stepanian, A.A., 252, 270
Stephens, S.A., 29, 55, 150, 152, 276, 287
Stern, C.P., 282, 283, 286
Stiller, B., 25
Stochaj, S., 25
Stocke, J.T., 205
Stoffel, H., 212
Stone, E.C., 52, 53, 116, 159, 161
Stone, R., 311
Strausz, S., 52
Streitmatter, R.E., 25, 53, 138, 152
Strickman, M.S., 223, 246
Strom, R.G., 207, 212
Strong, A.W., 75, 76, 79, 295, 305
Strong, I.B., 245
Sudan, R.N., 194, 205
Sugimoto, H., 53
Sunyaev, R.A., 157, 176, 188, 204, 205, 273, 278, 279, 286, 287, 290, 291, 301, 305
Sur, B., 54
Sutherland, P., 188, 205
Swanenburg, B.N., 282, 287, 290, 304, 305
Sweeney, W.E., 222, 246

Swordy, S.P., 38, 39, 53, 55, 105, 111, 117
Syrovatskii, S.I., 11, 25, 26, 119, 120, 122, 135, 178, 185, 310, 311
Szabelska, B., 72, 79, 116, 134, 135
Szabelski, J., 314, 323

Taam, R., 235, 247
Tabuki, T., 52
Takahashi, Y., 52
Tambovtsev, G.E., 53
Tananbaum, H., 305
Tan, L.C., 140, 141, 142, 144, 145, 150, 152
Tandon, S.N., 135
Taylor, J.H., 223, 245
Teegarden, B.J., 188, 205
Teraoka, K., 53
Terasawa, T., 186
Terashima, Y., 25, 135
Teshima, M., 255, 270
The, L.S., 188, 204, 247
Thode, L.E., 193, 194, 204, 205
Thomasson, P., 212
Thompson, D.J., 215, 222, 224, 235, 246, 261, 270
Titarchuk, L.G., 273, 278, 279, 287
Tittle, H.O., 53
Tkaczyk, W., 203, 271, 285, 286, 289, 292, 296, 305, 306
Toda, K., 53
Tominaga, T., 52
Tonev, W.D., 291, 304
Trigubov, Yu.V., 53
Trombka, I., 307, 311
Trumper, J., 256, 270, 286, 287, 304, 305
Tsao, C.H., 11, 17, 26, 31, 44, 54, 97, 98, 104, 106, 117, 136
Tucker, W.H., 205
Tueller, J., 173, 174, 176, 188, 189, 205, 246, 256, 258, 270
Tuffs, R., 286, 305
Tumer, O.T., 215, 218, 224, 226, 246, 247, 260, 261, 263, 270
Turtle, A.J., 202, 205
Tytler, D., 235, 245, 280, 281, 286

Ubertini, P., 176, 188, 205
Ulrich, M.H., 281, 287, 293, 295, 306
Ulvestad, J.S., 206
Unger, S.W., 105, 117
Urwin, S.C., 272, 285
Ushev, S.Z., 286

Vahia, M.N., 52
Vakulov, P.V., 53
Vanbeveren, D., 108, 117
Van den Bergh, S., 165, 166
Van der Bult, C.P.E.M., 67
Van der Hulst, J.M., 117
Van der Klis, M., 254, 255, 270
Van der Laan, H., 208, 211, 212
Van der Walt, D.J., 73
Van Dishoeck, E.F., 68
Vankov, H.P., 323
Varkovitskaya, A.Ya., 55
Vasiliev, Yu.Ya., 53
Vaughan, A.E., 270, 245
Verma, R.P., 135
Vestrand, J.S., 206, 305
Vestrand, T.W., 205, 286
Vettolani, G., 79
Vigroux, L., 285
Villa, G., 285
Virag, A., 161
Vogel, J.C., 72, 79
Vogel, K.R., 54
Voges, W., 256, 270, 287, 304, 305
Volk, H.J., 82, 85, 94, 96, 105, 108, 117, 134,
        178, 185
Von Ballmoos, P., 230, 241, 247
Vylet, V., 37, 55

Waddington, C.J., 31, 52, 53, 55, 116
Walker, G.a.H., 286
Walker, R.C., 205
Walker, R.M., 25, 26, 27, 52
Walker, R.N.F., 53
Wallace, P.T., 224, 226, 247, 261, 270
Wandel, A., 132, 136
Wasson, J.L., 157, 162
Watanabe, Z., 53
Watson, A.A., 42, 51, 255, 270
Watson, K.M., 194, 203
Watts, J.W., 52
Wdowczyk, J., 24, 26, 79, 116, 135, 313, 314,
        315, 317, 320, 323
Weaver, T.A., 50, 55, 108, 117, 168, 171,
        172, 176
Webber, W.R., 33, 35, 37, 38, 39, 43, 52, 53,
        54, 55, 99, 100, 101, 104, 113, 115,
        116, 117, 120, 127, 128, 135, 136
Webster, A.S., 208, 212
Weekes, T.C., 249, 252, 260, 261, 263, 264,
        265, 266, 268, 270, 280, 285, 286
Wefel, J.P., 26, 27, 29, 33, 49, 52, 53, 54, 55,

        116, 117, 135
Weiler, K.W., 105, 117, 205
Westergaard, N.J., 52
Wheaton, W.A., 305
White, G.L., 296, 297, 304, 306
White, R.S., 30, 167, 213, 218, 223, 224, 240,
        246, 247, 249, 268
Whitelock, P.A., 186
Whittet, D.C.B., 68
Wiedenbeck, M.E., 21, 26, 31, 32, 35, 43, 53,
        54, 100, 104, 116, 127, 128, 136
Wilczynska, B., 52
Wilczynski, H., 52
Wilkes, R.J., 52
Wilkinson, P.N., 117
Willingale, R., 282, 283, 287
Willis, A.G., 205, 210, 212
Wills, R.D., 224, 247, 286, 304, 305
Wilson, A.S., 205
Wilson, J.D., 27
Wilson, L.W., 123, 135
Wilson, R.B., 176
Wilson, R.W., 68
Wilson, W.E., 212
Winn, M.M., 315, 323
Witzel, A., 304
Wolfendale, A.W., 23, 24, 25, 26, 27, 65, 67,
        69, 70, 71, 73, 75, 78, 79, 96, 116,
        135, 157, 162, 238, 245, 305, 313,
        314, 315, 317, 320, 323
Wollan, E.O., 3, 25
Wolter, W., 52
Woodsworth, A.W., 279, 287
Woosley, S.E., 50, 55, 108, 117, 168, 171,
        172, 173, 174, 175, 176, 181, 186,
        188, 189, 205, 235, 247
Worley, A., 53
Worral, D.M., 295, 305, 306
Wosiek, B., 52
Wouthuysen, S.A., 27
Wu, X., 165, 166

Yakovlev, B.M., 53
Yamada, Y., 186
Yang, S., 286
Yashin, I.V., 53
Yiou, F., 79, 124, 136
Yodh, G.B., 251, 270
Yoshizumi, Y., 53
Young, E.C.M., 69, 79
Young, J.S., 35, 55
York, D.G., 72, 79, 161

343

Zakharov, V.E., 194, 205
Zamchalova, E.A., 54
Zatsepin, V.I., 40, 42, 55
Zdziarski, A.A., 279, 287
Zeldovich, Ya.B., 87, 96
Zensus, J.A., 272, 287
Zinner, E., 161
Zych, A.D., 246
Zyskin, Yu.L., 280, 287

SUBJECT INDEX

Abundances
    coronal, 101, 153, 157, 238
    cosmic ray $(Z \leq 30)$, 5, 29, 31, 119, 134, 153
    cosmic ray $(Z > 30)$ 6, 29, 36, 46, 47, 48
    cosmic ray source, 10, 17, 37, 39, 43, 44, 45, 46, 49, 51, 97, 99, 104, 105, 153, 154, 157
    isotopic, 17, 21, 29, 49, 50, 97, 113, 158, 160
    local galactic, 45, 46, 47, 49, 51, 57, 64, 97, 104, 108
    meteorites, 60, 100, 153, 157
    photospheric, 101, 238
    solar energetic particle, 101
    solar system, 6, 18, 46, 48, 50, 57, 64, 99
    solar wind, 101
    sun, 156, 238
Acceleration, 1, 10, 29, 46, 69, 87, 97, 101, 105, 134, 153, 160, 177, 185, 187, 213
    black holes, 213
    continuous, 131
    distributed, 119
    electron capture species, 19, 113, 114
    Fermi processes, 3, 13, 87, 89, 92, 155, 177, 187, 207, 208
    magnetohydrodynamic, 90, 180
    maximum energy, 94, 177, 178, 179, 180, 181
    neutron stars, 112, 213
    pulsars, 112, 213
    reacceleration, 94, 98, 112, 113, 114, 115, 131, 133, 134, 137, 148
    rigidity effects, 102
    shock waves, 16, 87, 90, 98, 105, 112, 134, 179, 212
    stochastic, 13, 133
    supernova remnants, 69, 74, 78, 87, 105, 110, 111, 112, 134, 177, 185, 187, 189, 213
Accretion, 63, 189, 190, 201, 215, 236, 256, 272, 289, 290, 291, 294, 296, 298, 300, 301, 302, 304
Actinides
    (see Abundances)
Active Galactic Nuclei (AGN), 22, 193, 196, 198, 214, 240, 252, 272, 297
    BL Lac, 239
    jets, 272, 285
    M87, 272
    neutrino emission, 297, 300, 302
    relativistic flows, 190
    (see also acceleration)
Age of Cosmic Rays, 119, 120
Air Shower arrays, 251, 268
Air Showers, extensive (EAS), 3, 24, 30, 42, 249, 250, 251, 262, 314, 319
Albedo, 36
Alfven waves, 88, 131, 138
Anisotropy, 92, 119, 314, 315, 322
ALICE experiment, 31, 49
Anomalous component, 36, 24
Anti-matter, 1
Anti-protons, 1, 24, 29, 137, 138, 151
Anuradha experiment, 31
Ariel-V, 297
Ariel-VI, 46, 47, 48
Atmospheric Cherenkov, 182, 183, 249, 250
    technique, 24
    imaging, 264

Binary systems, 112, 215, 239, 249, 256, 259, 272
    (see also Acceleration)
Black holes, 168, 187, 215, 229, 235, 236, 239, 240, 272, 282, 289, 290, 293, 294, 295, 300, 302, 303, 304
Blackbody radiation, 313, 316, 317, 321
Bremsstrahlung, 187, 189, 191, 200, 201, 236, 237, 271, 274, 279, 282, 284, 291, 292, 293, 294, 296, 307

Cen-A, 240, 272
Cen X-3, 249, 259, 266
Chemical selection
    (see First ionization potential)
Clouds, 77
    cosmic ray interactions, 36, 123
    giant molecular, 58, 63, 65, 66, 75, 78, 81, 123, 124, 157, 238
Color excess, 63
Coma cluster, 320
Composition of cosmic rays

arriving, 1, 5, 13, 30
  interplanetary, 30
  local interstellar, 30
  measured, 30
  source, 13, 30, 53
  (see also Abundances)
Confinement of cosmic rays, 49, 124
COS-B mission, 23, 71, 215, 216, 221, 222, 224, 226, 230, 235, 238, 280, 281, 282, 283, 284, 289, 290, 295, 296, 303, 307, 309
Cosmic rays, 1, 314
  anisotropy, 10, 133
  chronology, 19
  cosmogenic, 72, 74
  density in confinement region, 178, 307, 308, 315
  distribution in galaxy, 120, 238, 307, 310, 311
  energy spectrum, 1, 39, 40, 41, 73, 74, 75, 107, 119, 293, 315
  extragalactic, 24, 119, 313, 316, 317, 318
  gradients, 69, 71, 238
  history, 2
  halo, 124, 125, 127
  latitude effect, 3
  lifetime, 1, 20, 21, 49, 122, 124, 125, 126
  origin, 22, 23, 51, 97, 154, 249, 314
  point sources of, 24, 95
  radioisotopes, 119
Cosmology, 313, 317
COSMOS satellites, 40
Crab Nebula, 16, 24, 175, 180, 213, 215, 223, 227, 238, 252, 262, 263, 264, 266, 268
Crab pulsar, 175, 180, 213, 215, 216, 221, 222, 223, 249, 259, 260, 266
  light curves, 224, 225
  luminosity, 224
Cross Sections, 112
  anti-proton, 140
  calculations and cosmic-ray propagation, 10, 12, 30, 43
  fragmentation, 17, 39
  partial, 51
  semiempirical, 11, 98
  spallation, 98
Cygnus Loop, 72, 207
  break-out of shock, 208
  compression mechanism, 210

  filaments, 210
  magnetic field, 208, 210
  radio emission, 208
  spectrum, 209, 211
Cygnus X-1, 215, 233, 240
  gamma rays, 271
  x-rays, 236
Cygnus X-3, 215, 272
  gamma ray source, 24, 249, 252, 254, 266
  period, 252, 254, 255, 267
  pulsar, 254
  radio, emission, 255
  x-ray emission, 252

Diffusion, 10, 11, 89, 119, 123, 125, 126, 128
  coefficient, 70, 119, 120, 127, 177
  model, 119
Distributed acceleration
  (see Acceleration)

Electrons and positrons, 2, 22, 29, 70, 74, 95, 190, 192, 197, 207, 208, 211, 250
Electromagnetic showers, 3
Emulsion, 39
Energy spectra, 7, 92
Escape length, 120, 124, 147
Extensive air showers (EAS)
  (see Air Showers)
Extinction, 61, 62, 63, 66, 81

Ferm acceleration
  (see Acceleration)
First ionization potential (FIP), 45, 48, 100, 108, 154
  chemical selection by, 15, 46, 49, 101, 153, 238
  galactic cosmic rays, 45, 153
Flares
  (see Stellar)
Fragmentation, 10, 92, 119, 120
  (see also Cross Sections)
Fusion, 168

Galactic
  center, 57, 66, 213, 215, 216, 227, 229, 230, 240, 289, 290, 303, 317
  halo, 119, 121, 127, 238
  magnetic field, 7, 119, 310
  plane/disk, 119, 121, 123, 213, 229, 309
  radio emission, 131

wind, 112, 119, 127, 130
Galaxy
 collisions, 316, 317
 dynamics, 24, 98
GAMMA-1, 309
Gamma-ray astronomy, 1, 2, 22, 57, 69, 213, 250, 261, 290, 314
 extremely high energy (EHE), 249, 255
 high energy (HE), 213, 249, 278, 307
 history, 215
 techniques, 216, 220, 221, 249, 250
 ultra high energy (UHE), 23, 182, 185, 249, 250, 253
 very high energy (VHE), 23, 182, 185, 249, 250, 253, 263, 266, 268
Gamma-ray bursts, 182, 183, 184, 214, 234, 235, 263, 298
Gamma-ray emission, 153, 177
 accretion, 289, 296
 diffuse, 29, 57, 290, 307
 galaxies, 24, 307, 309, 310
 Geminga, 214, 216, 235, 238, 271, 272, 278, 275, 284
 LMC, 307, 308, 309, 310, 311
 SMC, 307, 308, 309
Gamma-ray lines, 168, 213, 214, 227
 cyclotron, 234, 256, 258
 from ^{26}Al, 213, 214, 229, 230
 from e+,e-, 213, 214, 218, 227, 228, 229, 234, 242, 279
 from ISM, 214, 236
 from SN 1987a, 167, 172, 231
 from sun, 215, 238
 particle interactions, 238, 271, 276
 nucleosynthesis, 231
 radioactive decay, 168, 172, 231, 232, 233
Gamma-ray sources, 75, 214, 222, 249, 252, 253, 266, 271, 290
 binary systems, 215, 252, 265
 3C273, 24, 236, 271, 278, 281, 283, 284, 255, 296
 catalogs, 252, 264, 266, 267, 268
 Cyg X-1, 271, 272, 278, 284
 inner galaxy, 76, 78
 neutrino luminosity, 300
 periodicity, 223
 (see also individual sources)
Gamma Ray Observatory (GRO), 71, 214, 215, 231, 242, 307, 309, 319
 BATSE, 234, 242, 243

 COMPTEL, 239, 242, 243
 EGRET, 242, 243, 308, 309
 OSSE, 214, 232, 233, 239, 242, 243
Gamma rays, 70, 95, 119, 185, 313
 absorption length, 170
 cosmological, 321
 detection techniques, 216, 217, 218, 219
 energetics, 271, 289, 291, 296, 319
 production processes, 202, 257, 271, 277, 291, 307
Ginga Satellite, 167, 188, 202, 203, 258, 259
GRIS detector, 173, 189, 229
GRASP detector, 233, 239
Gravitational waves (GW), 2

Hadron-hadron collisions, 138
HEAO-1 (A), 221, 235, 256, 280
HEAO-3 (C), 15, 33, 37, 39, 46, 47, 48, 221, 229
Hertzsprung-Russell diagram, 168
Her X-1, 24, 256, 257, 266
Hydrogen
 atomic, 62, 63, 75, 123, 237
 ionized, 62, 123
 molecular, 57, 65, 69, 75, 123, 235
Hydromagnetic waves, 127, 132, 195

IMB detector, 167
IMP-8, 31
Infrared astronomy, 58, 75, 76, 207
Initial mass function, 108
Injection of particles, 1, 13, 16, 93, 95, 97
Interstellar chemistry, 75
Interstellar dust/grains, 59, 69, 76, 79, 81, 82, 153
 abundances, 63, 64, 66
 accretion, 57, 63
 chondritic, 155, 157
 condensation, 153, 154, 155, 156, 159
 core, 62, 83
 element depletion, 64, 66, 158, 159
 H formation, 65, 81, 84
 ices, 57, 82
 mantles, 59, 62, 66, 81, 82, 84
 models, 57, 61, 65, 66, 81
 molecules, 59
 morphology, 57
 organics, 57, 58, 60, 64
 photoprocessing, 58, 59, 60
 refractory elements, 57, 58, 60, 64,

153, 156
relationship to gas, 57, 65, 66, 67
siderophile elements, 153, 156
volitility, 57
Interstellar medium (ISM), 1, 6, 21, 29, 51, 69, 88, 93, 97, 98, 115, 119, 131, 143, 178, 314
   clouds, 36, 58, 62, 66, 69, 77, 78, 81, 82, 84, 97, 157, 159, 213, 216, 238
   dynamics, 163
   gas, 57, 66, 69, 78, 119, 123, 131, 153, 156
   interactions in, 81, 82, 138, 308
   Kolmogorov, 149
   magnetic field, 88, 178, 208
Inverse Compton Process, 187, 188, 189, 191, 216, 218, 237, 271, 272, 279, 283, 307
Ionization potential
   (see First ionization potential)
IRAS satellit, 76, 77
ISEE-3 (ICE), 31

"Knee" in spectrum, 92
   (see also Energy Spectrum)

JACEE, 40, 42

Kamiokande detector, 167

Large Magellanic Cloud, 167, 180, 234, 307, 310
Leakage rate, 122
Leaky-box model, 39, 48, 115, 122, 124, 125, 126, 129, 132, 133, 137, 143, 147
LMC X-1, 173
LMC X-4, 266
Loop I, 70, 71, 72, 73
Loop III, 71, 73

Millimeter wave CO surveys, 57, 65, 75, 229, 238
Mir-Kavant Observatory, 167, 173, 188
Muons, 3
   (see also Air Showers)

NAE mission, 233, 239
Nebulae
   (see Clouds)
Neutrino astrophysics, 2
Neutrinos, 1, 2, 10, 22, 168, 177, 297
   from 3C273, 303, 304

from pions, 297, 298, 299
from SN 1987A, 181
luminosity, 302
production, 298, 299
Neutron stars, 23, 111, 168, 175, 187, 189, 213, 222, 234, 235, 239, 280
Novae, 213, 214, 230, 233
Nuclear interactions, 3
   (see also Cross Sections)
Nuclei, cosmic-ray
   (see Abundances)
Nucleosynthesis, 3, 7, 19, 24, 43, 97, 105, 109, 112, 159, 182, 213, 230, 231
   explosive, 161, 214
   neutron capture, 21, 46, 47, 48, 51, 233

Oort cloud, 75, 78
OSO-3, 215, 221
OSO-7, 221

Pair production, 3, 219
Particle beams, 187, 189, 201, 203
   energy loss, 190
   instabilities, 193
   plasma effects, 192
   waves, 195, 199
Pathlength distribution (Grammage distribution), 10, 29, 99, 120, 121, 124, 126, 132, 133, 149
   exponential, 11, 12, 31, 123, 133
   mean, 120
   truncation, 33, 123
   versus energy, 37, 39
Pi-zero decay, 22, 236, 237, 271, 275, 284, 292, 293, 294, 302, 307, 317
Plasma, relativistic, 291, 297, 298, 300, 303
Polarization of starlight, 62, 81
Positronium, 228
Positrons
   (see Electrons)
Propagation of cosmic rays, 1, 6, 10, 29, 30, 37, 43, 89, 92, 97, 120, 124, 177
Pulsar, 22, 23, 175, 181, 182, 184, 185, 188, 189, 213, 222, 249, 252, 264, 272, 314
   magnetic field, 176, 227
   period, 222

Quasars, 22, 194, 196, 240, 280, 293, 303

Radio-galaxies, 239, 241

Radio surveys, 119, 163, 207
Red giant/supergiant stars, 57, 58, 94, 105, 108, 109, 155, 157, 168, 180, 230, 278
Red shift, 174, 294, 301, 257, 262, 318

Salyut-6, 31
SAS-2 mission, 23, 70, 215, 216, 220, 221, 245, 252, 258, 282, 290, 295, 304, 307, 309, 319
Sco-X-1, 272
Secondary-to primary ratios, 29, 102, 119, 122, 134
Seyfert galaxies, 23, 239, 240, 241
Shock waves, 66, 72, 87, 178, 188, 210
    age, 72, 94
    Alfven waves, 88
    compression ratio, 88, 89, 92
    diffusion, 89, 177
    gyro-radius, 88, 89
    interplanetary, 91
    magnetosonic waves, 88
    particle spectrum, 91, 92
    reaction, 92, 94
    velocity, 90, 177
Skylab, 33
SMM satellite, 171, 221, 239, 240
Solar
    corona, 238
    modulation, 1, 7, 10, 30, 92
    photosphere/chromosphere, 238
    system formation, 58
Source composition
    (see Abundances)
Spacelab-2/CRN, 39, 42
Spallation
    (see Fragmentation)
Spectra
    (see Energy spectra)
SS433, 272
Star formation, 58, 66, 75, 78
Stellar
    evolution, 98, 109, 159, 168
    flares, 16, 101, 102
    mass loss, 108, 156, 185
    winds, 130
Stochastic processes
    (see Acceleration)
Supernovae, 3, 16, 51, 69, 93, 98, 107, 123, 130, 153, 157, 160, 168, 173, 175, 187, 190, 197, 213, 231
    envelope/ejecta, 153, 161, 168, 174, 187, 188, 232
    models, 168, 171
    Type II, 167, 168, 231, 233
Supernova remnants, 15, 16, 69, 70, 72, 87, 93, 94, 95, 98, 105, 134, 177, 187, 201, 203, 207, 210, 213, 232, 239, 266, 272, 314
    angular size, 164
    distance to, 163, 164, 166
    distribution, 74, 163
    envelopes, 161, 187, 196
    expansion, 161, 189
    identification, 163
    middle-age, 207
    nuclear disk, 165
    old, 111, 112, 115
    selection effects, 163, 165
    surface brightness, 163
    young, 106, 111, 177, 178, 181, 185, 212
Supernova 1987A, 167, 172, 179, 182, 185
    gamma rays, 171, 172, 174, 181, 187, 189, 202
    light curves, 188
    line spectra, 172
    mixing, 188, 204
    neutrino burst, 23, 167
    optical depth, 170
    pulsar, 175
    x-rays, 167, 187, 188, 202, 203
Synchroton radiation, 2, 3, 29, 71, 72, 95, 189, 191, 207, 227, 235, 307, 310
Synthesis telescope, 208

Transport Equation, 120, 130

UHURU mission, 252, 256

Vela pulsar, 213, 215, 216, 221, 222, 235, 238, 249, 261
    glitch, 226
    light curve, 224, 225
    luminosity, 226
Vela X-1, 24, 249, 258, 266
Virgo cluster, 10, 317, 318, 320, 321, 322
Voyager, 31

Whipple Observatory, 252, 264, 265
Wolf-Rayet stars, 50, 103, 104, 105, 107, 108, 109, 239

X-ray emission, 2, 72, 75, 202, 207, 258, 294

AGN, 231
binary systems, 258, 264, 272
bursts, 185
X-ray sources, 240, 241, 249, 272, 280, 295
(see also individual sources)

1-MONTH